Vertical Transportation:

Elevators and Escalators

Vertical Transportation:
Elevators and Escalators

George R. Strakosch
Otis Elevator Company

John Wiley & Sons, Inc.   *New York · London · Sydney*

Preface

If a multistory building is to operate successfully proper attention should be given to vertical transportation. As buildings and structures become taller, their success becomes more totally dependent on their elevators, escalators, and other forms of vertical transportation. Answering the many questions about vertical transportation is the purpose for which this book has been designed and to which it is dedicated.

The information contained in it is the result of questions posed and answers provided during 20 years in the field of vertical transportation. Many were based on my initial experience as an installer of elevators, and others were asked during the time I sold repairs and renovations.

The greatest part of this factual background was acquired in my capacity as traffic engineer for Otis Elevator Company, in which my responsibility for giving sound and proper advice on the number, size, speed, location, and operation of elevators in any type of building was foremost. It was while I was in that position that the inspiration for this book came to me, together with the discovery that no single source was available for the designer of a building to help him in terms of planning vertical transportation.

Vertical Transportation: Elevators and Escalators is not a handbook. No one page has the answer to a particular problem or building. Rather it is a guide to the ideas and practices that presently form the basis of elevator and escalator application to buildings. It emphasizes the ultimate use of such transportation: to serve people. This emphasis was created with the same logic and common sense that can be applied to any particular aspect of the subject.

The job is by no means complete. A truer title, perhaps, should be *An Introduction to Elevatoring,* for, as the reader will find, once basic understanding is established the problem will go beyond the building or structure into such aspects of contemporary culture as the use of building space and external transportation to and from that space.

Vertical Transportation: Elevators and Escalators attempts to cover the principal uses and applications of vertical transportation. The architect and architectural student should find help in planning the service core and establishing basic requirements for vertical transportation. The structural and mechanical engineer will be interested in the discussion of space requirements and their reaction on the structure. The electrical engineer and building-operating personnel will find something of value in the discussion of elevator operation, control, and power requirements. The building manager may find an answer to an operating problem by relating the basis of elevator planning to actual operation. Perhaps he will be able to understand his problem better. Even the average person who uses vertical transportation may find some of the safety aspects and over-all considerations that go into designing an elevator plant enlightening and reassuring.

Although all of the foregoing points have been considered, the problems of elevator application are too complex and specialized to be attempted by the novice. The actual task is the job of the various representatives of elevator manufacturers and vertical-transportation consulting engineers. If there is a true dedication to be made, it is to those persons who must live with the day-to-day activities of design, construction, operation, and maintenance. These specialists are usually no more than a telephone call away and should be consulted for the immense help they can give.

Many examples of actual building applications provide guidance and illustration. In addition, the current criteria of population and traffic rate, which form the real basis of elevatoring, are given. For the architect or engineer who is concerned with uncommon designs, such as observation towers, missile bases, or ships, some of the considerations that go into vertical transportation in those structures are presented. This aspect is close to me at present, for since writing this book, I have been appointed manager of special installations for Otis Elevator Company.

More persons than can be enumerated have contributed to the writing of this book. They include my associates and the friends I have made in all my activities. They are the men with whom I have worked, those who have asked me questions for which I have had to find answers, and the many students I have introduced to elevatoring, both at Otis management training classes and in various university classes in which I have lectured, in the talks I have given, and in the articles I have written. My special thanks go to them with the hope that this book will add to their knowledge.

New York, New York
April 1967

G. R. Strakosch

Contents

Vertical Transportation:

Elevators and Escalators

The Essentials of Elevatoring

EARLY BEGINNINGS

Since the time man has occupied more than one floor of a building, he has given consideration to some form of vertical transportation. The earliest forms were, of course, ladders, stairways, animal-powered hoists, and manually driven windlasses. Ancient Roman ruins show signs of shaftways where some guided movable platform type of hoist was installed. Guides or vertical rails are a characteristic of every modern elevator. In Tibet persons are transported up mountains in baskets drawn up by pulley and rope and driven by a windlass and manpower. An ingenious form of elevator, vintage about the eighteenth century, is shown in Figure 1.1 (note the guides for the one "manpower"). In the early part of the nineteenth century, steam-driven hoists made their appearance, primarily for the vertical transportation of material but occasionally for people. Results often were disastrous because the rope was of fiber and there was no means to stop the conveyance if the rope broke.

In the modern sense an elevator[1] is defined as a conveyance designed to lift people and/or material vertically. The conveyance must include a device to prevent it from falling in case the lifting means or linkage fails. Elevators as such did not exist until 1853 when Elisha Graves Otis invented the elevator safety device. This device was designed to prevent the free fall of the lifting platform if the hoisting rope parted. Guided hoisting platforms were common at that time, and Otis equipped one with a safety device that operated by causing a pair of spring-loaded

---

[1] In England and other parts of the world the word "lift" is used. An English "elevator" is a platform that can be moved vertically—similar to an American scaffold.

Figure 1.1   A very early type of vertical transportation.

dogs to engage the cog design of the guide rails when the tension of the hoisting rope was released (see Figure 1.2).

ELEVATOR SAFETIES

Although Otis' invention of the safety device improved the safety of elevators, it was not until 1857 that public acceptance of the elevator was apparent. In that year the first passenger elevator was installed in the store of E. V. Haughwout & Company in New York. This elevator traveled five floors at the then breathtaking speed of 40 fpm. Public and architectural approval followed this introduction of the passenger elevator. Aiding the technical development of the elevator was the availability of improved wire rope and the rapid advances in steam motive

Figure 1.2

power for hoisting. Spurring architectural development was an unprecedented demand for "downtown" space. The elevator however, remained a slow vertical "cog" railway for quite a few years. The introduction of the hydraulic elevator pushed up from below by a water powered hydraulic ram provided the incentive for competitive ingenuity. No small factor in the rapid development of the elevator was the appeal of the taller building as American cities grew during the 1870's and 1880's.

HYDRAULIC ELEVATORS

The hydraulic elevator reigned supreme for quite a few years; it was capable of higher rises and higher speeds than the steam-driven hoist-

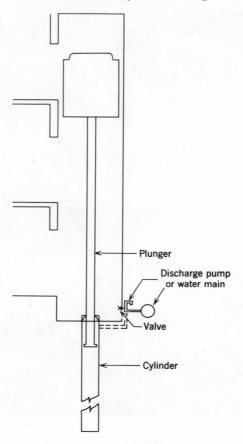

Figure 1.3   Hydraulic elevator.

type elevator with its limits of winding drums (Figure 1.3). The hydraulic elevator also evolved from the direct ram-driven elevator to the so-called geared or roped hydraulic (Figure 1.4) capable of speeds of 600 or 700 fpm and rises of 30 or more stories. The 30-story building did not appear until after 1900, well after steel-frame construction was introduced, but the hydraulic elevator served practically all of the 10- to 12-story buildings of the 1880 to 1900 era.

It was in this era that many of the aspects of elevators as we know them today were introduced. Hoistways became completely enclosed with doors. Before that time many hoistways were simply holes cut in the floor—sometimes protected by a rail or grill, often not. Simple signalling was introduced using bells and annunciators. Groups of elevators were installed, the first recorded group of four elevators being in the Boreel building in New York City and the majordomo of elevatored buildings —the starter—entered the scene.

The first electric elevator quietly made its appearance in 1889 at the Demarest Building in New York. This elevator was a modification of a steam-driven drum, machine-type elevator, the electric motor simply replacing the steam engine. It continued in service until 1920 when the building was torn down. Electric power was here to stay and the Otis Elevator Company installed the first automatic electric or push-button elevator in 1894.

With the tremendous building activity of the early 1900's and the increased size and height of such buildings at that time the questions of "How many elevators?"—"What size?"—"How fast?" and "Where should they be put?" began to arise. With these questions began the art—and art it was—of elevatoring. A typical answer to the problem was, "Joe Doe has two elevators in his building and seems to be getting by all right. Since my building is twice as big give me two twice the size." Realization rapidly came that persons in the latter building had to wait twice as long for service as in Joe Doe's building and complaints

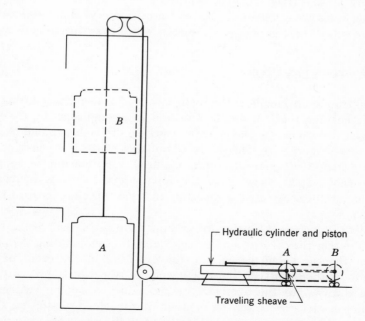

Figure 1.4   Roped (or geared) hydraulic elevator.

and building income reflected their dissatisfaction. The example is fictional though typical, and as a result elevatoring became more of a science than an art.

ELEVATORING

Elevatoring, in the modern sense, is the process of applying elevators and other equipment for the vertical transportation of personnel and material within buildings. Service should be provided in the minimum practical time and equipment should occupy a minimum of the building's space. The need for accuracy in this process became more and more apparent in the early 1900's as the mechanics of elevators became more firmly established in the forms we know today.

The mechanics of elevators changed radically in the early 1900's. As electricity became common, and with the introduction of the traction elevator, the hydraulic was rapidly superseded. Helping its demise was the rapid rise of building heights—the Singer Building, 612 ft; the Metropolitan Life Tower, 700 ft; the Woolworth building, 780 ft; all in New York City and all conceived and built by 1912. The roped hydraulic could not be stretched long enough to compete with such rises, and the direct ram-driven elevator required a hole as high as the rise. Telescoping rams were tried and proved unsatisfactory. But more final was the invention of the traction elevator which was introduced in 1903.

TRACTION ELEVATORS

The traction principle is the main means of transmitting lifting power to the hoisting ropes of an elevator and is accomplished by the friction between the grooves in the elevator machine drive sheave and the hoisting ropes (Figure 1.5). The safety advantages of the traction-type elevator are manyfold: multiple ropes are used, each capable of supporting the weight of the elevator so the rope safety factor is increased by the number of ropes used. Primarily, multiple ropes are used to increase traction area.

Safety is increased by the property of the drive sheave losing traction should either the car or counterweight land, thus eliminating the possibility of the car being drawn into the overhead in the event of switch failure. With drum-type hoisting machines, the car is prevented from being drawn into the overhead by mechanical stopping switches that disconnect elevator power. On a hydraulic machine, a stop on the ram prevents this occurrence. There is no limit to the rise with a traction-type

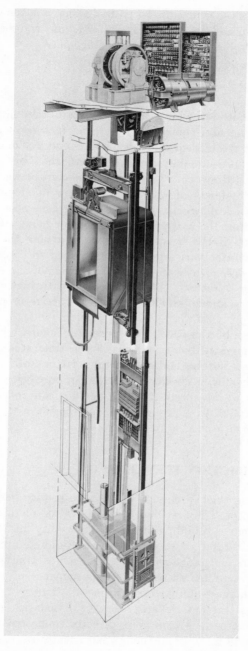

Figure 1.5   A gearless elevator installation.

7

elevator, whereas the drum, the roped hydraulic, and the direct hydraulic have definite limitations. The traction machine can be mounted over the hoistway without infringing on rentable space.

PERFORMANCE

More important, electricity allowed certain minimum standards of elevator operation and control so that time factors in an elevator trip could be firmly established and specified. Speed no longer depended on water or steam pressure but could be established by electrical design. The Ward-Leonard system of electric motor control was introduced and allowed the smoothness of operation common in elevators of today.

The Ward-Leonard system employs a motor generator driven by either an ac or dc motor, the output of the generator being directly connected to the armature of the hoisting machine. Varying the voltage on the field of the generator varies the voltage applied to the hoisting machine armature and consequently the speed and torque of the hoisting machine. Such systems or variations thereof are used with high-quality elevators of today and are known as either variable voltage or unit multivoltage elevators.

In the course of this book the operating characteristics of electric elevators are investigated and a basis for time study calculations of elevator trips are established. These time factors will become the basic tools of establishing necessary elevators for any type of building and will be related to the speed at which persons can be moved from place to place vertically. As a preliminary, familiarity with modern elevator types is necessary.

GEARLESS TRACTION ELEVATORS

The preceding brief discussion of elevator history introduced the traction-type elevator. The first high-rise application of this type of elevator was in the Beaver Building in New York City in 1903, followed by such notable installations as the Singer Building and the Woolworth Building. These elevators were of the gearless traction type that are at present the accepted standard for the higher-rise, higher-speed (over 350 fpm) and highest-quality elevator installation.

The gearless traction elevator consists of a large, slow-speed (50 to 200 rpm) dc motor of 4 to 8 poles directly connected to a drive sheave of about 30 to 48 in. in diameter. An electrically released, spring-applied brake is arranged to apply to the drive sheave. Slow-speed dc motors, though expensive and massive, are necessary to maintain sheave diameters that will conform to the bending radius of elevator steel ropes. This limitation is imposed by safety codes and good practice for long rope life and is generally established at a minimum of 40 times the diameter of the wire rope used. For example, a ½-in. wire rope would require a minimum sheave size of 20 in.

The slow speed of the direct drive gearless traction machine is necessitated by the speed of the elevator it serves. For example, for a 500-fpm elevator and sheave diameter of 30 in., a top speed of 86 rpm is required. To level this elevator to a landing at a maximum speed of 25 fpm, 4.3 rpm is necessary. Gearing has been tried with moderate success to gain these higher speeds. The heavy operating cycle of elevators (up to 25,000 miles per year) and the relative ease of maintenance of the gearless machines, as well as their dependability, makes them the preferred type for higher speeds.

On higher-speed gearless traction machines of 600 fpm or more, the double wrap principle is generally applied to obtain traction and to minimize rope wear. The ropes are wrapped from the car, around the drive sheave, around a secondary or idler sheave, around the drive sheave, and down to the counterweight (Figure 1.6). The groove seats are round providing support on the full half of the rope, eliminating pinching action and minimizing wear. Traction is obtained by the pressure of the ropes on the sheave. As may be noted, increasing the weight on the car or counterweight increases the force so that friction between the ropes and the sheave increases traction.

Elevators are roped either 1:1 or 2:1 (Figure 1.7) for both car and counterweight. In some unusual installations and special applications, 1:1 car and 2:1 counterweight roping has been used. In that event the

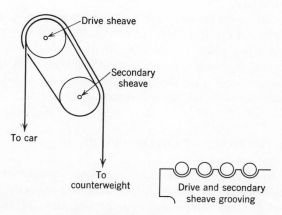

Figure 1.6

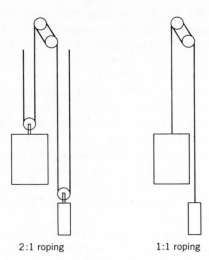

2:1 roping   1:1 roping

Figure 1.7

counterweight must be at least twice as heavy as the weight of the car. The 1:1 arrangement is the most popular for higher speeds and loads up to about 5000 lb. The 2:1 arrangement allows the use of a higher speed and therefore a smaller elevator motor. The mechanical advantage of 2:1 roping requires that only half the weight be lifted, so 2:1 is generally used whenever loads in excess of 4000 lb must be lifted. The economy of the faster motor which can be built smaller and lighter than lower-speed dc motors also makes 2:1 roping attractive for a full range of speed requirements from 350 to 500 fpm and for any lifting capacity.

The long life, smoothness, and high horsepower of gearless traction elevators provide a durable elevator service that can outlive the building itself. The original gearless machines in the Woolworth building were reused when that building's elevators were modernized in 1950. The gearless machine not only provides speed if necessary but also is capable of performance essential to any well-elevatored building.

GEARLESS MACHINES—PERFORMANCES

Essential to elevatoring considerations is the requirement that a gearless traction machine, no matter what its lifting capacity or speed, must be capable of minimum floor-to-floor operating time. Stated another way, the machine must be capable of starting a filled elevator car, accelerating it to a maximum speed for the distance traveled and slowing to a stop in a vertical distance of about 12 ft (average floor height) in a minimum time of about 4.5 to 5.0 sec. This must be performed under all conditions of loading and either up or down. The entire elevator system must be so arranged that such acceleration and retardation takes place without discomfort to the passenger from too rapid change in the rate of acceleration or retardation (with minimum jerk). Furthermore, the elevator must be capable of leveling, releveling, correcting for rope stretch, and changing passenger load at a floor with almost inperceptable movement. The aspects of performance are discussed further in a later chapter.

GEARED TRACTION MACHINES

As the name implies, the geared traction elevator machine utilizes a reduction gear to drive the hoisting sheave. A high-speed ac or dc motor drives a worm and gear reduction unit which in turn drives the hoisting sheave, the net result being the slow sheave speed and high torque necessary for elevator work. A brake, usually located at the coupling between the motor and gear reduction unit, is applied by spring and released electrically to stop the elevator and/or hold the car at a floor level.

The geared traction machine is used for elevators and dumbwaiters of all capacities from 25 to 30,000 lbs or more and speeds from 25 to 350 fpm. The complete flexibility of worm gear ratios and motor speeds and horsepowers as well as drive sheave diameters and roping arrangements (1:1, 2:1, and, sometimes, 3:1) makes this vast range of application practical.

The geared traction elevator is an outgrowth of the earlier drum-type elevators. The steam engine gave way to the electric motor and gear (Figure 1.8) and the drum gave way to the drive sheave (Figure 1.9). The grooved drive sheave was an outgrowth of the traction principle applied to gearless elevators; instead of ropes being wrapped around the sheave, grooves were cut into the sheave and friction was created by the pinching action of the grooves on the rope (Figure 1.10). Various types of grooving are used for different loads and traction requirements. Generally, the sharper the angle the greater the traction (and usually, greater rope and sheave wear).

Geared machines are driven by either single-speed or two-speed ac motors or by dc motors utilizing the Ward-Leonard means of control. The a-c motor machines are used for speeds from 25 to 150 fpm (occasionally, 200 fpm) and stopping is accomplished by disconnecting the power from the motor and stopping the car by a combination of slide and

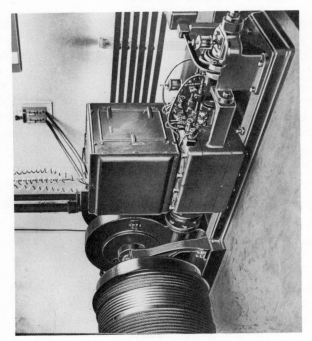

Figure 1.8

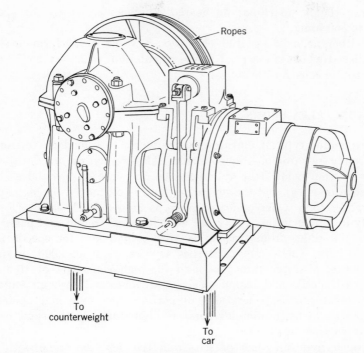

Ropes

To
counterweight

To
car

Figure 1.9   Geared traction machine with alternating-current motor.

brake action. Two-speed ac operation employs a double-wound motor, a fast-speed winding for full-speed running and a slow-speed winding (at one-half to one-quarter full speed) for stopping, leveling, and, if required, releveling. Operation is generally to start at full speed, run, switch to low speed at a measured distance from the stop and accomplish the final stop by combination of brake and slide. The floor-level accuracy of plus or minus $\frac{1}{2}$ to 1 in. can be obtained under all conditions of load as contrasted with single-speed accuracy of 1 to 3 in. which will vary with load. In contrast, the dc Ward-Leonard drive allows the car to be stopped electrically before the brake is applied, resulting in leveling accuracy from $\frac{1}{2}$ to $\frac{3}{4}$ in. under all conditions of load, and much softer

Grooving

Figure 1.10

stops than the ac machine; dc geared machines are used for speeds from 50 to 350 fpm.

With either ac or dc geared elevators, a value of performance can be established which is essential in the calculations of elevator efficiency for elevatoring considerations.

HYDRAULIC ELEVATORS

A third major type of elevator in use today is a modern version of the hydraulic elevator mentioned earlier. Modern hydraulics are direct-ram-driven from below (the cylinder extending into the ground as high as the elevator rises) and the operating fluid is oil moved by high-speed pumps rather than water under pressure as used in early types (Figure 1.11). Hydraulic elevators today are used for both freight and passenger service in buildings from two to six stories high and for speeds from 25 to 150 fpm. Single-ram capacities will range from 2000 lb to 10 tons or more. Multiple rams are used for high capacities of 10 to 50 tons. Varied speeds and high capacities are obtained through multiple pumps. Elevatoring considerations of performance time and operating characteristics of hydraulic elevators are approximately the same as for ac geared traction machines.

The roped hydraulic has passed from the elevator scene with one notable exception—it is still used to lift the deck-edge airplane elevators on aircraft carriers. They are operated under extremely high pressures at speeds of 200 fpm.

ESCALATORS AND MOVING RAMPS

A very potent factor in vertical transportation is the escalator (moving stairway) and moving inclined ramps. Before the 1950's escalators were mainly found in stores and transportation terminals. Today their use has expanded to office buildings, schools, hospitals, banks, and other places where either large flows of people are expected or it is desired to direct people vertically in a certain path. Escalators and elevators are often used in combination either to provide necessary traffic-handling ability or to improve elevator operation by directing people to one elevator loading level. Many office buildings and factories have found escalators ideal for rapid shift changes or speedy floor-to-floor communication.

Moving rampways, inclined, flat, or contoured, are growing in popularity as a means of transporting people and are closely related to the escalator form of vertical transportation (Figure 1.12). The passenger-

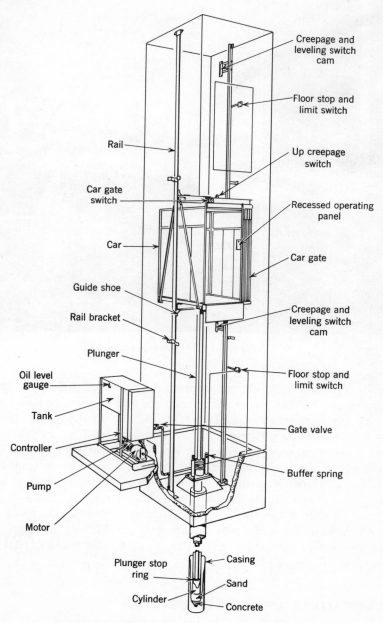

Figure 1.11 A typical freight installation.

15

Figure 1.12   Moving ramp.

handling ability of such conveyances is based on speed and density of passenger loading, either per step or per unit of area. Nominal ratings are usually in passengers per hour. Qualification of capacities and application of the moving stairway or ramp are discussed in later chapters.

As a historical note, the escalator was first introduced by Otis Elevator Company at the Paris Exposition in 1900. It was a far cry from today's flat, finely cleated step, the first model being little more than an endless series of inclined "indentations" that were boarded at the same angle of rise (Figure 1.13). Development rapidly followed, the main points of which were flat steps, flat boarding and debarking areas, narrower step cleats and combs, extended newels, and most recently, glass balustrading (Figure 1.14).

DUMBWAITERS AND CONVEYORS

Other forms of vertical transportation discussed and applied in the later chapters in this book are dumbwaiters and vertical conveyors. Mod-

Figure 1.13

ern buildings use these devices for a variety of purposes: delivery of books in libraries, distribution of mail in office buildings, delivery of food and supplies in hospitals, and so on. The dumbwaiter (Figure 1.15) is actually a small elevator with all the performance characteristics of an elevator. Loading and unloading can be either at counter or floor level, either manual or automatic. Size can vary from letter size to car sizes consisting of any arrangement of 9 ft^2 or less of platform area and a car no more than 4 ft high. This is a limitation imposed by elevator safety codes (covered in detail in a later chapter), and anything over that size must be classified as an elevator. Dumbwaiters need not have safeties and are strictly for material handling. They are always operated from the landing, not from the cab as in an elevator.

Vertical conveyors are generally specialized and require some form of container designed for use with the conveyor (Figure 1.16). This container is loaded (either manually or automatically) on a endless chain with up loads on one side and down loads on the other side.

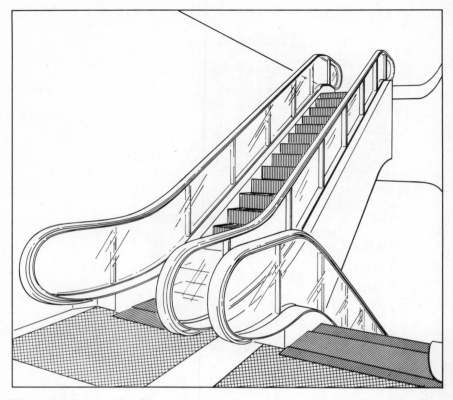

Figure 1.14   Escal-Aire®, the glass escalator; General Motors Futurama, New York World's Fair.

Unloading is done automatically and the container is rolled onto a floor station. Some types of conveyor move continuously whereas others stop and go as loads are applied.

The foregoing represents the principal forms of vertical transportation. Applying these forms is our main course of study and, in reality, the major part of elevatoring. Our earlier definition of elevatoring can be restated in the following section.

STUDY OF ELEVATORING

Elevatoring is the study of requirements of vertical transportation of personnel and material in a building, under all operating conditions.

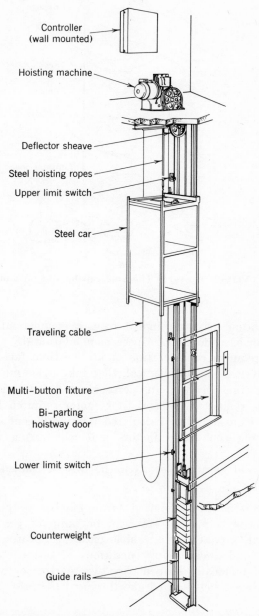

Controller (wall mounted)

Hoisting machine

Deflector sheave

Steel hoisting ropes

Upper limit switch

Steel car

Traveling cable

Multi-button fixture

Bi-parting hoistway door

Lower limit switch

Counterweight

Guide rails

Figure 1.15   Electric dumbwaiter; machine-above arrangement.

19

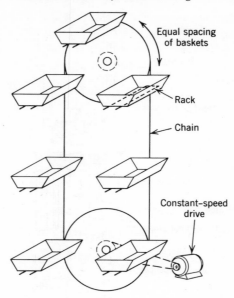

Figure 1.16   Vertical conveyor (baskets can be slid on and off racks).

Such transportation may be studied from a commercial aspect, as in an office building, or a functional aspect, as in a hospital.

Elevatoring requires consideration of all the time factors and movements, both physical and mechanical, that take place during the operations providing transportation for persons and/or material. These time factors must be related to a total time factor required for the output of service based on actual or calculated input. Efficient elevatoring requires minimizing such time factors and maximizing the output of service.

The time elements of an elevator trip that will be studied and evaluated are as follows:

Loading time—the time required for a number of people to board an elevator car or a moving stairway or ramp or the time required to load material, a pallet, or a vehicle onto an elevator. Loading time must be considered under many conditions of operation consisting of but not limited to ideally shaped elevators, narrow or wide cars, wide doors, narrow doors, well-located elevators and partially filled or empty elevators.

Transfer time—the time to partially unload (or reload) an elevator at an intermediate stop. Transfer time is based on all the considerations of loading time plus, essentially, the density of the passenger or other load remaining on the elevator, the direction of the transfer either entering or leaving, and relation of the elevator to other facilities in the building.

These two elements, loading and transfer time, are the most elusive and the most difficult to establish firmly because in general these times are based on people—the most unpredictable element in an elevator or escalator trip. Qualifications have been made on hundreds of studies of human behavior and conclusions are reluctantly (because of the doubt that such a person exists) based on "the average person."

The other factors in an elevator or escalator trip are the mechanical times which, fortunately can be established accurately and assured by specifications that can be developed before installing an elevator or escalator. These time factors are as follows:

Door-closing time—a function of door weight (mass). Width of opening and type of opening—center (Figure 1.17*a*) single-slide (1.17*b*), two-speed (1.17*c*), or swing for passenger application and sliding or vertical biparting (Figure 1.17*d*) for freight application—involve different masses that affect closing speed. The kinetic energy of closing doors is limited by elevator safety codes and is usually established at no more than 7 ft-lb. In practical terms this means that the familiar 3-ft 6-in. center-opening sliding door will require about 2.3 sec to close. Closing time is a vital consideration in elevatoring, for the closing operation on a typical elevator occurs hundreds of times a day. An elevator cannot

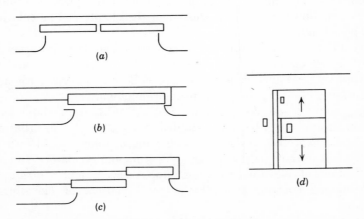

Figure 1.17 (*a*) **Center-opening;** (*b*) **single-slide;** (*c*) **two-speed; and** (*d*) **biparting.**

leave a floor until the doors are essentially closed and locked, a logical and important safety requirement.

Door-opening time can be minimized by proper arrangement and by power operation. Door-opening time can and should be much faster than closing time and doors can start to open while an elevator is leveling to a stop. This premature opening must be limited so that the opening is not wide enough to allow passenger transfer before the elevator is level enough with the landing to avoid a tripping hazard. The time necessary to open the doors will vary with the width and type of doors. For example, center-opening doors take less time than single-slide or other types, and wide openings require more time than narrower openings.

Operating time—a function of the speed and control arrangement of the elevator and the number of stops the car will make. Two considerations are necessary in elevator work: the time require for a floor-to-floor operation and the time required for full-speed operation. The operating speed of escalators or moving ramps is constant and must be qualified only under load conditions.

Because the floor-to-floor operations of elevators are repeated over and over again, a measure of the probable number of stops an elevator will make in the course of a single trip is required. Knowing or estimating the number of stops provides the total time for all time functions and leads to the cycle time or round-trip time of an elevator. The number of stops can be established by applying a statistical formula, by inspecting the various attractions of each floor at which an elevator is required to stop, or a combination of both statistical and logical determination. The various approaches are discussed in the chapter on calculating elevator performance.

Once all the time factors are ascertained and the time required to serve a given number of people is determined, the number and size of elevators or escalators in a building can be established. Although this is the essence of our studies, elevatoring cannot end here.

The grouping and operation as well as location of those elevators (or escalators) must be also established so that the installation will provide the expected service. The following chapters established principles of arrangement and location of elevators and escalators. In addition, qualification of elevator grouping, stops served, lobby arrangements, skip-stopping, control, and all the total aspects of elevatoring are presented.

CHAPTER TWO

The Basis
of Elevatoring a Building

POPULATION

Before any thought is given to the elevators in a building, a thorough and detailed study must be made of how people will occupy that building. This is an obvious prerequisite to the design and size of the building itself. It must have been conceived for a practical or economic basis, it must be expected to perform its function, that is, house or provide working space for a given number of persons, and it must be expected to endure for a considerable number of years.

Basic factors in elevatoring a building include the number of occupants and visitors, their distribution by floors, and the times and rates of arrival, departure, and floor-to-floor movement. We can determine the average density of population in an existing building based on so many square feet of space per person. We can also determine that persons in or coming to or going from an existing building require so many units of vertical transportation. If these findings are related to a future building of similar nature, a reasonable provision for vertical transportation can be made.

Density of population and the intensity of elevator traffic for all types of buildings are suggested in later sections of this book. You will note the term "suggested"; the actual use of the building is beyond the realm or control of the architect and the elevator engineer. The depth to which basic population and usage research can go (and how much experience is available) will help determined how well the building is elevatored. When the degree of uncertainty is high, the basis of elevatoring should be conservative, or the fantastic expense of adding additional equipment will be faced.

ELEVATOR TRAFFIC

In every type of building there is a critical elevator traffic period. The type, direction, and intensity of elevator traffic during this period determines the quantity and quality of elevator service for a particular building. If the elevators serve traffic well during the critical time, they should be capable of satisfying traffic at all other times.

Critical traffic periods vary with building types and in various areas of the country and the world. For example, in office buildings in downtown areas served by mass transit, the critical traffic period is the morning in-rush. If elevators are sufficient to serve the peak of that in-rush period, the rest of the day usually presents no problem. In other cities the critical traffic in an office building may be the noontime period when lunch hours may be standardized and the entire building may go to and return from lunch within a minimum time.

The critical traffic period in many hospitals may be in the forenoon when doctors are visiting patients, transfers for treatment are being made, operations are performed, and essential hospital traffic reaches a peak. In other hospitals, perhaps because of administrative rules, critical traffic may occur during visiting hours.

In apartment houses the critical traffic is usually the late afternoon or early evening period when tenants are returning from work, children are coming home from school, wives returning from shopping, and others are leaving for evening entertainment. A downtown apartment with a predominant business-person tenancy may find that the critical traffic period is in the morning when practically everyone is leaving for work.

Once the critical traffic period for a building is determined and evaluated in terms of required elevator handling capacity, the choice of the proper number, speed, size, and location of elevators may proceed.

Critical traffic periods for various types of building have been determined by observations, traffic studies and tests, discussions with building managers and owners, and by research into use and population requirements. The degree and nature of this traffic is reviewed in the sections of this book dealing with various building types.

THE ENVIRONMENTAL CONSIDERATIONS OF ELEVATORING

The environmental considerations of elevatoring cover the process of locating elevators in a building, providing proper access space to such elevators, designing and shaping them to best accommodate people, determining door sizes and arrangements, and other considerations to make sure the maximum use and benefit is gained from the total elevator plant in a building.

The cost of elevators, including the direct costs of installation and maintenance and the indirect cost of the space they require, is far too high to tolerate an inefficient installation. Elevators must be placed, arranged, and designed to provide the necessary service with the least investment. Unsatisfactory elevator service can damage a building's reputation and cause incalculable loss in the productive time of its occupants.

With costs and results in mind, the factors that make a superior elevator installation will be presented.

Car or Platform Shape

The elevator platform—the area on which passengers ride—must be large enough to accommodate a passenger (or freight) load without undue crowding and allow each passenger ready access to and from the elevator doors.

An average person will require about 2 ft^2 of floor area to feel comfortable. Passengers can be crowded, however, to about 1.5 ft^2 for the average man or to 1.0 ft^2 for a woman—the combination of men and women requiring about 1.3 ft^2. If no one is pushing or forcing people to crowd, (the usual case with automatic elevators), each person will take two square feet. There is one important exception: at office building quitting time, passenger loading in elevators often attains the minimum of about 1.3 ft^2 per person density.

The average space per passenger in elevator cars means that the elevator capacity—expressed in pounds and translated to square feet so that the car will not exceed its rated load if packed full—must be arranged in the best dimensions to accommodate the shape of people. The arrangement of ranks and files has been found to be best, and inside car dimensions shown in Table 2.1 for common-size passenger elevators have been established as industry standards.

As an example, the average loading of a 3000-lb elevator is 16 passengers. You will note from Figure 2.1 how these 16 persons will generally arrange themselves inside the elevator car. Note also that there is sufficient room for the person in back to pass those in front (it seems the one in back is always the one who wants to get off first).

In Figure 2.2 note how the same area, with a different width and depth, leads to awkward loading situations. More ranks of passengers

Table 2.1

Capacity (pounds)	Inside Car Area (square feet)	Inside Car Size	Average Loading Persons
2000	23.2	6'0" wide × 3'8" deep	10
2500	28.3	6'8" wide × 4'3" deep	12
3000	31.7	6'8" wide × 4'9" deep	16
3500	37.5	7'2" wide × 4'9" deep	19

now make access to the door difficult and generally require someone to step out of the car to let others out. These complications add a time delay to each elevator stop, which accumulates during the total trip and seriously reduces efficiency. The deep, narrow arrangement also leads to loss in passenger capacity—15 passengers versus the 16 passengers shown in Figure 2.1. Part of this loss is from the extra space required for doors, but most is from platform shape.

Study of the two illustrations suggests the conclusion that the most efficient elevator car is only one person deep! This is true but not practical because efficient door arrangement must also be considered.

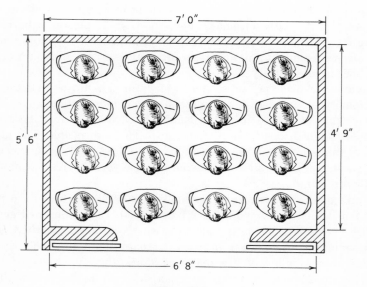

Figure 2.1

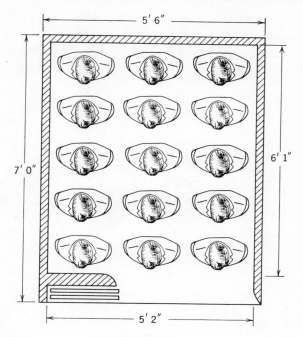

Figure 2.2

Door Arrangement

The most efficient door is one that opens and closes in minimum time and allows two persons to enter or leave an elevator simultaneously. The doors must also be reasonably economical and adaptable to efficient platform sizes. The 3 ft 6 in. center-opening door meets most of these requirements and is the most popular for high-quality elevators; it is wide enough to allow two persons to transfer simultaneously (Figure 2.3), can fit the average 6 ft 8 in. or 7 ft wide platform and can be opened in slightly more than a second. Closing speed, as we mentioned previously, must be within the 7 ft-lb kinetic energy limitation. Because each panel of the door is half the weight of the entire door (no more than 100 or so pounds per panel) and the distance traveled is only half the opening width, the 3 ft 6 in. center-opening door can be closed in slightly more than two seconds to meet this kinetic energy limitation.

Doors narrower than 3 ft 6 in. can be considered one-person doors. Note how awkward it becomes for two people to pass each other (Figure 2.3); the natural tendency is to allow one person to leave while the other holds up elevator service until he can enter.

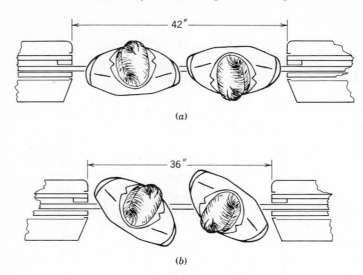

(a)

(b)

Figure 2.3

Wider doors are often necessary for special purposes, such as the 4 ft door on a hospital elevator that must accommodate a hospital bed or on a freight elevator that must accommodate wide containers or carts. In these cases the efficiency of the door is secondary to the function the elevator must perform.

In apartment houses the economy of the single-slide door prevails. Because passengers are expected to move at a somewhat more leisurely pace, some efficiency may be justifiably sacrificed for economy. For ultimate economy swing doors are often provided in three- or four-story apartment houses in which elevators are more of a convenience than a necessity.

Lighting and Signals

The interior of an elevator car should be well lighted and the lights arranged so that they cannot be turned off by unauthorized persons. To this end there should be either a locked light switch or no light switch. The car threshold should have a minimum of 5 ft-candles of light as prescribed by the American Standard Safety Code for Elevators since inaccuracy in floor level stops can create a possible tripping hazard.

A person should be able to look at an elevator and tell whether it will travel up or down when it leaves his floor. With a single-car installation in a normally quiet building this is not serious, for if he is the only one on the floor the car will generally travel in the direction he chooses.

With more than one car serving a floor, some form of directional indication becomes essential, for a car going either way may stop. Lighted directional arrows in the door jamb of the arriving elevator offer a simple, relatively inexpensive solution to this dilemma (Figure 2.4). The most effective way is to provide lanterns over or next to each hoistway entrance which will inform the prospective passenger of the next car to arrive at his floor and the direction it will travel when it leaves his floor (Figure 2.5). Such lanterns should be arranged to light up sufficiently in advance of a car's arrival at each floor to give passengers time to walk to the entrance of the arriving car and be ready to board it. This is not always accomplished, but as will be noted later each second thus saved in passenger boarding time is worth extra elevator capacity. The lantern must also be prominent enough so that a person may see it from the point where he is likely to stand. Note, in Figure 2.5, arrangement *C*, that a lantern on a transom or in a depression cannot be seen. Arrangement *B* would be much better.

Figure 2.4

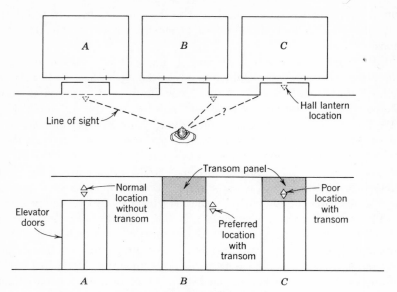

Figure 2.5   Hall lanterns should be located to be seen.

Hall call buttons that light when touched or pressed inform the prospective passenger that his call for service has been acknowledged. In the absence of an indicating lantern on the elevator, a lighted button that goes out when the car arrives is a simple substitute for directional information.

With one- or two-car installations, the inclusion of some form of direction and motion indicator in the hall call station provides passenger assurance that a car is on its way. These devices include miniature mechanical or electrical indicating dials showing the location of each car or the more modern digital readout devices (Figure 2.6). The serious

Figure 2.6   Digital readout.

objection to such devices is the fact that the car may be filled and bypass that call, or is bypassing because it is on a form of special service and not answering hall calls. Because the waiting passenger does not know this he is quick to complain when he is bypassed. More than two such devices in the same hall fixture, as would be required when more than two cars are serving the same landing, can hopelessly confuse the passenger and are not recommended.

Once the passenger is in the elevator car he should be readily able to indicate where he is headed and be promptly informed when he arrives. The car call buttons should be conveniently located so passengers can register calls as quickly as they enter an elevator, the side locations proving to be the most acceptable (Figure 2.7).

Some form of position indicator in the elevator car is required and should be plainly visible to all passengers. This is especially necessary in busier buildings. Car position indicators over the car door jamb, the

Figure 2.7   Car operating panels.

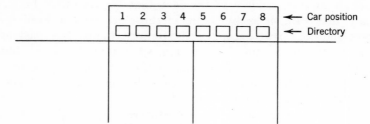

Figure 2.8   Car position indicator and directory.

most acceptable location, are often combined with directories to show what is on each floor of an office building, department store or hotel (Figure 2.8). Other messages have also been placed in the same spot —advertising, clocks, or thermometers showing outside temperature. In many buildings, especially hotels and hospitals, in which the usual passenger may not be accustomed to riding in elevators, the floor designation may be helpfully placed on the jamb of the hoistway door so it may be seen when the door opens. In budget apartment houses this approach has been a means of saving the expense of a car position indicator.

LOCATING ELEVATORS IN A BUILDING

Elevators and escalators should be accessible and centrally located. All entrances should lead to the vertical transportation center, which should be near the main entrance of the building. If a parking lot or subway entrance is near the building it is reasonable to expect that most passenger traffic will come from that direction. If the flow is expected to be heavy, escalators or moving walkways can be employed to guide passengers to the elevator lobby.

Centralizing elevators in a building allows all parts of each floor to be equally accessible to the elevators. Elevators located on one end of a building detract from the desirability of the other end and adds considerable extra time for passengers to cover the horizontal distance (Figure 2.9).

Experience has shown that the walking distance from the elevators to the farthest office or suite should not exceed about 200 ft, with a preferred maximum distance of about 150 ft. For example, in a building 300 ft long, the elevators should be located at the center point (Figure

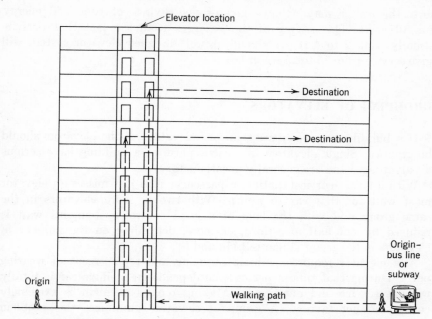

Figure 2.9 **Noncentralized elevators mean additional walking time.**

2.10). Buildings with X, Y, or T floor layouts have a natural center point.

In some buildings, where the busiest entrance is near one end rather than the middle, a central location for the elevators may still be desirable. If people use the main entrance only when entering or leaving the building but use elevators repeatedly during the day, locating them

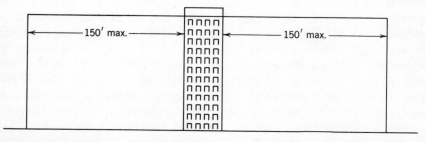

Figure 2.10 **Distance from elevator core to farthest office not to exceed 150'.**

near the center may achieve greater net savings of time and energy for all users. This saving of time accrues from the fact that persons usually walk 2 to 4 ft per second. A well-designed elevator system will give service from 15 to 25 sec or less.

GROUPING OF ELEVATORS

If a building requires more than one elevator, all the elevators should be grouped. Single elevators in various parts of a building have serious disadvantages and are generally unsatisfactory.

With a single-car installation, a passenger who just misses an elevator must wait for that car to return. With two or more elevators in the same group and with the help of a good control system, his wait is reduced by one-half, one-third, or more, depending on the number of elevators in the group (Figures 2.11a and b).

Any elevator requires periodic servicing and replacement of wearing parts. During that time a person who depends on a single car is totally without service and must walk. Making repairs at night is extremely costly and not favored. A group of elevators minimizes this problem and permits periodic repairs without total passenger inconvenience.

If a tenant is moving into or out of a building, or if building renovations are scheduled, one car of a group of elevators can be assigned to these tasks. With a single car such moving or renovation is a weekend or nighttime proposition or the passenger again must walk (Figures 2.11c and d).

Notable exceptions where elevators are not grouped (if there is more than one elevator in a building) are single-service elevators designed for specialized use in apartment houses, motels, nursing homes, or office buildings. These service elevators are mainly for building maintenance purposes, moving operations, or food service, and, as such, are generally subject to marring, scuffing, and other damages. They should not be considered for general passenger use and the car interior should be of durable material. If passengers must be carried, removable pads can be used and building services made to wait. Food service elevators for upper-floor dining facilities, hospitals, or other buildings, are in the category of possible acceptable single-car installations. A garage shuttle elevator serving the basement garage in an office building is also a possible exception—provided no more than a few stops are served, handling capacity is sufficient, and there is a convenient stairway. The safe-deposit elevator in a bank is a logical single-car installation.

The architect should provide interconnecting passageways between single elevators. Failure to do so will completely deny elevator service to a portion of the building. The lack of these interconnections is serious if the building is of any height or if the elevator is essential to a building's operation, as in a hospital or housing for the elderly.

As a general rule, if elevator service is essential to the building operation and no alternate means of vertical transportation is available, more than one elevator should be considered.

SERVING FLOORS

All elevators in a group should serve the same floors. This is a common-sense rule that is often violated for false economy. If, for example, only one car out of a group of three, serves the basement, a person wishing to go to the basement from an upper floor has only one chance out of three that the next elevator that comes along will take him to the basement. Conversely, a person in the basement must wait three times as long for elevator service than an upper-floor passenger. Ideally, all cars should serve the basement but if not, a special shuttle elevator might be considered, to run only between the main floor and the basement. This latter scheme is the alternative to be favored if multiple basements exist and a large group of main passenger elevators is required. The difference in the cost of providing entrances on all the main elevators at the basement levels and the cost of the shuttle elevator or elevators may be nil.

The expedient of providing a separate call button at an upper floor to call the single car that serves the basement has often been tried and never proved satisfactory. The average person will operate both the normal call button and the basement call button, take the first car that comes along, and cause the basement car to make a false stop. These false stops will add up in lost elevator efficiency over the years to more than pay for the cost of the extra entrances on all elevators.

The rule that all elevators in a group should serve all stops applies to penthouse and intermediate floors as well as to basement floors. As operations within the building expand during the years, the search for extra working space becomes desperate and any floor served by an elevator is a likely area for expansion. A mechanical floor can be changed to a partial file area, a structure can be built on the roof, the basement can be rented—all good reasons why each floor in a building should

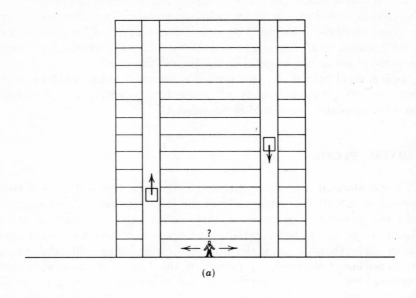

(a)

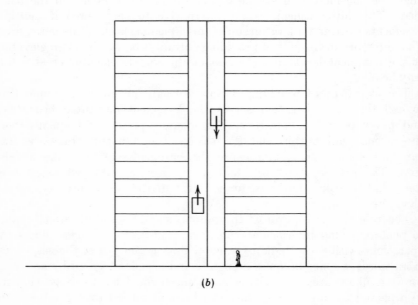

(b)

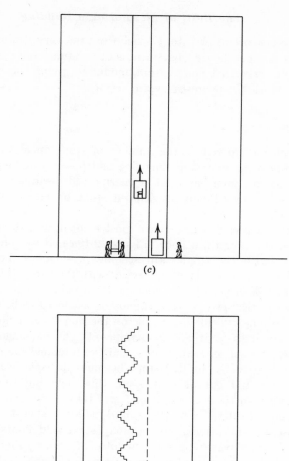

(c)

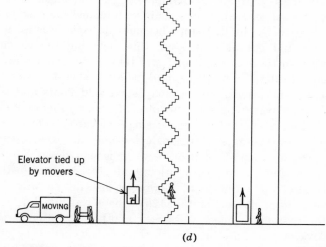

Elevator tied up
by movers

(d)

Figure 2.11 (*a*) **Widely separated elevators reduce transportation efficiency;** (*b*) **grouping elevators avoids passenger indecision;** (*c*) **grouped
elevators afford continuity of service;** (*d*) **separating elevators can deny
service.**

37

have a full measure of elevator service from the very beginning. A potent example is the penthouse apartment suite; having only one car out of two or three serve that floor is tantamount to giving the most expensive area in the house the poorest elevator service.

Skip Stops

Many schemes to reduce the number of stops an elevator will make, thereby improving operating efficiency and possibly reducing equipment, have been tried. Each has relative merits and disadvantages. The most notable are schemes involving skipped stops on either single or groups of elevators.

Single-car skip-stop schemes are most elementary; the elevator serves every other or every third floor (Figures 2.12a and b). The disadvantage is obvious: with the single-skip scheme persons on the floor skipped must walk down to get elevator service; with the every-third-skip scheme they must walk either up one floor or down two. In apartment buildings elderly or handicapped persons cannot be asked to walk up stairs, baby carriages become difficult for people on the nonelevator floors to manipulate, and moving operations are hampered. The passenger load remains but is concentrated on fewer floors, and the intended increase in elevator capacity owing to the limited stops becomes dubious because more persons move in and out at each stop, thus delaying the elevator. The main saving is in the lower cost of fewer total elevator entrances, which may be from 5 to 10 per cent of the total installation cost.

In two-car installations, one car may serve odd floors and the other, even floors, thereby saving one entrance per floor (Figure 2.12a). The total installation is equivalent to two single elevators side by side with most of the disadvantages of a single-car and the sole advantage of only having to walk one floor if an elevator is shut down. Service is not improved as it would be in a conventional, all-stop, two-car installation.

Another skip-stop variation is a two-car installation with both cars serving every other floor (Figure 2.12b) where waiting time is reduced but half the passengers must walk. Still another variation is the intermediate elevator landing scheme with the cars serving every other floor (Figure 2.12c); passengers must walk up or down only half a floor.

Skip-stop elevators may be used advantageously to create duplex apartments, where the feeling of luxury offsets the inconvenience of the alternate-floor elevator stopping. Another special application is in schools during class change periods when alternate floor stopping can increase elevator capacity and reduce loading by requiring many students to walk a floor or two to their next class.

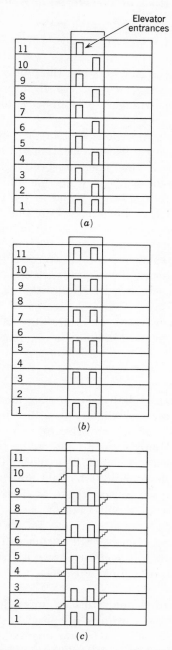

Figure 2.12 (a) Odd-even skip-stopping; (b) alternate-floor skip-stop-ping; (c) intermediate landing.

ARRANGEMENT

As essential as grouping elevators and the proper location of the group in a building is the arrangement of the elevators in the group. As a rule elevators should be arranged to minimize walking distance between cars.

With any group of elevators, one spot in the lobby is usually favored by waiting passengers, often near the location of the elevator call button. As an elevator arrives at that floor prospective passengers must react and walk to the elevator while it waits for him. Because an average passenger walks at a rate between 2 and 4 fps, the time spent by the elevator at each stop must be adjusted to this rate of walking.

Advance hall lantern operation will help minimize that waiting time. Excessive distances between the cars in a group results in longer time delays at each stop, which cannot be overcome by lantern operation. Excessive delay from this cause, coupled with other inefficiencies resulting from poor group arrangement, may require the installation of additional elevators.

Experience has demonstrated the desirability of the elevator arrangements illustrated and discussed in the following pages.

Two-Car Groupings

For a two-car group, side-by-side arrangement is best. Passengers face both cars and react immediately to a direction lantern or arriving car. Two cars facing each other constitute an acceptable alternative as the passenger need only turn around to be facing an elevator.

Separation of the elevators should be avoided. The greater the separation, the longer each elevator must be held until a passenger can arrive at that car. Excessive separation tends to destroy the advantages of group operation; passengers will wait at the call button, and, rather than run for the second car if it is too far away, will let it go and reregister a call. Adding a second call button will not relieve this situation but will only result in the effect of two individual elevators serving the same floors, each providing only half the service of which it is capable.

The lobby in front of the elevators on upper floors should, as a minimum, be as wide as the elevators are deep (usually from 4 to 6 ft) if elevators are side by side, and from one and one-half to two times as deep if the cars are opposite each other (Figure 2.13). The side-by-side arrangement requires more space in the main floor lobby because more

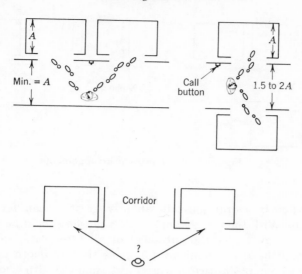

Figure 2.13   Two-car arrangements.

persons are expected to wait in this area. With the cars opposite each other, an assembly area should be provided and the elevator lobby dead-ended (alcove arrangement). It is extremely dangerous to have a door located in this area because waiting persons might lean on or could be struck by a swinging door.

In hospitals or other buildings, where elevators carry vehicles, the lobby must be wide enough to accommodate them. Vehicles must be pushed straight in or out of the elevator to avoid hitting the protective edge on the car door. About two additional feet must be allowed to accommodate an attendant.

Three-Car Groupings

Arrangements of three cars in a row or two cars opposite one are acceptable, the main problem being the location of the elevator call button. The type of elevator door may influence the choice. With center-opening doors, three cars in a row may be preferable as this will give the elevators a balanced appearance (Figure 2.14). With two-speed or single-slide doors, unequal space between elevator fronts (Figure 2.14) may make the two-opposite-one arrangement desirable.

There is very little difference in walking time with either of the three-car arrangements, as the turn-around reaction time offsets the shorter

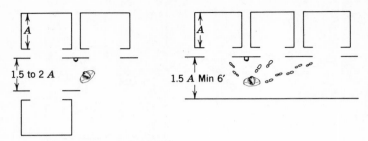

Figure 2.14   Three-car arrangements.

distance. Lobby widths must be slightly greater than for two-car arrangements. With the row arrangement, a person should be able to stand back far enough to see the entrances of all three cars; thus the lobby width should be a minimum of 1.5 times the car depth or about 6 ft. With the one-opposite-two arrangement, lobby width should be from one and one-half to two times the car depth, or a minimum of about 8 ft.

Four-Car Groupings

Four elevators in a group are common in larger, busier buildings. Experience has shown that a two-opposite-two arrangement is the most efficient.

The alternative arrangement, four cars in a row, has notable disadvantages and tends to become unacceptable with larger elevators (over 3000 lb) because of the increasing distance between the call button and the last car in the row. With average-sized elevators, this walking distance is about 12 ft. Unless the arrival of an elevator is signaled in advance and passengers react promptly, the elevator must be held at the floor for at least 4 to 5 sec. This time is about two seconds over the alternative arrangement of two cars opposite two. Because elevators make from five to 10 stops per trip, these extra seconds add appreciably to the total round-trip time of the elevator. Efficiency of the installation is reduced solely by poor arrangement, and would possibly necessitate faster or larger elevators.

The preferred two-opposite-two arrangement (Figure 2.15) should have a lobby from one and one-half to two times the depth of an individual elevator but no less than 9 ft for those times when all cars arrive at the main lobby filled and passengers entering or leaving must pass each other. The closed-end alcove arrangement is acceptable, for even

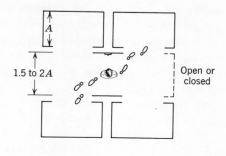

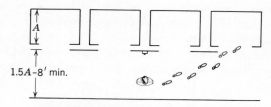

Figure 2.15   Four-car arrangements.

if persons wait at the end of the alcove they are only a car length away from the next car to arrive or depart.

If architectural factors necessitate four cars in a row and the time penalty of such an arrangement is acceptable, the lobby should be at least one and one-half times the depth of an individual elevator but no less than 8 ft. This width will allow a person to stand back far enough to see the directional lantern of any elevator. At the main floor the lobby should be wider and longer to accommodate the assembly of people waiting to board the elevators. This is especially necessary during the incoming rush and to provide quick exit for outgoing passengers.

Six-Car Groupings

Groups of six elevators are often found in large office buildings, public buildings, and large hospitals. Six elevators frequently provide the combination of quantity and quality of elevator service required in these busy buildings. The arrangement of six cars, three opposite three, seems to satisfy most architectural core schemes.

The best arrangement (and to many persons, the only arrangement) is three cars opposite three (Figure 2.16a). The waiting passenger can see all six elevators simply by turning around. The distance to the next arriving elevator is a minimum and the car need be held at a stop for a minimum time. The main floor lobby can be either alcoved (one end closed) or open at both ends.

The lobby width for a six-car group of elevators should be from one and three fourths to two times the depth of an individual elevator but no less than 9 ft. If the lobby is to be used as a passage for other than elevator passengers (never recommended at the main floor), its width should be no less than 11 ft.

Elevator lobbies can be too wide as well as too narrow. The wider the lobby the longer elevators must be held at floor stops for passengers to get to them. For this reason, an elevator lobby for a six-car group should be no wider than 14 ft.

An acceptable arrangement other than three cars opposite three, is two cars opposite four (Figure 2.16b). Passenger response time now be-

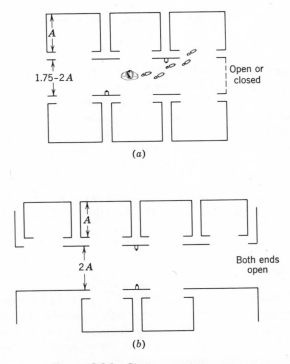

(a)

(b)

Figure 2.16   Six-car arrangements.

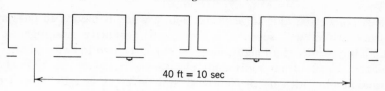

40 ft = 10 sec

Figure 2.17   Unacceptable six-car arrangement.

gins to become appreciable however, and finally, as with six cars in a row, becomes totally unacceptable. It was formerly believed necessary in a department store to have all the elevators visible to passengers. This may have been true so that attendants of manually operated elevators could see the approaching passengers but in-line arrangement is hard to justify in view of the universality of automatic operation today and the time factor of holding elevators for passengers. Even if extra time per stop is allowed for the slowest passenger, the random rotation of elevator arrivals at a floor may result in the two end cars arriving simultaneously. If one fills quickly the passengers who could not board must run to the other end and risk missing that car also (Figure 2.17).

Eight-Car Groupings

The largest practical group of elevators in a building is eight cars—four opposite four. The main lobby is required to be open at both end, each of which must be equally accessible to a main entrance to the building, for the handling capacity of eight elevators will require passengers to assemble both in the elevator lobby and in the space beyond both ends of the lobby (Figure 2.18). Equally important is that departing

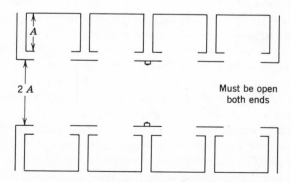

Figure 2.18   Eight-car arrangement.

passengers must be able to leave the lobby without having to pass other elevators, which will soon be arriving with capacity passenger loads.

The lobby width of an eight-car group must be two to two and one-half times the depth of an individual elevator and never less than 10 ft. The maximum width of the lobby should never exceed 16 ft, and even then the passenger response time to an elevator will be long enough to require extra waiting time at hall calls for some of the cars.

Hall call buttons should be located at the center of the lobby, on opposite sides. The best place for persons to wait and where they usually do wait, is dead center so they may see each elevator. Passengers can then respond as quickly as possible, with minimum walking distance.

Using the main floor elevator lobby as a passage is not recommended, as accommodating any kind of traffic other than elevator traffic would require too wide a lobby. At the upper floors such an arrangement is possible because traffic is expected to be minimal. A main floor lobby, which is open-ended, and upper-floor lobbies in an alcove arrangement are completely acceptable.

One of the best alternatives to an eight-car arrangement is to avoid the necessity of an eight-car group. This may be done by replanning the elevators into two four-car groups or, if a building requires more than eight elevators, into combinations of four- and six-car groups. There is no general rule; each building's needs must be analyzed individually and the most satisfactory solution determined. These calculations are demonstrated in a later chapter when the requirements of quantity and quality of elevator service are discussed.

Unique Arrangements

Certain distinctive elevator arrangements have either unique merit or serious disadvantages. The architecture of particular buildings, rather than economic considerations, is usually responsible for their use.

The angular arrangement of elevators is feasible with a single group of cars serving a building, but has certain inherent disadvantages that must be compensated for by additional elevator service. As can be noted in Figure 2.19a, cars at the narrow end of the lobby must be a minimum distance apart, which tends to make the wide-end cars too far apart. This leads to extra time losses per upper-floor hall call stop.

The cornered arrangement in Figure 2.19b consolidates the elevator lobby but leads to interference between passengers entering or leaving the corner cars. This is serious if the full capacity of the elevators is required, and is not recommended for that reason.

The circular arrangement (Figure 2.19c) is a variation of the angular

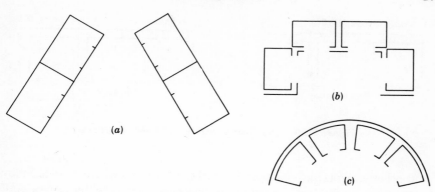

Figure 2.19

and cornered, with a premium in cost because of the shape and special mechanical features of the elevator car and doors. The closeness of the elevator fronts requires either special door arrangements or substantial extra hoistway space to accommodate conventional elevator doors. Traffic congestion possible with such an arrangement of elevators is an equally important discouraging factor.

Odd-shaped elevator cars and other unique arrangements of elevators are discussed in the section on elevators for special applications later in this book.

Front and Rear (or Side) Entrances

One of the most important of the special arrangements of elevators is the use of both front and rear (or side) entrances on one or more elevators in a group. This is one of the areas of elevatoring in which the operation of the elevators must be closely coordinated with their arrangement.

As a general rule, when two sets of entrances are furnished on one elevator in a group but are not on all of the elevators, one set or another but never both should be in operation at one time. The reason is the same as if only one car in a group serves an odd floor: special controls must be furnished to intercept that car for the rear entrance and a person's wait at a rear-entrance landing may become intolerable.

A suitable arrangement for rear or side entrances is the use of one of the cars in a group as a part-time service elevator. The elevator is then disconnected from group operation and made to serve a separate hall call button for rear or side service (Figure 2.20).

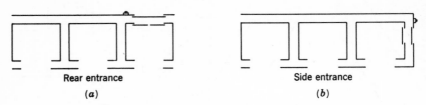

Rear entrance

(*a*)

Side entrance

(*b*)

Figure 2.20   (*a*) Rear-entrance; (*b*) side entrance.

Another acceptable arrangement is in a hospital where a rear lobby is provided for patient vehicular service and a front lobby serves staff and visitor traffic. During peak patient activity hours the cars are operated from rear entrances only; at peak passenger hours, cars are operated at front entrances only (Figure 2.21). Specific administrative control is required, however, to establish entrances to be served at various hours. The section on hospital elevators covers this arrangement more fully.

A third practical application of front and rear entrances is the use of a group of elevators between old and new structures to bridge uneven floors. Here all elevators in a group should serve both the front and rear entrances at all times and car call buttons should be provided for each opening. For example, if the third floor rear is a different level

Service corridor

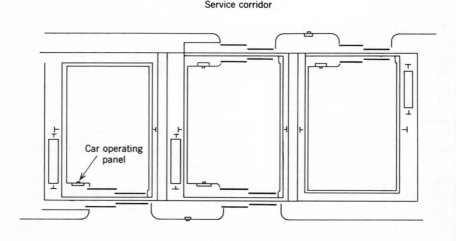

Car operating panel

Passenger corridor

Figure 2.21   Three car hospital grouping.

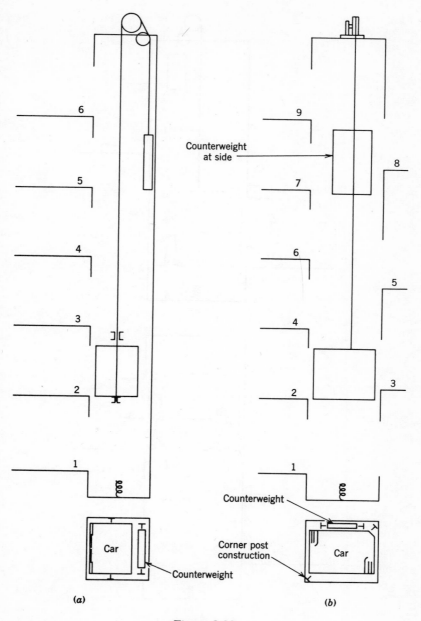

Figure 2.22

49

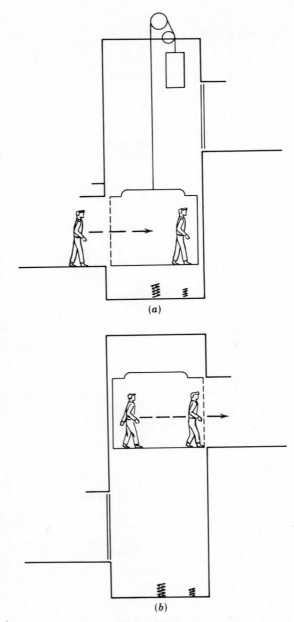

Figure 2.23   (a) Loading; (b) unloading.

from the third floor front, a person should be able to choose the level he requires. Separate buttons should be provided even if both front and rear are on the same level. Front and rear openings served in this way make for a building with elevator requirements almost equivalent to one with as many floors as the total number of openings. Because most of an elevator's trip time in a low building is spent in stopping, the increased number of possible stops tends to increase total trip time. Serving both front and rear entrances requires additional elevator capacity (Figure 2.22).

When a passenger elevator serves only two stops front and rear openings allow prompter loading or unloading of the car. Passengers can walk directly into the elevator and face the entrance from which they will leave, and a loading group at the opposite entrance can follow them in as they are leaving (Figure 2.23).

Front and rear entrance on automobile and freight elevators may expedite loading and unloading. An auto that can be driven off without backing can often be unloaded in half the time.

Other special elevator arrangements are discussed in the sections dealing with specific building types and special applications.

CHAPTER THREE

Passenger Service Requirements

If we know how many people will require elevator service within a given period of time, the task of providing that service is one of time and motion study. It embraces many variables, one of the most important being passenger reactions to elevators.

THE ELEVATOR TRIP

In modern buildings people are accustomed to pressing or touching a call button to summon an elevator and will move to an elevator that opens its doors to offer them service. Usually, but not universally, passengers will note a signal showing direction of car travel and will choose the car corresponding to the desired direction. In a building with light traffic and a tendency for only one elevator to stop at a floor at one time, passengers may ignore the lantern and get into the next elevator that arrives. In busier buildings there is a strong possibility of two cars stopping at a floor at one time. If a passenger has taken the wrong car once or twice he is conditioned to note the directional signal.

Once the passenger boards the elevator car he is expected to operate a car button for the floor he wants to reach. Failure to do so may take him where he does not want to go, which quickly teaches him to register a car call each time. The passenger must do one more thing before his trip is complete: to get off at his floor he must note where the elevator is stopping as shown by the car position indicator over the car door jamb and leave the car at his stop.

THE REQUIREMENTS OF GOOD ELEVATOR SERVICE

The elevator engineer is interested in the passenger's state of mind during his trip. While he is waiting at some intermediate floor his impatience is growing. In a commercial atmosphere he is less tolerant of waiting than in a residential or relaxed atmosphere. Frequent studies have indicated that passengers become impatient after waiting about 30 sec in a commercial building, and about 60 sec in a residential building.

From these observations come the first requirement for good elevator service—the elevator system must be designed to provide service for a person within 30 sec in commercial buildings and within 60 sec in residential buildings.

The second requirement is to provide sufficient quantity of elevator service for the maximum passenger load expected within a predetermined period. This can be accomplished by either a platform of sufficient area to accommodate all persons wishing to ride or, alternatively, a sufficient number of rapidly moving smaller platforms. The alternative of more platforms is usually preferred because it also satisfies the first rule for frequency of service.

A good example in vertical transportation is the escalator. Platforms are provided with minimum waiting time (usually zero seconds waiting because the stairs are constantly moving) so that a person has immediate access to vertical transportation. Because the platforms are large enough to accommodate only one or two persons at a time, if more than one or two require service at the same instant, someone must wait. The wait is usually painless, however, for the prospective passenger can see the escalator is in service and the extent of his wait. On the other hand, a person waiting for an elevator at an upper floor may not be able to see if the cars are in service and is therefore relatively intolerant of waiting.

Once a person boards an escalator he knows he will be delivered to the next floor in a relatively short period of time, and except for the extreme high-rise escalators in some subway stations, he can see the top landing. An elevator passenger often does not know how long he is going to be in the car. If it serves many floors in a busy building and the number of elevators is limited, a person may be on an elevator for a considerable period of time.

Studies have found that about 60 to 90 sec becomes the limit of tolerance for persons in an elevator making several stops, each for one person. Tolerance will lengthen to about 120 sec if a few persons are being served at each stop; the "average person" feels more tolerant if two persons are being served. Finally, if monotony is relieved by a changing scene and perhaps, a few pretty girls, our passenger may tolerate a ride as long as 150 sec. These time factors are necessarily approximate since an individual's tolerance varies with the urgency of his mission or other factors affecting feelings or atmosphere.

The third requirement of good elevator service, therefore, is to design the system so that a person will not be required to ride a car longer than a "reasonable" time. If the first two requirements are met, the third is usually satisfied as a natural consequence.

CALCULATING THE TIME FACTORS—TWO-STOP ELEVATORS

To calculate the total time for an elevator trip, a practical procedure is to break the trip down into its components. A simple example of a two-stop elevator will be followed by analysis of more complex and many-stop trips.

Suppose we have an elevator that makes two stops about 10 ft apart and wish to calculate how long it will take a person to ride to the higher or lower landing.

When the passenger arrives at the landing and operates the elevator call button he is, in effect, starting his trip. When he leaves the elevator at the other landing he has completed his trip. Once the call is registered the elevator is serving the passenger and the time factors will be as follows.

Referring to Figure 3.1, if a car is at the lower landing when the passenger arrives and operates the call button, the elevator doors need only open (a). A typical door requires about 2 to 3 sec to open depending on the width and type of door. About 2 sec must be allowed for the passenger to enter the car and operate the car button (b). The doors must close again (about 3 sec) and the car must travel the 10 ft to the next landing (about 7.5 sec) (c). The doors must again open and since this can start before the elevator has stopped, opening the final width may take about 2 sec, with another 2 sec for the passenger to leave (d). The total time consumed by that passenger is 19.5 sec.

Before another person can get service more time must necessarily elapse. The doors must close again (3 sec), and the car return to the opposite landing (7.5 sec). At this point the cycle can be repeated. The elevator's total cycle time or round-trip time has been 30 sec. Thus 30 sec is the approximate time a person who just missed the elevator at the first floor will have to wait for it to return and give him service

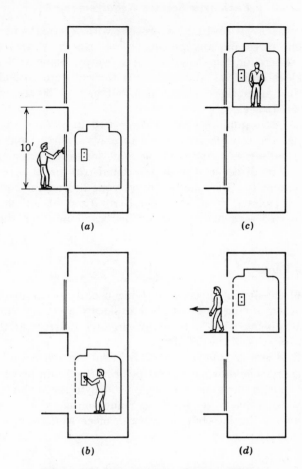

Figure 3.1   Passenger or elevator action:

(a) Passenger operates button, doors open; approximate time: 3   sec
(b) Passenger enters car, operates button (2 sec),
doors close (3 sec); approximate time: 5   sec
(c) Passenger carried bottom to top: 7.5   sec
Doors reopen (starting before elevator stops) (3 sec
less 1 sec premature opening):   2   sec
(d) Passenger leaves: 2   sec
Time to serve one passenger: 19.5   sec
To return for another passenger at lower floor:
   Doors close: 3   sec
   Run, top to bottom: 7.5   sec
Total round-trip time: 30.0   sec

55

If we view this as a continuous process with a stream of passengers moving in one direction, any passenger can expect to wait an average of one-half the round-trip time of the elevator. Some will arrive just before the elevator leaves and will have to wait zero seconds, whereas others will just miss the elevator and will have a 30-sec wait, so the average wait is 15 sec.

The foregoing example serves to show two important considerations in elevatoring: the total time required to serve a person and its relation to elevator handling capacity, and the wait for an elevator as indicated by interval and its direct relationship to round-trip time.

Handling capacity—the number of persons served in a given period of time—is calculated from the round-trip time of an elevator. The basic time period is generally established as 5 min for the following reasons.

Five-Minute Peaks

Peak requirements in an office building usually occur in the morning when persons are trying to be at their desks by a certain starting time. Human nature being what it is, many employees arrive at the building within a few minutes of the deadline.

Figure 3.2 shows a typical arrival rate at an office building lobby where prospective elevator passengers peak in the 5 min preceeding starting time. If enough elevators are not provided to serve this peak, lobby congestion persists past the deadline. Some conscientious people arrive earlier to avoid being late but, in general, office workers consider them-

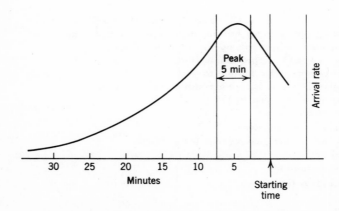

Figure 3.2   Typical arrival rate at an office building.

selves on the job if they arrive at the building at the normal starting time. It is the responsibility of their employer to transport them quickly up from the lobby to their office floors.

Because elevators for office buildings received the most attention when formal study of elevatoring began, the standard of a 5-min peak has persisted. We have also found 5 min as a convenient time period to measure peak traffic on elevators in any type of building. For that reason our calculations are concerned with a critical 5-min traffic peak and 5-min elevator handling capacity.

Handling Capacity

Translating our first example into 5-min handling capacity by means of the formula, we find that the elevator has a 5-min handling capacity of 10 persons:

5-min handling capacity

$$= \frac{\text{number of passengers per trip} \times 300 \text{ sec}}{\text{round-trip time in sec}},$$

$$(3.1)$$

$$\frac{(1) \text{ passenger per trip} \times 300}{30} = 10 \text{ passengers/5 min.}$$

If only one passenger is served per trip in one direction, our 5-min handling capacity is only 10 persons; with two passengers per trip (or one person up and one person down per trip) in the same time, capacity would be 20, and so on. If more passengers are served each trip, however, the time factors, especially entering and exiting transfer time, would increase.

Interval

Interval or the time between elevators is determined directly from round-trip time and is inversely proportional to the number of elevators in a group. It is calculated by the formula:

$$\text{interval} = \frac{\text{round-trip time of an elevator}}{\text{number of elevators in the group}} \quad (3.2)$$

In our example, with only one elevator, interval is equal to round-trip time. Obviously the interval measures the theoretical longest time a person should have to wait for an elevator. In practice interval varies from trip to trip because of passenger delays or random traffic on an elevator, and should be stated as an average for a given period of time.

If in our example (Figure 3.1) we had two elevators side by side and operating so that when one car is at one floor the other is at the other floor, round-trip time would be substantially the same, handling capacity would be doubled, and the interval would be halved. Instead of waiting 30 sec if he just missed an elevator, the passenger would wait 15 sec because the other car would replace the car that left.

Waiting Time

Here we introduce the concept of waiting time related to interval. The theoretical average wait of all persons is one-half the interval, the interval being the theoretical longest wait of any person. The term theoretical is used for three reasons: (a) intervals must be considered as averages for a period of time; (b) the operating system must maintain uniform exact spacing of elevators; and (c) sufficient traffic must be present. With the best available operating systems, average waiting times will be greater than half the interval, about 55 to 75 per cent or more depending on the refinement of the operating system.

A two-stop elevator is the simplest and most efficient elevator system. Everyone that gets on at one landing is expected to get off at the other landing. Transfer time is minimized and no question of probable stops occurs since there is only one possible stop.

Even groups of two-stop elevators have very little complexity. Scheduling can be simple: If traffic is two-way, one car should be at the top and another car at the bottom; with one-way traffic, elevators should be concentrated top or bottom.

Multistop Elevators

Elevatoring calculations become more complex with three or more stops. With three stops, for example, a number of elevator trips are possible: a person at the lower landing may wish to go either to the middle or top landing; a person at the second landing may wish to go either to the top or bottom landing; or a person at the top may wish to go either to the second or the lower landing.

The time required for a typical trip may be calculated on either of two bases. The more conservative basis assumes that the elevator will make every stop up and down. A second more typical and more complex method determines the probable stops the elevator will make related to the traffic it is expected to handle. We will investigate the latter approach in detail.

Probable Stops

The first step in calculating the time required for a typical trip is to determine the number of stops an elevator will make in a round trip. This depends on the following factors:

1. The number of persons entering the elevator at the lobby floor greatly influences the number of stops the elevator makes. If the elevator serves more floors than the number of passengers on the car during that particular trip, assuming passengers enter at the ground floor only, the elevator is not expected to make more stops than passengers carried. The chances are it will make fewer stops than the number of passengers carried.

Viewed differently, the number of floors the elevator serves influences the number of stops an elevator is expected to make with a given passenger load. For example, an elevator that serves 20 floors and is expected to carry 10 persons per trip will probably make 10 stops each trip, whereas an elevator that serves 10 floors and carries 10 passengers per trip will probably make fewer than 10 stops per trip.

2. The normal working or residential population of each floor the elevator serves also influences the number of stops an elevator makes. For example, if some floor served by the elevator is a storage or mechanical floor, the elevator's tendency to stop there is greatly reduced. If one floor has 100 persons and the other floors have only 10, the tendency to stop at the 100-person floor is greatly increased.

3. The expected direction of traffic imposed on an elevator influences the number of stops each trip. For example:

(a) When everyone is coming into the building, the elevator generally makes only up car stops and returns to the lobby floor without down stops.

(b) When persons are traveling between upper floors in a building each person causes the elevator to make two stops: an up or down hall call for that person to board the elevator and a subsequent car call for that person to leave.

(c) When visitors are coming to and going from the building or when the occupants are leaving and returning during lunch or other times, up car stops are generated by persons entering the elevator at the lobby and down hall stops by persons on upper floors. Under extremely busy situations and with inadequate elevators, it is possible for an elevator to make every stop up and every stop down, resulting in intolerably long round-trip times in a building of any height. This is especially true if elevators have large capacities and carry many persons, which causes many stops.

(d) When many persons wish to leave the building within a short period of time, as at quitting time in an office building, a different pattern of stops is likely. The elevators are expected to make only down hall stops and to fill quickly at each stop. Because at least a carload of persons is eagerly awaiting the elevator and each person is concentrating on leaving the building as quickly as possible, the number of down stops in a typical trip may be far fewer than an equivalent up trip for the same number of persons.

As may be seen, determining probable stops requires a knowledge of critical traffic in the building under consideration. Timing and the nature of the critical traffic for each type of building is discussed in later sections of this book. One form of traffic may be critical in many types of buildings or many types of traffic may occur in one building during various times of the day, so that probable stops will be related to the various types of elevator traffic.

In the following chapters we discuss the major traffic periods and the necessary time required for elevators to serve passengers during those periods. With this information and with a known building, elevatoring for the critical traffic period can be established. If elevators can handle the critical traffic, and if they are properly operated, they will also be adequate for the other traffic loads imposed on them.

CHAPTER FOUR

Incoming Traffic

INCOMING TRAFFIC

Incoming traffic provides one of the critical traffic periods in office buildings and occurs to a greater or lesser degree in any building. The number of elevators required to serve a given number of persons during this period is calculated and their operation discussed. In succeeding chapters two-way and outgoing traffic are similarly discussed.

We go into incoming traffic calculations in detail as this traffic type is important in any building. In addition, the method of calculation that we establish in our study of incoming traffic can be extended to include any traffic type.

Incoming or up peak traffic exists when all persons arriving at a lobby floor are seeking transportation to upper floors (Figure 4.1). Little or no down traffic is expected during this period. A single elevator trip during this period consists of the following elements:

1. Loading time at the lobby.
2. Door closing time and running time to the next stop.
3. Door opening time and time to transfer part of the passenger load at that floor.
4. Door closing time and running time to the next stop.
5. Door opening time, transfer time, etc. until the highest stop is reached.
6. Door closing time and running time back to the lobby.
7. Door opening time at lobby and repeat loading time.

As may be seen, the elevator trip is made up of various time elements related to such factors as the number of people entering and leaving,

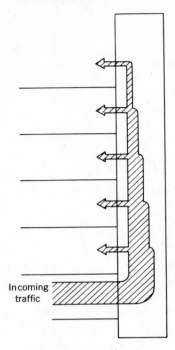

Incoming
traffic

Figure 4.1

the speed of the elevator, and the time to open and close the doors. Of prime importance is the number of stops the elevator will make on its up trip. Two methods are suggested for estimating the number of stops. The method selected will depend on the information available about the distribution of the building's population, working hours, and employee's activities within the building. The more that is known about these factors, the more practical and accurate the probable stop value will be. The less that is known, the more theoretical the probable stop value will be.

In a building in which a great deal is known about the per floor population it is possible to assign a stop value to each floor. Table 4.1 is based on an 11-story building. The population per floor is as indicated and everyone is expected to report for work at the same time. We assume that each elevator in this building has a normal capacity of 10 persons. For this table we have made the reasonable assumption that the expected number of stops (probable stops) is proportional to the number of persons an elevator can carry. If we assume the top floor population as 5 instead of 100 as shown, an elevator would stop there only once out of every 20 trips instead of every trip. If people on the tenth floor, for example, started work say 15 min later, the expected stopping at the tenth floor would be greatly reduced during the time the other floors required service.

Seldom is as much information available as shown in Table 4.1. If it were the task of elevatoring could be reduced, as is possible with a known building in which the elevators are manually operated and there is a desire to automate them. A study of the existing situation can determine the average number of stops made each trip and, if suffi-

Table 4.1

Floor Number	Population per Floor	Expected Stop
11	100	1
10	100	1
9	100	1
8	100	1
7	50	$\frac{1}{2}$
6	50	$\frac{1}{2}$
5	25	$\frac{1}{4}$
4	25	$\frac{1}{4}$
3	10	$\frac{1}{10}$
2	5	$\frac{1}{20}$
	Expected stops	5.65

cient elevators are available, the degree of improvement possible with automatic operation.

In estimating probable stops for a building yet to be built we must give due regard to the real-life situation. We will not know that all starting times are the same, we will only know that so many square feet of area are available for the per floor population and we will not know the difference in attraction for each floor.

We can be reasonably certain, however, that in any elevator trip the elevator will stop at upper floors in proportion to the number of persons in a car and the number of floors that elevator serves. This forms the basis of second method of estimating probable stops.

If we assume that population on each floor is equal and that persons are entering a building in a random fashion so that all must be in place by a given time, there is a distinct possibility that one or more persons will get off the elevator at the same floor within the same trip. A statistical calculation of the probable number of passengers leaving the elevator at a given floor at the same time provides the following formula:

$$\text{Probable stops} = S - S\left(\frac{S-1}{S}\right)^p \qquad (4.3)$$

which becomes the formula for probable stopping of an elevator with a given passenger load wherein

S = the number of possible stops above the lobby,
p = the number of passengers carried on each trip.

Formula 4.3 is the one used in planning elevators for buildings when little is known about the distribution of future population and each floor is assumed equal in population. Unless it is reasonably certain that the uppermost floor will have less attraction than any lower floor, or the number of floors served is greater than the average passenger load per trip, it also must be presumed that the elevator will travel to the top floor on each trip.

Applying the formula to a 10-passenger, 10-upper-floor elevator trip, a probable stop value of approximately 6.5 stops is obtained. Chart 4 shows approximate probable stop values for various car loadings and

Chart 4

Passengers per trip

Upper floors served	10	12	14	16	18	20	22
18	8	9	10	11	12	13	13
16	8	9	10	10	11	12	12
14	7	8	9	9	10	11	11
12	7	8	9	9	10	10	10
10	6	7	8	8	9	9	9
8	6	6	7	7	8	8	8
6	5	5	6	6	7	7	7

Probable stops

various numbers of upper floor stops. Car loading should not be more than 80 per cent capacity; left to themselves, passengers will seldom fill an elevator to more than that during the up peak. Although a greater per cent can be attained if someone encourages loading, crowding on elevators will increase upper floor transfer time, so that 80 per cent capacity is considered acceptable.

Loading Time

Table 4.2 gives loads and loading times for various standard size elevator cars. Loading times are based on entrances of at least 3 ft 6 in. wide (3 ft 0 in. for the 2000-lb car). The 3 ft 6 in. entrance is the minimum size through which two persons can pass at once. For each inch that an entrance may fall short of this minimum, lobby loading

Table 4.2 Lobby loading time

Capacity (pounds)	Inside Dimensions	80 Per Cent Load (people)	Time to Load (seconds)
2000	6′0″ wide × 3′8″ deep	10	8
2500	6′8″ wide × 4′3″ deep	12	11
3000	6′8″ wide × 4′9″ deep	16	14
3500	7′2″ wide × 4′9″ deep	19	16
4000	7′6″ wide × 5′5″ deep	22	17

Table 4.3. Door closing time

Door Width	Door Type	Time for Doors to Close and Car to Start (seconds)
3′0″	Single-slide	4.3
3′0″	Two-speed	3.8
3′0″	Center-opening	2.9
3′6″	Single-slide	4.9
3′6″	Two-speed	4.4
3′6″	Center-opening	3.3
4′0″	Two-speed	5.0
4′0″	Center-opening	3.7

and upper-floor transfer times are increased by at least 1 per cent. Similarly, each foot the platform dimensions differs from the standard entails both a loading time and an upper-floor transfer time penalty of at least 5 per cent.

When the elevator is filled at the lobby floor it takes time for the doors to close and the car to start moving to the next landing. This time varies with the size and type of hoistway doors as in Table 4.3. Repeated for each stop, these times become an important factor in round-trip calculations.

Once the door is closed it takes a bit more time to insure that the door is locked and for the elevator motor to "build up" to run to the next floor. For this requirement, 0.8 sec is added to each door closing time in the table. More time must be allowed if door mechanisms are slower or if build-up time is longer than the values given.

Door closing time is established by safety codes based on kinetic energy and the values shown are within code limitations for average weight, hollow metal doors.

Ignore for the moment the time it takes an elevator to travel from floor to floor; the next element in an elevator trip is the door opening at the next stop. Well-designed elevators should have doors that start opening as the elevator levels to the floor (premature opening) and open wide enough for passengers to start moving in or out the instant the car stops. This procedure can save at least half the door opening time—a time saving repeated for each stop of the trip. Premature door operation can reduce opening time as in Table 4.4. It is important that the elevator installation provided is capable of accomplishing good premature door-opening operation. Also important is a two-speed door mechanism—fast opening and slower closing.

Once the elevator has stopped at an upper floor some passengers in the car are likely to leave. Persons in front can get out quickly, persons in the rear, if the car is crowded, may require considerably longer time. Because there is an infinite number of combinations of car loading and passenger exiting, an arbitrary time value per stop is assigned to this

Table 4.4. Door opening time

| Door Type | Size | Time Required Prior to Transfer (seconds) | |
		w/o premature (complete opening)	w/premature
Single-slide	3'0''	2.5	1.0
	3'6''	2.9	1.4
Two-speed	3'0''	2.9	0.8
	3'6''	3.1	0.9
	4'0''	3.7	1.0
Center-opening	3'0''	2.3	0.5
	3'6''	2.5	0.6
	4'0''	2.7	0.8

action no matter how many people exit or how full the car is. Table 4.5 shows values for the standard shapes of cars. Add 5 per cent to the time shown for each foot of deviation from the standard dimensions.

In addition to the loading and unloading and door opening and closing, running time is the other element in the round-trip time of an elevator. Part of the running time is spent in getting the elevator up to speed and slowing it down to a stop.

Persons can feel changes of acceleration and retardation but are not too conscious of constant acceleration or retardation; therefore elevator equipment must be able to overcome inertia and get the car up to speed or slow it down to a stop smoothly. The machinery must be also capable of moving the car a distance of 11 to 12 ft, a floor height, in minimum

Table 4.5. Transfer time

Capacity (pounds)	Inside Dimensions	Time to Exit per Stop (seconds)
2000	6'0" wide × 3'8" deep	1.2
2500	6'8" wide × 4'3" deep	1.5
3000	6'8" wide × 4'9" deep	1.6
3500	7'2" wide × 4'9" deep	1.8
4000	7'6" wide × 5'5" deep	2.0

time. Heavy-duty equipment such as a gearless machine can move an elevator from floor to floor in about 4 to 5 sec. Less powerful equipment, such as a geared or hydraulic elevator, will require from 6 to 8 sec for the same distance, depending on the ultimate speed the machine can develop.

Floor-to-floor speed seldom exceeds about 350 to 400 fpm regardless of the ultimate speed of the elevator. Like horsepower in an automobile, however, the heavy-duty gearless equipment is necessary for minimum floor to floor time.

A sample set of time-distance curves for various speeds of elevators is shown in Chapter 7, page 117. Note that the curve includes both acceleration and retardation time so that the total time to travel the distance shown is indicated by a point on a curve.

Since time-distance curves vary with all elevator speeds, a means to approximate running time will be given which can be developed quickly and easily for any speed and elevatoring situation.

Running Time

For elevators of 500 fpm or more assume 1.8 sec to attain a reasonable floor-to-floor speed and 1.8 sec to retard to a stop or 3.6 sec for starting and stopping on each run. Add to this the time required to run the full distance at constant full speed which will partially compensate for the distance traveled. For very fast elevators, 800 fpm and more, an extra time factor, as shown in Chapter 7, will be required.

As an example, assume that a 700-fpm elevator is traveling 20 ft:

$$\text{Start and stop:} \qquad 3.6 \text{ sec}$$

$$\text{Run 20 ft:} \frac{20 \times 60 \text{ sec}}{700 \text{ fpm}} = \underline{1.7 \text{ sec}}$$
$$5.3 \text{ sec total}$$

Actual time from elevator tests is 5.2 sec, which indicates a difference so small that it will not matter in our approximate calculations.

For elevators of from 100 to 350 fpm assume 2.2 sec to accelerate to full speed and 2.2 sec to retard to a stop or a total of 4.4 sec for starting and stopping. Add the time required to run the given distance at full speed.

For example, assume that a 200-fpm elevator is traveling 12 ft:

$$\text{Start and stop:} \qquad 4.4 \text{ sec}$$
$$\text{Run 12 ft:} \qquad \underline{3.6 \text{ sec}}$$
$$8.0 \text{ sec total}$$

Actual time from elevator tests in 7.8 sec.

You will note that the time calculated will always be a conservative estimate as the distance traveled during acceleration and retardation is not added. If the equipment under consideration for a particular job requires longer for acceleration for floor-to-floor travel, an extra time value must be considered. If equipment levels at slow speed, if the transition from fast to slow speed is not swift and smooth, or if the leveling speed operation is too long, floor-to-floor operating time may be as long as 8, 10, or more sec.

Based on the foregoing analysis, elevator round-trip time can be calculated with relative ease as in this example.

Incoming Traffic Calculations

Suppose we want to know how many persons a 3500-lb elevator at 500 fpm from 3 ft to 6 in. center-opening doors, in an 11-story building with 12-ft floor heights, can serve during a 5-min incoming traffic peak period.

1. Table 4.2, page 65, shows that the capacity of a 3500-lb elevator is 19 people.

2. The chart of probable stops, page 64, shows that 19 passengers will make approximately 9 stops on the 10 upper floors in this building.

Time to load 19 passengers (Table 4.2):	16.0 sec
Time to close 3 ft 6 in. center-opening doors and to start car (Table 4.3):	3.3 sec
Time to open the doors when the car returns to the lobby (Table 4.4):	0.6 sec
Time to start the car and to stop the car when it returns to the lobby:	3.6 sec

3. The total time spent near the lobby: **23.5 sec**

Time to open the doors at an upper floor stop:	0.6 sec
Time to transfer passengers at each upper floor stop: (Table 4.5):	1.8 sec
Time to close door at each stop:	3.3 sec
Time to start and stop at each stop:	3.6 sec
Total time spent at stopping and leaving each upper floor stop:	9.3 sec

4. Nine probable upper floor stops × 9.3 sec per stop equals total stopping time: **83.7 sec**

5. Time to run back to first floor from top floor stop and to run from stop to stop exclusive of time required to get up to speed and to stop:

$$\frac{\text{rise (10 floors} \times 12') \times 2 \text{ (up and down)} \times 60 \text{ sec}}{500 \text{ fpm}} = \textbf{28.8 sec}$$

6. Total of all time factors equals round-trip time:	136.0 sec
7. Allowance for inefficiencies 5 per cent of items 3 and 4:	5.4 sec
Total round-trip time:	141.4 sec
Or approximately:	141 sec

8. Elevator 5-min capacity:

$$\frac{19 \text{ passengers per trip} \times 300 \text{ sec}}{\text{Round-trip time 141 sec}} = 40 \text{ passengers}$$

In other words the single elevator in our example can serve **19** passengers in 141 sec or a total of 40 passengers in 5 min.

Item 7, a 5 per cent factor for inefficiency, is added to compensate for the rounding off of probable stops, door time, transfer time, and starting and stopping time and to simplify calculations. It could also

Table 4.6

Car Size and Loading	2000 lb	2500 lb	3000 lb	3500 lb	4000 lb
	10	12	16	19	22
Lobby Time[a]	16	20	23	25	26
Upper Floor Time	8.7	9.5	9.6	9.8	10.0

[a] Rounded off to nearest second.

be called a confidence factor representing the difference between our assumptions and possible actual conditions.

All the time factors affecting a single stop were lumped together (see item 4). By charting these time factors, Table 4.6, we can establish a time value per upper floor stop as well as a lobby time factor related to car loading to simplify future calculations. The values in the table are based on 500 fpm or more, add 0.8 sec to each value for less than 500 fpm; 3 ft 0 in. center-opening doors for 2000 lb and 3 ft 6 in. center-opening doors for all other car sizes, standard size platforms, and a 5 per cent inefficiency are included. Add correction factors as discussed.

Figure 4.2 shows the net result of combining all the time factors into a single quantity. The total height of the building is averaged into equal floor heights and the stopping, door operation, transfer, and starting times are combined into a time factor.

Calculations for a typical elevatoring problem appear in Example 4.1. Although four larger elevators provide the necessary *quantity* of elevator service, the *quality* of service expected in a good office building would require five elevators. Building parameters can be based on the proper combination of elevator size and numbers. A chart of office building area and height related to number of elevators is shown in the chapter on commercial buildings.

Full Trip Probability

If the top floor served by a group of elevators does not have sufficient attraction so that the elevators will travel to that floor on each trip, the average trip will be shorter than the full rise of the hoistway.

Averaging the number of trips the elevators will make to the top is one way to allow for this factor. Alternatively, the probability of a top floor trip can be determined by studying the particular building.

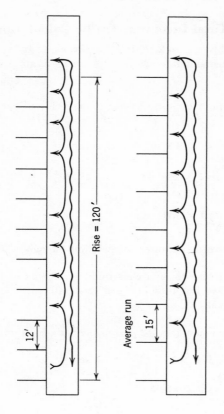

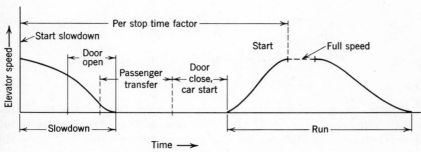

Figure 4.2

71

Example 4.1. Total Incoming Traffic Calculation

Given: 15-story building, lobby (1) to 2, 20 ft; typical floor 12 ft.

Required: Elevatoring to accommodate 125 persons during 5-min peak morning in-rush

Procedure:

Assume: four 3500 @ 500 fpm elevators, serving floors 1–15, 19 passengers per trip, 11 probable stops.

$$
\begin{aligned}
\text{Stops: } 11 \times 9.8 &= 107.8 \text{ sec} \\
\text{Lobby:} &= 25.0 \text{ sec} \\
\text{Run: } \frac{186' \times 2 \times 60}{500} &= \underline{44.6 \text{ sec}} \\
&= 177.4 \text{ sec} \\
\text{HC} = \frac{19 \times 300}{177} &= 32 \text{ persons}
\end{aligned}
$$

$^{125}\!/_{32}$ = 4 elevators required for handling capacity

Interval: $^{177}\!/_4$ = 44 sec. Too long for first-class building. Should be 30 sec.

Observe: 4 cars can carry load but time between cars (interval) too long, need fifth car to improve interval.

Recalculate:

Assume: five 2500 @ 700 fpm elevators, 12 passengers per trip, 9 probable stops

$$
\begin{aligned}
\text{Stops: } 9 \times 9.5 &= 85.5 \text{ sec} \\
\text{Lobby:} &= 20.0 \text{ sec} \\
\text{Run: } \frac{186 \times 2 \times 60}{700} &= \underline{32.0 \text{ sec}} \\
&= 137.5 \text{ sec} \\
\text{HC} = \frac{12 \times 300}{138} &= 26 \text{ persons}
\end{aligned}
$$

$^{125}\!/_{26}$ = 5 elevators required for handling capacity

Interval: $^{138}\!/_5$ = 27 sec. Good.

Assume, as an example, that a building is set back so the population of the top floor is one-half that of a lower floor. An elevator would therefore travel to the top, on the average, every other trip, provided the control system has provisions for reversing the car at its highest car call. This consideration would reduce the probable number of stops by possibly a half stop each trip. The probable stop calculation can thereby be corrected for this short trip each time. Similarly the rise traveled by the elevators could be corrected to reflect the difference of one-half of a floor. These differences may influence decisions between two sizes of elevators or car speeds.

When the future use or population of a building is unknown, it may not be possible to determine logically the probability of a top-floor stop. Instead the planner may use Chart 4 in which a heavy line has blocked off certain probable stop figures. Numbers below this line indicate areas in which the average trip will probably include the top landing and no provisions for a short trip should be made. Numbers above the heavy line indicate the probability of a short trip · and, if nothing more is known about the building, each trip may be reduced by one-half of a stop. Stated otherwise, if, for example, the normal probable number of stops is 10, the adjusted probable stop factor will be 9.5. For conservatism, the rise of the elevators should not be reduced.

If Example 4.1 is recalculated on the basis of short trips, the following results would be obtained:

Four 3500 @ 500 fpm elevators serving floors 1–15
Round-trip time: 172.5 sec
5-min capacity per elevator: 33 persons
4 elevators required; interval: 43 sec

Five 2500 @ 700 fpm elevators serving floors 1–15
Round-trip time: 132.7 sec
5-min capacity per elevator: 27 persons
5 elevators required; interval: 26 sec

When all other economic factors are considered, the foregoing may encourage the building of one more floor if five elevators are provided.

INCOMING TRAFFIC INTERVAL

Calculations of elevator requirements for incoming traffic yield an interval or average time between elevators leaving the lobby floor. This is the average time a person who just misses an elevator has to wait before the next one leaves. As can be seen from the calculations, the interval includes the loading time of the elevator.

For efficient loading, a carload of people should arrive and enter the elevator during the time allowed for loading. We may visualize at least one carload waiting to enter each elevator as it returns to the lobby, a concept that makes the interval become the average time each person waits for elevator service during periods of peak incoming traffic.

Incoming traffic interval differs somewhat from operating interval as described earlier in the discussion about a two-stop installation. With incoming traffic, *loading* interval represents the average wait for service

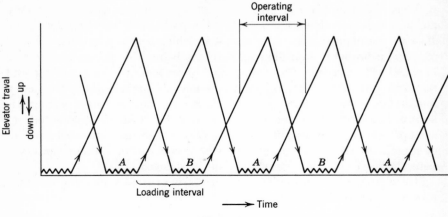

Figure 4.3

at the lobby; *operating* interval is related to the wait for service at an upper floor. Loading interval and waiting time are approximately equal but operating interval, theoretically, is twice waiting time at an upper floor. This distinction is shown graphically in Figure 4.3.

Figure 4.3 shows a two-car operation. With four cars, all other time factors remaining equal, loading time and loading interval are almost equal. The next car arrives at the lobby as the last car leaves and a person's wait for service is spent in the car. With eight cars and all other time factors remaining equal, two cars must be loaded simultaneously to avoid wasting carrying capacity.

INCOMING TRAFFIC OPERATION OF ELEVATORS

To provide a sufficient quantity and quality of elevator service during incoming traffic periods, elevator operation must conform to that traffic. For proper operation elevators must be controlled as follows:

1. Each car must depart from the lobby as soon as it is filled to a desired percentage of capacity.
2. Loading time should start as soon as the first call is registered in the car, assuming the first person who enters operates a car button.
3. The elevator should travel no higher than required by calls registered in the car.
4. The elevator should return to the lobby without stopping.
5. Passengers should be encouraged to load as promptly as possible.

6. If the interval between elevators is less than the average loading time or if random distribution causes more than one car to be at the lobby at one time, more than one car should be loaded at one time.

7. Cars should not be held beyond the time allowed for loading.

These requirements must be translated into automatic operations by the elevator control system. Modern systems do this without human intervention since no elevator attendant is present and an elevator starter cannot make decisions with necessary speed and accuracy. Automatic operations should include the features discussed in the following paragraphs.

In office buildings especially and in other buildings as well, the incoming traffic peak usually begins after a long period of quiet. If the control system has shut down the elevators, that is, parked them with doors closed, they must be activated as traffic occurs in the building. Because traffic is now entirely incoming, someone entering the building will operate a call button at the lobby floor to summon a car or activate a car parked there with the doors closed.

When the elevator responds, its doors open and one or more passengers operate call buttons in the car for their floors. If the car does not fill these passengers should not be held at the lobby more than 10 to 15 sec. If the car fills quickly, as indicated by a load-weighing device on the elevator, the car should depart immediately and another elevator become activated since quick loading of a car signifies continuing incoming traffic.

Once the car has started it should serve its car calls and return to the lobby immediately after serving the highest call. A continuing flow of traffic into the lobby will be indicated by filled cars or a multiplicity of car calls in cars that are at the lobby and by no appreciable hall call activity.

Cars should be controlled so that they depart from the lobby after a period of time equal to the expected loading time or depart as soon as filled to an adjustable percentage of load.

A lighted sign in the lobby should indicate to passengers the next car to depart. Even if it has not yet arrived at the lobby, its sign should be lighted so persons gather at the entrance, ready to load promptly when the car does arrive. If more than one car is expected to load at one time, all cars that return to the lobby should have their doors open to encourage simultaneous loading.

If there are no cars at the lobby and previous cars have left the lobby filled, a heavy incoming rush is indicated. During this period the elevators should automatically bypass hall calls until at least one car has returned to the lobby for incoming passengers. Elevators can bypass hall calls whenever lobby traffic requires this priority or bypassing can be restricted to certain periods of the day. At lunchtime, when both down traffic and incoming traffic becomes heavy, elevator service should be shared equally and the lobby should not have priority.

Restricting operations and giving priority to incoming traffic only during certain periods of the day can be accomplished by a time clock. Such clocks can be set to recognize days of the week and restrict operations to certain times on weekdays only. The clock can have the elevators in position for a known recurring incoming rush and also sustain operations during momentary lulls. Negative information, that no rush has occurred at a certain time, can indicate to a sophisticated elevator system that a particular day is a holiday and that elevator activity should not be maintained.

Once rapid loading and a multiplicity of car calls at the lobby ceases for a time or upper-floor hall calls become numerous, the incoming rush has subsided and the mode of elevator operation should change. Depending on the intensity of this subsequent two-way or interfloor traffic, elevator operation should be changed, as is discussed in the following chapter.

HANDLING INCOMING TRAFFIC PROBLEMS

If service demand in a building has changed or if it had an inadequate number of elevators from the start, certain measures may improve the handling capacity of its elevators during the incoming traffic period.

One of these measures was previously suggested—bypassing upper floor hall calls to prevent them from interfering with the service to the lobby traffic during times when no elevator is at the lobby. Bypassing could be extended so no hall calls are answered at any time during the critical incoming peak. As may be seen from our calculations, stopping for one call in a direction opposite to the peak traffic increases trip time by at least 9 or 10 sec with a corresponding reduction in handling capacity. The importance of serving hall calls becomes a guiding factor in this decision.

Up-Peak Zoning

Incoming traffic capacity can also be increased by reducing the number of stops each elevator makes. If enough elevators are in a group they may be zoned. Some of the elevators may be designated and controlled to serve the lower floors served and the others the upper floors. Separate means of control should be provided for each subgroup and stopping

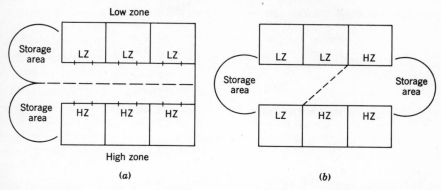

Figure 4.4 (*a*) Poor arrangement for incoming zoning; (*b*) good arrangement for incoming zoning.

for hall calls should be restricted. Special signs should be provided at the lobbies and the car buttons of the floors not served must be deactivated. Zoning should be restricted to specified periods and incoming passengers conditioned to expect restricted service at those times. There should be ample space for passengers at the lobby with the elevators arranged for ready access from the passenger waiting space. Figure 4.4*b* shows a preferable lobby arrangement for zoning.

Zoning increases handling capacity at the expense of interval. For example, one six-car group would be replaced by two three-car groups. From the calculation in Example 4.2, the handling capacity of a typical group of elevators is increased by 33 per cent at the expense of a greatly increased (50 per cent) loading interval. If persons are backing up in the lobby their waiting time is increasing so any means to get them to their floors would be welcome.

Example 4.2. Effect of Incoming Traffic Zoning

Original: Six 3500 @ 500, serving floors 1–12, rise 132 ft (12-ft floors)

$$
\begin{aligned}
\text{Stops:} &= 98.0 \text{ sec} \\
\text{Lobby:} &= 25.0 \text{ sec} \\
\text{Run: } \frac{132 \times 2 \times 60}{500} &= \underline{32.0 \text{ sec}} \\
&\ 155.0 \text{ sec} \\
\text{Round-trip time:} &= 155 \text{ sec} \\
\text{Interval: } {}^{155}\!\!/\!_{6} &= 26 \text{ sec} \\
\text{HC: 6 cars} = 6 \times \frac{19 \times 300}{155} &= 217 \text{ persons}
\end{aligned}
$$

With zoning:

Low group: Three 3500 @ 500, serving floors 1–7

$$\text{Stops: } 7 \times 9.8 \qquad\qquad = \quad 69.0 \text{ sec}$$
$$\text{Lobby: } \qquad\qquad\qquad = \quad 25.0 \text{ sec}$$
$$\text{Run: } \frac{72 \times 2 \times 60}{500} \qquad = \quad \underline{17.0 \text{ sec}}$$
$$111.0 \text{ sec}$$

Round-trip time: $\qquad$ = 111 sec
Interval: $111\frac{1}{3}$ $\qquad\qquad$ = 37 sec

$$\text{HC: 3 cars} = 3 \times \frac{19 \times 300}{111} = 154 \text{ persons}$$

High group: Three 3500 @ 500, serving floors 1, 8–12

$$\text{Stops: } 7 \times 9.8 \qquad\qquad = \quad 69.0 \text{ sec}$$
$$\text{Lobby: } \qquad\qquad\qquad = \quad 25.0 \text{ sec}$$
$$\text{Run: } \frac{132 \times 2 \times 60}{500} \qquad = \quad \underline{32.0 \text{ sec}}$$
$$126.0 \text{ sec}$$

Round-trip time: $\qquad$ = 126 sec
Interval: $= 126\frac{2}{3}$ $\qquad\quad$ = 42 sec

$$\text{HC: 3 cars} = 3 \times \frac{19 \times 300}{126} = 135 \text{ persons}$$

Group capacity: $\qquad\qquad$ = 289 persons
Gain by zoning: 72 persons or 33 per cent
Interval increase: 50 per cent longer.

Incoming traffic zoning has other limitations. Once a group of elevators is arranged for zoning, people must be conditioned as to what to expect. Once zoning is initiated it must be continued for a period of time, since people do not pay close attention to signs and become confused if zoned and unzoned operations alternate spasmodically. One subgroup, even though it may momentarily have idle elevator capacity consequently cannot temporarily aid the other subgroup. An alert lobby attendant can control initiation or discontinuance of zoning where it is required only temporarily.

High- and Low-Rise Elevators

It is a consequence of zoning that the concept of high- and low-rise elevators came into being. Instead of having all the elevators in a building serve all the floors, the elevators were broken into permanent groups, one group serving the lower floors of the building, a second group the next higher floors, and so on. The grouping of elevators is a characteristic of almost every major building of any height built today.

Each group of elevators has its own operating system and is calculated in a manner similar to the up-peak or up-peak zoning calculations. The essential difference is that sufficient elevators must be provided in any group to maintain a good loading and operating interval. To serve the higher floors in the building, the time required to transverse the express run or "blind" hoistway is reduced by higher-speed elevators. In 40- and 50-story buildings the highest rise groups of elevators, those serving the uppermost floors, may have speeds of 1000, 1200, or more fpm.

Utmost efficiency in providing elevators may be gained by establishing various-sized groups of elevators in a given building. For example, the low rise could be a four-car group, the mid rise a six-car group, and the high rise an eight-car group, all designed to provide the necessary handling capacity and to stay within a reasonable 30-sec interval.

Multiple-Entrance Floors

A building with multiple-entrance or lobby floors requires extra elevator capacity. If ample capacity is not available, limiting incoming traffic to one entrance floor can improve elevator service and perhaps ease a difficult situation.

Reviewing the calculations for incoming traffic handling capacity, we note that only one time allowance was included for the lobby or loading floor. If passengers are expected to board elevators at more than one floor, this time allowance must be increased in proportion to the number of passengers expected to enter at each floor.

For example, if a building has two entrance floors and half the incoming passengers are expected to arrive at each, two lobby stops are necessary. The time to make a round trip will automatically be increased by at least 10 sec in order to operate to the lower level. To insure full use of elevator capacity, each elevator must stop at both loading levels. The loading time spent at the lower loading level will be equal to about half the average loading time. The trip back up will require additional time so that approximately a minimum of 15 sec extra is required to serve the second terminal.

If elevators are filled at the lower level and bypass persons on the upper level, the latter will soon discover that they must go to the lower level for reasonable service. Escalators or shuttle elevators should then be provided. Preferably, the escalators or shuttle elevators should carry all passengers to the upper level, thus eliminating an extra elevator stop, reducing the distance traveled, and increasing the efficiency of the entire system.

Garage Floors

Similar arrangements are helpful for multilevel garages below the main entrance level. To provide service for passengers on the garage levels, all elevators must stop at those levels. Each stop adds 15 to 20 sec to the normal incoming traffic round-trip time, but a shuttle elevator would avoid this loss in elevator efficiency. Passengers then enjoy the convenience of parking in the building and the benefit of improved elevator service to their floors.

Parking floors above the lobby level but below the office floors or other usable space creates more serious problems. If parking is used by tenants in the building each parking level represents a potential loading level in calculating elevator round-trip time and handling capacity. A time factor proportional to the number of stops expected at parking levels must be added. If parking is open to both tenants and transients, still another time factor must be included proportional to the persons expected to leave the building from the parking levels.

As an example, if floors 2 through 6 are parking floors and about 50 per cent of the spaces are to be used by transients, and remaining parking patrons represent 50 per cent of the tenant population, the following additional stops may be expected. If each elevator is expected to carry 12 persons on a trip, 6 persons who work in the building are expected to enter the elevator at the ground floor and 6 parkers who work in the building are expected to enter on floors 2 through 6. The latter 6 persons will create about 3 additional stops during the up elevator trip. In addition, as the elevator returns to the lobby floor it must stop at least two or three more times to pick up the 6 transient parkers leaving the building. These people must be unloaded before the elevator can begin to serve incoming passengers again. In all, the 5 garage levels add about 5 additional stops (about 50 sec) to the round trip of an elevator, plus extra unloading time at the lobby.

The best solution is shuttle elevators between the lobby and parking levels with main elevators running directly from the lobby to the office floors. This improves tenant security as well as elevator service. Persons cannot enter the building or leave without passing through the main lobby. The parking area can be used in the evening whereby access to the upper floors of the building is controlled and use of its main elevators is minimized.

If main elevators must serve parking areas, elevator controls should be provided to minimize the impact of the extra stops. The number of stops any elevator makes at the garage levels should be limited to only a proportional measure of service. Limiting the number of elevators that will answer down calls at garage levels is a means of limiting elevator service in that area. How extensive such limitations are depends on the particular building.

GENERAL CONCLUSIONS

Incoming traffic problems are usually those of handling capacity and are often met by reducing time delays. The foregoing gave examples of means to reduce time delay and increase incoming handling of elevators.

But maximizing incoming traffic handling by zoning or other means that reduce the number of elevators may create a critical traffic situation at some other time of the day. Calculations of incoming traffic must be compared with other types of traffic in reaching final elevatoring decisions.

The foregoing chapter has introduced elevator time-study calculations. Comparing time factors in a calculation with those observed in actual installations aids in a personal evaluation of elevatoring problems. Means can be discovered to speed up a trip: better door opening operation, faster floor-to-floor time, or means to get doors closed and a car started sooner.

Each opportunity should be utilized to investigate various phases of the elevator trip as well as the loading and unloading of people from the elevator car. The result will be improved transportation and a more serviceable building.

Analysis was begun with incoming traffic because it is not complex and its time factors can be calculated with relative ease. The following chapter discusses two-way and interfloor traffic, rounding out the treatment of elevatoring previously presented.

CHAPTER FIVE

Two-Way and Interfloor Traffic

THE IMPORTANCE OF TWO-WAY TRAFFIC CONSIDERATIONS

Once a building is occupied its residential or working population will want to enter or leave the building at various times during the day. Some people may be entering at the same time as others are leaving, as at lunchtime (two-way traffic), or people will be going from one floor to another (interfloor traffic).

In many buildings the elevator peak traffic is two-way traffic. In a hotel guests are often checking out or going to activities while other groups are checking in or returning from meetings.

In buildings other than hotels the peak traffic is between floors. In a hospital, for example, traffic is heaviest when patients are being transferred for treatment, doctors are making visits, volunteers are tending to patients' needs, and other personnel are moving from floor to floor.

Traffic situations like these require elevators to make stops in both the up and down directions during the same round trip.

Two-way traffic may be relatively simple; persons enter the elevator at the lobby floor and leave at various stops during the up trip. On its down trip the elevator picks up passengers at various floors and lets them out at the lobby floor. Compared with purely incoming traffic, the round trip will now be considerably longer but the elevator will serve many more persons, the up passengers plus the down passenger on each round trip.

The interfloor traffic trip is more complex. During an up trip, for example, an elevator makes one stop to pick up a passenger and another stop to let him off. Each hall stop for a passenger usually requires two stops for the elevator. The round-trip time is therefore exceedingly long in relation to the number of passengers served.

During extremely heavy interfloor traffic, as in schools during class change periods and in department stores during rush buying seasons, it is conceivable that each elevator will make every stop up and every stop down!

Calculations for two-way and interfloor traffic follow the course outlined for incoming traffic. During these periods elevators should be operated to equalize waiting time for all elevator users.

TWO-WAY AND INTERFLOOR TRAFFIC REQUIREMENTS

To calculate how many elevators are required to serve a two-way or interfloor traffic situation, we begin by ascertaining passenger demand. Intensity of demand is a function of the building population, whereas its complexity depends on the distribution of that population among the floors of the building.

Determining population should be an easy matter. The building has been designed to accommodate certain activities or facilities: so many hospital beds and related staff, so many students, or, in an apartment or hotel, so many sleeping rooms. These factors determine the population.

Next, we need to know how many of these people will require elevator service during some critical period.

As with incoming elevator traffic, we are concerned with a critical 5-min period. Such a period is easy to determine; it has been evaluated in all types of buildings and, if longer periods of traffic demand persist, can indicate average intensity over the longer period. In schools the entire peak may occur during a 5-min period since this is all the time the students may be allowed to change classes. Should 10 min be allowed, elevator traffic will peak in the middle 5 min of the longer peroid.

For each building type discussed later in this book a qualifying percentage of population is given for the critical traffic period. The percentage, representing expected elevator passenger demand during a critical 5-min period, may vary from a low of about 6 per cent for apartments to a high of about 40 per cent for school buildings.

Characteristics of two-way or interfloor traffic depend not only on the building types but also on the relative attraction of each floor in a building. In a hotel, for example, the location of meeting room or ballroom floors and their relation to the lobby or guest rooms have a direct influence on the number of stops an elevator makes. In a school, hospital, or office building the cafeteria location may greatly influence the stopping on each elevator trip. This chapter gives guidance of a general nature; more specific suggestion for building types appear in later chapters.

Interfloor traffic can be a problem in an office building. If a single tenant or organization occupies many floors, traffic between various divisions of such an organization may adversely affect elevator service.

Under certain conditions, a separate interdepartmental elevator may prevent overburdening the main building elevators. In a large organization mail distribution, for example, may require almost continuous use of an elevator. One organization has a mail elevator complete with racks in which mail is sorted to permit delivery with minimum delay.

Changing habits are making two-way traffic more critical than the incoming peak in office buildings in many areas. When persons drive to the office their arrival is influenced by the accessibility of parking rather than by the time they are due at work. Arrivals may be spread over a longer period, which reduces up-peak elevator traffic. During the lunch period half the building population may be leaving while the other half is returning. The percentage of building population the elevators must serve during a peak 5 min of this period of time may be twice that served during a peak 5-min period in the morning.

Factors like these must be considered in calculating elevator requirements for two-way and interfloor traffic. The consequence of insufficient elevators for this period is impaired service for passengers. They must wait too long for an elevator and, once aboard, may face an unduly long trip marked by excessive stops for entering and leaving passengers.

Capacity is seldom the problem—it would be a poorly designed installation if an elevator that stopped for a passenger had no room for him. Waiting time and riding time are the more critical aspects so that elevators must necessarily pass the floors in a building with sufficient frequency in order to provide prompt service to all passengers.

A European device, the paternoster, has a series of continuously moving platforms (Figure 5.1). The passenger must leap onto a moving platform and off at his floor of destination. If he passes his floor he can stay on and make the full cycle up and over or down and under. Although the paternoster is a relatively slow-speed device (about 60 fpm), its use demands agility and its installation is not allowed in the United States.

With conventional elevators passengers can be transported only if the cars are intercepted, slowed, and stopped. A passenger's wait for

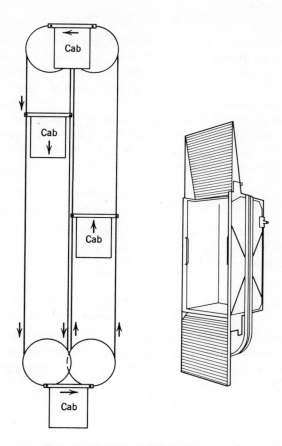

Figure 5.1 **"Paternoster" elevator.**

service becomes a function of the elevator operating interval. To provide service with acceptable average waits, the operating interval must be no longer than the maximum wait that passengers will tolerate.

In hurried, commercial atmospheres this tolerance seldom exceeds 30 to 35 sec. In a more relaxed residential atmosphere, a wait of about 60 sec is tolerated before tempers rise and people complain. An interval of from 30 to 60 sec is therefore necessary for most types of buildings. With service of this frequency during peak conditions passenger waiting times should be of acceptable duration.

CALCULATIONS FOR TWO-WAY TRAFFIC

Calculating the round-trip time of elevators serving two-way and interfloor traffic can follow the format used for incoming traffic. The time for each stop is established and multiplied by the number of expected stops, to which is added lobby time and nonstop running time. The total is an approximate round-trip time.

To establish the number of expected stops, a passenger load per trip in each direction must be determined. The total of up passengers plus down passengers times 300 sec (for 5 min) divided by the round-trip time per trip gives an elevator's 5 min capacity:

$$\text{Five-minute handling capacity} = \frac{(\text{up plus down passengers}) \times 300 \text{ sec}}{\text{round-trip time in seconds}}$$

Operating interval or average time between elevators passing a given upper floor in the building in either direction is found by dividing the round trip time of a single elevator by the number of elevators in the group.

$$\text{Operating interval} = \frac{\text{average round-trip time per elevator}}{\text{number of elevators in group}}$$

The principle is the same as in calculating the interval for incoming traffic, but emphasis shifts from loading interval at the lobby for incoming traffic to waiting time at an upper floor for interfloor or two-way traffic.

Probable Stops

The number of stops an elevator makes in any trip is a function of the number of passengers it carries, the number of floors the elevator serves, the relative attraction of each floor, and the relationship of each floor to the others in the building. Establishing probable stops for a building before the occupancy of that building requires a great deal of estimation.

Prevailing practices of people in known buildings can help in this estimation and give an indication of the number of stops elevators will make during two-way trips. People, for example, usually go to lunch at noon or to a coffee break in midmorning. In specialized buildings, such as hospitals or hotels, activities take place that can be measured, evaluated, and projected to the next hospital or hotel to be built.

In any building certain floors will be sure stops for each elevator trip. The lobby is one such floor; the cafeteria floor would be another.

Entrances to the building from parking areas on several levels will cause elevator stopping relative to the attraction of each such floor. During two-way traffic, the probability of passengers going to or from the top floor of a building is proportional to the relative population on that floor.

As a beginning, we have at least two certain stops in each two-way or interfloor elevator trip—the lobby and some upper floor in the building. Stopping at other floors is a function of the number of people using the car during each trip. For two-way traffic, because we are concerned with persons boarding the car at the entrance floor or floors, the number of up stops is approximately the same as for incoming traffic. No provision should be made for short trips, as this becomes highly unlikely unless the top floor served has a minimum attraction.

On the down trip, because persons are at each floor waiting to be picked up, and people often go to lunch with companions, the number of stops made are a percentage of the number made on the up trip, less one. The number is less one because the top stop is both an up and down stop and should not be counted twice. The percentage of stops in the down direction compared to up may be arbitrarily taken as 75 per cent based on actual values from 70 to 80 per cent.

The probable stop value for two-way traffic then becomes:

Two-way probable stops = up probable stops
$$+ \ 0.75 \ (\text{up probable stops}) - 1$$
Two-way probable stops = 1.75 (up probable stops) − 1

When many floors are to be served, the likelihood of each passenger causing a stop is increased. If, for example, an elevator is expected to carry 10 passengers in a trip and can make say 20 stops, it is almost certain to make 10 stops. Similarly, if an elevator is expected to carry 10 passengers in each direction and can make only 5 stops, it is almost certain to make every stop up and down. These later considerations will prove especially valuable in approximating two-way trips in apartment buildings or any situation in which minimum car loading is expected.

Elevator capacity must be ample for two-way and interfloor traffic. We will assume the elevator car is filled equally in both directions although this is seldom the case in actual situations. Essentially, the platform must be large enough to serve the required number of persons in each direction in each trip. As a rule, the car should not be filled to more than an average of one-half its up-peak capacity in two-way traffic calculations. With capacity loads the trip time usually becomes much too long, the transfer time at each stop is unduly lengthened, and no reserve capacity remains for momentary traffic surges or inbalance between up and down traffic.

Chart 2

Passengers per trip	2	4	6	8	10	12	14	16	18	20	22	24	26
30	2	4	6	8	10	12	14	16	18	20	20	21	22
28	2	4	6	8	10	12	14	16	17	18	19	20	21
26	2	4	6	8	10	12	14	15	16	17	18	19	20
24	2	4	6	8	10	12	13	14	15	16	17	18	19
22	2	4	6	8	10	11	12	13	14	15	16	17	18
20	2	4	6	8	9	10	11	12	13	14	15	16	17
18	2	4	6	7	8	9	10	11	12	13	13	14	15
16	2	4	6	7	8	9	10	10	11	12	12	12	13
14	2	4	5	6	7	8	9	9	10	11	11	12	12
12	2	4	5	6	7	8	9	9	10	10	10	11	12
10	2	4	5	5	6	7	8	8	9	9	9	10	10
8	2	3	4	5	6	6	7	7	8	8	8	8	8
6	2	3	3	4	5	5	6	6	6	6	6	6	6
4	2	3	3	4	4	4	4	4	4	4	4	4	4

Upper floors served

Probable stops—equal attraction per floor

An expanded version of the up probable stop chart, Chart 2, is presented to provide values for expected light and heavy loadings.

For interfloor traffic determining probable stops under extreme conditions is quite simple. Because each passenger requires two elevator stops, one to pick him up and one to let him off, the number of stops will be twice the number of passengers in each direction less one for the highest stop. For example, if two persons are expected to travel up and two persons down, an elevator will make about seven stops. We say "about" because one or more of those stops may be coincidental, that is, a person will get on where a passenger made a car stop or vice versa. Stated otherwise, some hall calls are expected to be coincidental with car calls. A coincidence factor can be established but because it must apply only to a particular building we will be conservative and assume none.

As may be seen, interfloor traffic trips can be time consuming and if a large number of persons are traveling up and down, the elevators will make almost every stop in each direction. This is particularly true in school situations during class changes. In offices and hospitals the general average is about every other stop up and down with the elevator filled to about 50 per cent of its up-peak capacity.

Transfer Time

Somewhat more time is required to load a single passenger or a group at an intermediate stop or to let passengers off at an upper stop during two-way than during the incoming traffic period. Certain minimum requirements should be included in any calculation. A person can move out of a moderately loaded elevator in about 1 sec or less providing he is ready to get off at the next stop. A passenger in the hall requires about 2 sec to enter a car if he is alerted by a hall lantern and is waiting in front of the entrance when the car arrives.

In our calculations we will use a combined average of 3 sec per stop for both entering and leaving passengers. As a safety factor all the time factors will be increased by 15 per cent for each stop.

Since cars are not expected to be filled to capacity, the values used are equal for any size car. These values for elevators with 3 ft 6 in. center opening doors are as follows:

1. Time to stop and start		3.6 sec
2. Time to open doors		0.6 sec
3. Time to transfer		3.0 sec
4. Time to close doors		3.3 sec
	Total	10.5
	Plus 15 per cent	1.5
		12.0 sec

We must allow a minimum of 12 sec plus 1.0 sec for each person entering and leaving the elevator at the main lobby stop. For example, if 10 persons are expected to travel up from the lobby and 10 are expected to exit at the lobby each trip, the lobby stop time should be 12 sec plus 20 sec for the entering and leaving passengers or a total of 32 sec.

Each foregoing value must be modified for extreme conditions as, for example, in school buildings. Extra transfer time should be included for each passenger carried over 50 per cent of the up-peak capacity of the elevator.

For example, suppose the up-peak capacity of the elevator is 16 passengers (a 3000 lb car) and 16 passengers are expected to be riding in each direction, on the average, during a two-way or interfloor traffic trip. Extra time of 1.0 sec per passenger for half the passengers per direction should be allowed. For the 16-passenger car, the extra time would be 8 sec for up and 8 sec for down or a total of 16 sec extra transfer time for intermediate stops. The extra time recognizes the difficulty a passenger would have getting out of or into a filled car.

As discussed for the up-peak situation, time compensation adjustment should also be allowed for narrow or wide doors different from the 3 ft 6 in. standard center opening entrances. Additional time should be allowed for other than standard-shaped platforms. Unless elevator lobbies are adequate, still additional transfer time will be required.

Sample Calculations. Examples 5.1 and 5.2 show the complete calculations for two-way and interfloor traffic. Both moderate car loadings and full car loadings are shown.

For two-way traffic, handling capacity is simply defined, as all persons have obvious destinations. Handling capacity is measured in terms of persons traveling to and from the lobby.

In the interfloor traffic examples, handling capacity is the net number of persons transferred to and from the lobby and does not account for additional persons carried from floor to floor.

It is essential that the standard of elevator demand be established. If the demand is defined as persons carried from floor to floor, elevators effectively carry many more persons during interfloor traffic than is shown by only a lobby count. This is best explained by a sketch:

Up		Down	
20 ◄—		◄— 20	In and out at first floor per trip, 40 persons.
20 ◄—		◄— 20	In and out at all floors—floor-to-floor per
20 —►		—► 20	trip, 120 persons.
20 —►		—► 20	
20 ◄—		◄— 20	
20 passengers in		20 passengers out	

Note that the total interfloor trip only carried 40 persons to and from the lobby but 120 persons from floor to floor. The essential point is to define and measure demand in terms of the problem.

For simplicity, demands for interfloor traffic will be expressed in terms of lobby or traffic in and out of the building. If between-floor traffic must be analyzed, percentages of persons traveling one, two, three, or more floors as well as the percentage of passengers traveling to and from the lobby must be ascertained. Generally, if a high interfloor traffic demand is expected, escalators are the best way to serve that demand.

In Example 5.1, part B, a round trip time of 262 sec was calculated. A person riding in an elevator for that length of time would be expected to complain from the sheer boredom of a long trip. Since the example assumed both up and down traffic, persons going to and from the top floor of the building would be on the elevators about half the round trip time or about $2\frac{1}{4}$ min. Even this is too long, and if such traffic were common and expected to extend over a period of time of about 15 to 30 min, two groups of four elevators each (high rise and low rise) would be indicated even though it meant an additional elevator in the building.

Having four elevators serve floors 1 through 6 and four cars serve floors 1 and 7 through 12 would expedite traffic to and from the lobby and greatly reduce the average passenger trip. Fewer hoistway entrances would be required, the elevator system could be installed in less building space, and passengers would be happier. Depending on equipment specifications, the eight elevators might even cost no more than the seven cars serving all floors.

Example 5.1. Two-way Traffic

A. Given: Two-way traffic peak, 120 persons, 12-story building, 10-ft floor heights.

Assume: Four 3000 @ 500 fpm elevators—8 passengers up, 8 passengers down.

$$\text{Stops: } 1.75 \times (6) - 1 = 10.5 - 1 = \quad 9.5 \text{ stops}$$
$$\text{Lobby: } 12 + 16 \times 1 \quad\quad = \quad 28.0 \text{ sec}$$

$$\text{Stop time: } 9.5 \times 12 \quad\quad = 114.0 \text{ sec}$$
$$\text{Lobby:} \quad\quad\quad\quad\quad\quad = \quad 28.0 \text{ sec}$$
$$\text{Run: } \frac{(11 \times 10) \times 2 \times 60}{500} = \underline{\quad 26.4 \text{ sec}}$$
$$168.4 \text{ sec}$$

$$\text{HC: } \frac{(8 + 8) \times 300}{168} = \quad 29 \text{ persons/elevator} \times 4 = 116$$
$$\text{persons}$$

$$\text{Interval: } {}^{168}\!\!/_{4} \quad\quad = \quad 42 \text{ sec}$$

5 cars required for good interval and handling capacity.

B. Given: Two-way traffic peak, 250 persons, 12-story building, 10-ft floor heights.

Assume: 3000 @ 500 fpm elevators, 16 passengers up, 16 passengers down.

$$\text{Stops: } 1.75 \times (9) - 1 = 15.75 - 1 = \quad 14.75 \text{ stops}$$

$$\text{Stop time: } 14.75 \times 12 \quad\quad = 177.0 \text{ sec}$$
$$\text{Lobby: } 12 + (32 \times 1) \quad\quad = \quad 44.0 \text{ sec}$$
$$\text{Extra transfer: } 2(1. \times 8) \quad\quad = \quad 16.0 \text{ sec}$$
$$\text{Run: } \frac{(11 \times 10) \times 2 \times 60}{500} = \underline{\quad 26.4 \text{ sec}}$$
$$263.4 \text{ sec. Long trip time.}$$

$$\text{HC: } \frac{(16 + 16) \times 300}{263} = \quad 37 \text{ persons/elevator}$$

$$^{250}\!\!/_{37} = 6.7 - 7 \text{ elevators required}$$

$$\text{Interval } \frac{263.0}{7} \quad\quad\quad = \quad 38 \text{ sec.}$$

Example 5.2. Interfloor Traffic

A. Given: Interfloor traffic requirement 90 persons in 5 min (lobby count), 8-story hospital, 10-ft floor heights.

Assume: Three 3500 @ 500 fpm elevators, 6 passengers up, 6 down.

Assume: Elevators make every other stop.

$$\text{Stops: } 7 \times 12 \qquad\qquad = \quad 84.0 \text{ sec}$$
$$\text{Lobby: } 12 + (12 \times 1.0) \quad = \quad 24.0 \text{ sec}$$
$$\text{Run: } \frac{(7 \times 10) \times 2 \times 60}{500} \quad = \quad \underline{16.8 \text{ sec}}$$
$$\qquad\qquad\qquad\qquad\qquad\qquad 124.8 \text{ sec}$$

$$\text{HC: } \frac{(6 + 6) \times 300}{125} \qquad = \quad 29 \text{ person/elevator} \times 3 = 87. \text{ O.K.}$$

$$\text{Interval: } 125/_3 \qquad\qquad = \quad 42.0 \text{ sec. Acceptable.}$$

B. Given: Interfloor traffic requirement 250 persons in 5 min (lobby count), 6-story school, 12-ft floor heights.

Assume: 4000 @ 500 fpm elevators, 22 passengers up, 22 down.

$$\text{Stops: } 9 \times 12 \qquad\qquad\;\, = 108.0 \text{ sec}$$
$$\text{Lobby: } 12 + (22 \times 1) \quad\; = \quad 34.0 \text{ sec}$$
$$\text{Extra transfer: } 2(1 \times 11) = \quad 22.0 \text{ sec}$$
$$\text{Run: } \frac{(5 \times 12) \times 2 \times 60}{500} \quad = \quad \underline{14.4 \text{ sec}}$$
$$\qquad\qquad\qquad\qquad\qquad\qquad 178.4 \text{ sec}$$

$$\text{HC: } \frac{(22 + 22) \times 300}{178} \quad = \quad 74.0 \text{ persons}$$

$$250/_{74} \qquad\qquad\qquad\;\; = \quad 3.3 \text{ elevators. Should be 3 larger elevators.}$$
$$\text{Interval: } 178/_3 \qquad\qquad = \quad 59 \text{ sec. Too long; would be longer for 3 larger}$$
$$\qquad\qquad\qquad\qquad\qquad\qquad\qquad \text{elevators.}$$

Four elevators required for acceptable handling capacity and interval. 3500 lb is indicated.

ELEVATORS OPERATION DURING TWO-WAY AND INTERFLOOR TRAFFIC

When the number of elevators for interfloor and two-way traffic situations are calculated, a primary objective is to minimize waiting time by providing a short interval of service. Interval depends largely on the effectiveness of elevator operation and is mainly the result of the sophistication of the group supervisory system provided.

Minimizing the time an average passenger would spend on the elevator is of secondary concern. Riding time is a function of elevator layout and arrangement as well as the number of floors served and the size of each car.

With modern automatic elevators all decisions to start or "dispatch" an elevator are made by electronic devices. The simplest will start an elevator whenever a call is registered with little regard for closeness to the car ahead or "elevator spacing." As a result, cars often operate in close proximity and the group of elevators offers service very little better than one large elevator.

An on-call operation of this type can only be effective when traffic is light and elevators are sufficient so that each car can operate almost independently of the others. Our calculations have indicated that if only one or two persons are seeking service, even the most elementary operating system will suffice.

Where many people are seeking service at a given time, elevators require more skillful automatic control to maintain a proper distribution in time. Each prospective passenger will then have an equal opportunity to board the elevators and his average wait will not exceed that of any other passenger.

To begin our study of elevator operation let us first classify elevator traffic into three categories as follows:

1. Light traffic, when the number of passengers seeking service at a given time is no more than two or three times the number of elevators available to give service.

2. Medium to heavy traffic, when the number of passengers seeking service at one time will not fill the elevators to more than one-half their capacity.

3. Heavy traffic, when the number of persons seeking service will fill elevators between 50 and 100 per cent of capacity.

By assuring the most efficient operation during the medium and heavy traffic situations the number of elevators required are minimized.

Light Traffic

During light traffic elevators may often park and wait for the next call. The cars should be distributed among the floors of the building so they are within minimum operating time of a next expected call. It is also essential that the cars travel no farther than necessary to serve their existing calls and park in anticipation of subsequent calls. Because traffic is light there is little need to operate the elevators continuously and on-call operation is perfectly feasible.

An arrangement for light traffic operation is shown in Figures 5.2*a* and 5.2*b*. Waiting cars are parked in areas (1 and 2) that have been

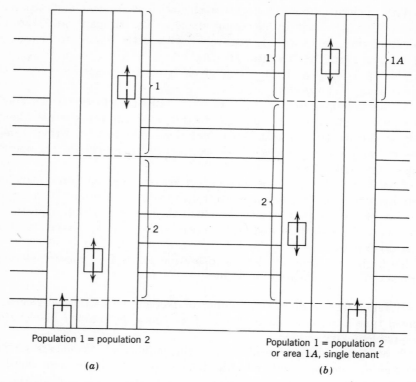

Population 1 = population 2

(a)

Population 1 = population 2
or area 1A, single tenant

(b)

Figure 5.2 (*a*) **Population** 1 = **population** 2; (*b*) **population** 1 = **population 2 or area** 1A, **single tenant.**

established on the basis of population of the various floors or the expected activity caused by a single tenant on a group of floors. Each car should move to the next call in its area with minimum delay and be free to travel either up or down from that call as passengers desire.

One car is stationed at the lobby, where the probability of a call is high. If that car leaves another car should promptly take its place and the former lobby car should park, after completing its call, in the zone of the car it displaced.

Because elevators can give individual service, each car should only operate to the highest or lowest call in the area it covers, remaining in that area to answer the next call. If a car is taken from one area to another, and the car in the latter area is also moved to another area, the former car should assume responsibility for the new area. If for any reason an area is temporarily unoccupied, an elevator in an adjacent area should be free to answer calls in the unoccupied area.

Medium Traffic

When traffic increases and elevators must share the passenger load, they seldom have occasion to park. For efficient service elevators should be continuously distributed in controlled spacing so that the operating time between each car is approximately equal. Elevators should be operated continuously whether or not calls are registered and should be scheduled on the basis of the prevailing traffic, whether equal in both directions or weighted either up or down. For this purpose traffic is considered in terms of the time required for the elevator trip. Traffic is equal in both directions if the time required to make an up trip is equal to that required to make a down trip with all intermediate stops considered, as shown in Figure 5.3.

Figures 5.3*a* and *b* show a distribution of elevators. As long as the time between each car is more or less equal, any passenger will have an equal opportunity to intercept any car within the operating interval. In Figure 5.3*b* the effect of introducing calls between the cars is shown. If no control were established car *B* would soon overtake car *A* and car *C* would soon overtake car *D*. The net result would be equivalent to a two-car system rather than a four-car system. Cars *A* and *B* and cars *C* and *D* would be operating like two single elevators and the interval between elevators would be double (quality of service halved).

This result could be overcome by proper dispatching moves. Car *B* could be short-tripped and reversed at the down hall call shown providing it had no higher car calls. The time car *C* spends at the lobby could be minimized so the balance of cars traveling up and down as well as the time between the individual cars would be restored.

Decisions of this nature were the function of the elevator starter for manually operated elevators. As may be seen, with a fast moving system a starter could never keep up with all the changing traffic situations and electrical control is a necessity.

Modern elevator supervisory systems should be based on the ability of electrical components to make rapid decisions and take action. Many such systems are available and the most sophisticated of these modern systems uses an electronic computer to calculate the interval for each car on each trip and in each direction. Electronics are used to account for many more variables than a human elevator starter could ever do.

Some of the necessary dispatching action is shown in Figures 5.4*a* and *b*. If we plot each elevator trip on a time base as shown and introduce

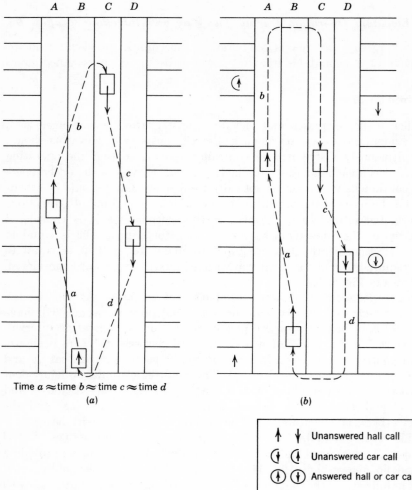

Time $a \approx$ time $b \approx$ time $c \approx$ time d

(a)

(b)

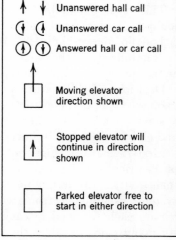

↑	↓	Unanswered hall call
↻↓	↺↑	Unanswered car call
⊕↓	⊕↑	Answered hall or car call
[↑]		Moving elevator direction shown
[↑]		Stopped elevator will continue in direction shown
[ ]		Parked elevator free to start in either direction

Key to symbols

Figure 5.3 (*a*) Time *a* ≈ time *b* ≈ time *c* ≈ time *d* (≈ about equal to); (*b*) time *a* decreasing, time *b* increasing, time *c* decreasing, time *d* increasing.

96

calls into the system, we get a graph as shown in section *A*, Figure 5.4*a*. For simplification, the time consumed by stops is lumped with running time and a total up and down trip time is shown in section *B*.

As long as the time required to make an up trip is equal to the time required for a down trip as shown in section *B*, the dispatch of a car from the lower terminal is simultaneous with a dispatch from the upper terminal. This is true with any even-number group of elevators. Dispatches from an odd-number group would alternate for equal traffic in both directions.

As the time to make a trip in one direction is lengthened or shortened by changing passenger demands, and the signals are given on schedule, the elevators can be made to operate on a desired pattern matched with the prevailing traffic. Note in area *C* (Figure 5.4*a*) how a car is held at the top for a short time to adjust it to the traffic pattern

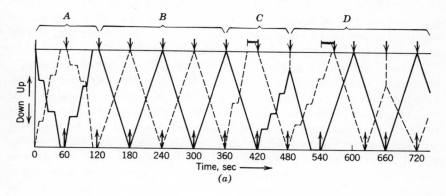

(a)

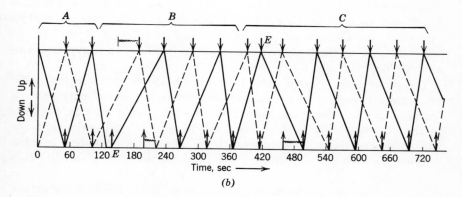

(b)

Figure 5.4

and how a car is short-tripped to catch up to the pattern. Further adjustment in the time between dispatches would be made (Figure 5.4*a*, area *D*) to compensate for long or short trip trends but, basically, the simultaneous top and bottom dispatch would be the rule as long as traffic in both directions is more or less equal in the time required.

Figure 5.4*b* shows traffic biased in a heavier up or heavier down fashion. Area *A* shows the equal traffic situation; area *B* shows bias in the up direction by the extra long up trip. Note that an extra or early dispatch at the lower terminal (*E*) changes the pattern of operation from simultaneous to alternative dispatching and restores a schedule to the elevators. The bias in area *C* is in the opposite direction—the up trip is short and the down trip long. Again an extra dispatch balances elevator traffic against dispatching operation.

We have shown a simple dispatching sequence for two cars. The pattern for four or six cars, changing each trip of each elevator to correspond to the traffic it encounters, would be much more complex. What is important is that the supervisory system, when provided with a group of elevators expected to encounter traffic of the nature described, should consider all the factors in order to perform properly.

A group supervisory system should be designed to anticipate constantly what may occur with the prevalent traffic, rather than waiting to react to what occurs; circuits should be provided to force elevators on their way, based on indicators of demand. If the supervisory system fails to do this the elevators can be hopelessly overwhelmed and heavy traffic will exist where only moderate traffic existed before. As can be appreciated, elevator traffic is dynamic—it is always changing—and if it is not served when it occurs passengers will pile up at every floor, where they will register both up and down calls in frustration and make the situation worse. A few seconds can change the entire aspect of a system from good to bad; hence everything possible must be done to control such traffic and the response of the elevators to it.

A summary of the operations required for medium to heavy two-way and interfloor traffic should include the following items.

The supervisory system must have the ability to measure the traffic an elevator is expected to encounter and dispatch it accordingly on each trip and in each direction. Such traffic factors would include car calls in the car, the loading of the car, the number of hall calls that car will encounter, the spacing between that car and the preceding car, the relation between up and down traffic, and the location of all the cars in the system.

In addition, the group supervisory system must decide whether the elevators should be quickly changed from concentration on down or up traffic to traffic in the opposite direction, whether to travel an elevator through to the top or bottom terminal or short-trip that car, where to send cars to be fed into prevalent traffic demand, and when to change the time spacing between elevators.

All of the foregoing constitutes a formidable task that electronic devices, now becoming available, are beginning to accomplish by gathering, storing, and computing all the necessary information. Because the factors *are* dynamic, the job calls for a highly specialized analog computer. Once the calls are counted they must be weighted. Elevators are not traveling at constant speed but rather running, stopping, or starting; people's habits are not predictable, and one call can change the entire aspect of an elevator system in less than a second. We have dealt with averages in our computation. In real life discrete trips and people must be dealt with. We presume the average will make the most passengers satisfied.

Heavy Traffic

Once traffic becomes exceedingly heavy in both directions, we find the cars filling on the up trip (either at each floor or at the lobby similar to up peak operation) and filling in the down direction. With such extreme traffic the situation becomes one of panic operation. The cars will probably make every stop up and they should go no higher than the highest up hall call or car call and be immediately reversed. On the down trip the cars may make every stop down and perhaps bypass the lower of the down hall calls because of capacity load in the car and load bypass arrangement. The time the elevator spends at the lobby should be the minimum required for passenger transfer.

Hall calls that are bypassed should be given a measure of preference. An upper limit of waiting time can be established, and any car in the proper direction, with capacity and without intervening car calls, can be bypassed to the call that has waited overly long.

Bypassing must be used with discretion. The bypassed call becomes a tentative long-wait call—with indiscriminate bypassing, many calls could wait overly long and a hopeless situation could develop. To avoid this it is necessary to do everything possible to dispatch elevators at the first indication of traffic rather than wait for a traffic situation to develop.

Overwhelming situations can occur in any building. It is most noticeable in schools during class change periods and in hotels during the time when convention meetings break up. Everyone in the building wants to go some place at the same time, and if enough elevators were provided there would be little room for usable area on the building's floors. The best approach is to recognize the problem and make ample provisions to move people to an area where waiting is more tolerable, such as a lounge or cafeteria.

One of the most appropriate means is by escalators or large stairways. Elevator service to certain floors should be discontinued and elevator entrance lobbies blocked so that people will not be frustrated by waiting for elevators that may not stop because they are filled to capacity. Only one floor should be designated to load the heavy incoming crowd and all persons directed to that floor. Additional efficiency can be gained by restricting the stops the elevators will make such as up car and down hall call stops only if such is feasible.

In schools during class change periods students can be encouraged to use stairways by restricting the floors the elevators serve to every second or third. Handicapped students can be directed to service or other elevators or required to wait until the rush has subsided. Reducing the number of stops on the main elevators will reduce round-trip time and improve handling capacity.

Other solutions to the overwhelming traffic problem is to restrict service to incidental floors such as basements or penthouses. These floors could be manually or automatically cut out and lighted signs could inform passengers to use stairs. In a building that is initially underelevatored or where a change in the building use has created handling capacity problems, the feasibility of adding additional elevators or dividing the existing elevators into subgroups as described for incoming traffic should be considered. Permanently removing time-consuming and poorly productive elevator stops such as in basements or garage floors should be attempted. Perhaps an auxiliary small elevator could be installed to assume that function.

GENERAL CONCLUSIONS

Two-way and interfloor traffic can be the most serious of the traffic situations encountered in any building. Not only must sufficient elevators be provided to serve the expected traffic but they must be operated in such a way that their most efficient use is assured. Failure to do so will create a heavy traffic situation where, perhaps, only moderate traffic should exist.

All the inefficiencies of poor elevator shape, size, layout, and so on, as described for incoming traffic, will be amplified during the heavier two-way traffic situations. Poor operating intervals will cause immeasurable employee time loss by riding and waiting passengers. When we consider the number of passengers riding and waiting at a given time, we see that 5 or 10 sec extra time spent per trip will add up to thousands of man-hours lost by inefficient elevators each year. This cost can be avoided by proper design and operation.

As with all the examples and calculations given in this book, these are offered as a guide to the thinking process of elevatoring. Ample professional help is available and should be sought once a decision to establish elevatoring for any building is made.

CHAPTER SIX

Outgoing Traffic

THE IMPORTANCE OF OUTGOING TRAFFIC

When the quitting bell sounds or when lunch time arrives, a building's occupants are ready to leave and will demand elevator service. During these outgoing traffic peaks passengers, by sheer numbers alone, may overwhelm an elevator system unless provisions are made for this contingency.

The most elementary of these provisions is sufficient elevator capacity to serve the outgoing traffic demand expected. In office buildings, especially, the outgoing 5-min peak traffic may exceed any other traffic peak by 40 or 50 per cent. Proper design and operation of an elevator system can provide this capacity without more elevators than are normally required to serve other traffic periods.

Another consideration is a reliable means to prevent an elevator filled to capacity from responding to hall calls. For this load weighing and bypassing operation, automatic elevators can be equipped with any of several devices, the most sophisticated of which will measure only the live load on the platform. Devices of this nature should be capable of adjustment; average capacity load in one building may never be attained in another but the problem of efficient outgoing traffic operation will remain.

Since demand is usually scattered among the various floors and an elevator is loaded promptly when it arrives at each floor, advantage may be taken of this in calculating outgoing traffic performance. Because persons are on their own time, so to speak, and anxious to get out of a building, they willingly load elevators to near capacity and often beyond. If the area is available, loads will exceed the average 80 per cent loading experienced during incoming traffic periods. So much so

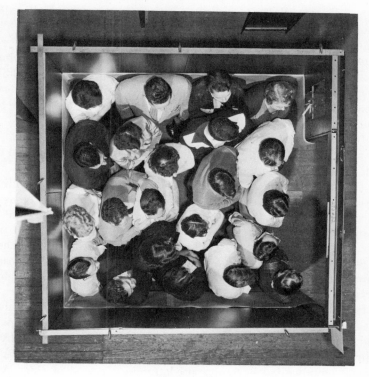

Figure 6.1

that the American Safety Code for elevators requires the elevator brake to be able to slow down and stop a down traveling car filled to 125 per cent of rated elevator capacity. Figure 6.1 shows moderate loading of an elevator during a down peak period. The 3000-lb elevator shown in the photo has a normal full load capacity of 19 persons, but 22 persons are crowded into the car.

OUTGOING TRAFFIC REQUIREMENTS

Normally an elevator system should be capable of evacuating the population of a building within 15 to 30 min. This period may be lengthened or shortened depending on particular tenant needs. Although the primary need is capacity, and quality of service is secondary, service should be available at every floor at intervals no longer than 60 sec. A sophisticated elevator control system will have a means to provide equal service to all floors once a multiplicity of down hall calls are apparent. The sequence of operations might be as follows:

If all floors are receiving outgoing traffic service, the elevators should be equally spaced in time in the down direction, unloaded in minimum time at the lobby, and immediately returned up into the building to serve additional outgoing traffic. Elevators may be allowed to serve up hall calls as long as these calls do not interfere with service to the outgoing rush.

As the cars fill at upper floors they tend to bypass hall calls in the lower section of the building. When this occurs all but one or two elevators in the group should then bypass up hall calls.

As the waiting time of calls in the lower section of the building increases beyond a predetermined value, some elevators should be assigned to serve only the lower portion of the building. At what point these cars are to turn back can be calculated or observed from actual performance. To facilitate any up traffic, it should be restricted to the cars that serve the upper portion of the building by having only those stop for up hall calls. These procedures will tend to equalize the elevator capacity available to all floors of the building.

If traffic continues to increase until hall calls tend to wait beyond a predetermined period of time, a preferential "spotting" operation should be instituted. After elevators are unloaded at the lobby they are directed to any floor at which passengers (as indicated by a down hall call) have waited beyond a predetermined period of time. At that call the elevator reverses and, if it is not filled, it continues to pick up down hall calls until it fills or reaches to the lobby. Under extreme conditions with this operation, elevators become, in effect, two-stop elevators, completely loaded at one floor and completely unloaded at another. This is the most efficient operation that can be gained from any elevator.

Obviously, if extreme conditions for down traffic occur with any frequency in a building, service to any odd floors, up hall calls, basements, and so on, should be temporarily suspended. Any traffic opposed to the outward rush will reduce the systems efficiency and should be considered in that light. Naturally, if up service is necessary and outgoing traffic demands all the available elevator service, additional equipment, staggered quitting times, or other approaches to the problem are necessary.

Calculations for Outgoing Traffic

Intensity of outgoing traffic is seldom the main consideration in elevatoring a building. Under certain circumstances, however, it can be exceedingly important. For example, if elevators serve an upper-floor meeting room or auditorium they require sufficient capacity for the orderly evacuation of that facility. In theaters, classroom buildings, stores, and so forth, evacuation ability may be of prime interest in elevatoring. For upper-floor "sky lobby" arrangements discussed in a later chapter, shuttle elevators must be predicated on the down peak capacity of the local elevators they serve.

Determining the capacity of an elevator system during outgoing traffic periods can proceed in a manner similar to incoming traffic with the following essential differences.

The mode of operation must be established. Will the peak be severe enough to warrant two-stop operation—loading at one floor and unloading at a lower floor, or are many stops in the down direction expected?

Elevators may carry greater loads than during the incoming peak; 100 per cent rather than 80 per cent loading can be considered.

Loading can be efficient. An average of 0.6 sec per person can be used provided there is sufficient door width and a reasonably shaped platform. We presume passengers will be attentive to hall lanterns and be at the entrance when an elevator arrives at a floor.

In view of the foregoing discussion an average time value per stop can be established in the following manner:

1. Time to start and stop	3.6 sec
2. Time to open doors	0.6 sec
3. Time to close doors	3.3 sec
	7.5 sec plus
4. Time to transfer	0.6 sec times the number of transferring passengers

5. Inefficiency factor 15 per cent

Therefore the total time per trip can be represented in the following fashion.

$$
\text{Outgoing round-trip time} = (\text{number of stops} + 1^*) \times 7.5 \text{ sec} \quad (a)
$$
$$
+ 2 \times (\text{number of passengers}) \times 0.6 \quad (b)
$$
$$
+ 0.15\,(a + b)
$$
$$
+ \frac{\text{rise} \times 2 \times 60}{\text{speed fpm}}
$$

The foregoing equation is based on 3 ft 6 in. center-opening doors and elevators speed of 500 fpm or more. Adjustments in time for other conditions must be made as described for incoming traffic.

* The +1 is for the lobby stop.

Outgoing handling capacity and interval are calculated as for other conditions.

$$\text{5-minute handling capacity} = \frac{\text{number of passengers down} \times 300 \text{ sec}}{\text{round-trip time}}$$

$$\text{Interval} = \frac{\text{round-trip time}}{\text{number of elevators}}$$

The interval for average conditions should not exceed 60 sec. This is predicated on the intention of offering all passengers service within 60 sec during the peak outgoing traffic 5 min period.

The intensity of outgoing traffic will vary in all types of buildings. We will arbitrarily assume that it is 40 per cent more intense than at any other critical period. Hence, if the elevators have been designed to serve a 12 per cent 5-min incoming peak, they should be calculated to serve 140×12 per cent or a 16.8 per cent outgoing 5-min peak. This figure may be modified for particular buildings to a lesser or greater percentage or to provide sufficient capacity to evacuate the building within a given time.

PROBABLE STOPS

The number of stops an elevator makes during the outgoing traffic period depends on how much it fills at each stop. If sufficient passengers are waiting at a floor to fill any car that stops there, it usually descends directly to the lobby. This situation can be determined from information about a particular building: the population of each floor, the nature of population (executive or clerical, for example), the quitting time or reason for leaving that floor. An outgoing traffic schedule or flow chart can then be established and elevator service calculated accordingly.

When the exact nature of the occupancy cannot be known in advance, as in designing a building for general office use, probable stopping must be estimated. We assume that quitting times are sufficiently staggered so that the peak will not exceed the 5-min average. We also assume that each floor has an equal possibility of originating outgoing passengers. With these assumptions, probable down stopping will be approximately 75 per cent of incoming probable stopping. As outlined in the discussion of two-way traffic, people tend to leave in groups or with a partner, and experience has shown that average stopping is between 60 and 80 per cent of up peak or incoming traffic stopping.

Chart 4, page 64, gives the values for probable incoming stopping for all conditions of loading. These values should be reduced to 75 per cent and the lobby stop accounted for.

If the top floor is equal in population to any other floor, only slight advantage of short trips or travel to the highest down hall call can be taken. As a conservative measure, all trips should be figures to the top landing unless many more stops can be served than the number of passengers the elevator can carry. This decision must be based on judgment or investigation into demands of the persons who will occupy the building.

SAMPLE CALCULATIONS

The calculations on the following pages exemplify a few situations to which outgoing traffic studies may apply. Example 6.1A may be considered a typical situation in a diversified office building. Note that if sufficient cars are provided to serve incoming and two-way traffic demands, outgoing traffic is served with comparative ease. The combination of increased loading and the minimum delay in passenger transfer makes this possible. Note also that if provisions for zoning the elevators were to be applied to example A as in example C, outgoing capacity can be substantially increased.

In example 6.1B an evacuation situation is shown. The elevators described can do a creditable job in getting students out of the building. This may not be the prime consideration in elevatoring a school, however; class change periods with their tremendous interfloor traffic may be the factor that determines the number elevators. The example does point out that reliable vertical transportation can augment other means of exit such as stairs, a fact seldom recognized in contemporary building codes.

Example 6.1C gives one means of solving an extreme outgoing traffic problem and relates actual elevator operation to the traffic served. Stated otherwise, evacuation of a building can be expedited by minimizing the number of stops elevators make, provided each floor in the building has equal access to vertical transportation. Dependence on performance such as is shown in example C would require an elevator operating scheme that is responsive to outgoing traffic and designed to zone each elevator as it leaves the exiting floor into an area of the building. Each area should be so designated to represent equal traffic demand and the elevators arranged so that each area would have an elevator assigned to it. Assignments would be changed each trip to provide equal service to all areas.

Example 6.1. Outgoing Traffic

A. Given: Building population 1000 persons. 15 stories, 5-2500 @ 700 fpm elevators, rise 186 ft, up-peak capacity 130 persons (see Chapter 4, example 4.1).

Determine: Down peak capacity. Will elevators accommodate 16.8 per cent during 5 min of down peak? 2500-lb capacity = 12 passengers incoming, 15 outgoing.

Procedure: Stops: Incoming probable stops: 9.0

$$
\begin{aligned}
\text{Outgoing probable stops: } & 0.75(9) &&= 6.75 \\
\text{Add for lobby: } & 6.75 + 1 &&= 7.75 \\
\text{Stop time} & 7.75 \times 7.5 &&= 58(A) \\
\text{Transfer time} & 2(15 \times 0.6) &&= 18(B) \\
\text{Inefficiency 15 per cent (A and B)} &= 0.15(58 + 18) &&= 11
\end{aligned}
$$

$$
\text{Running time} \qquad \frac{186 \times 2 \times 60}{700} = \underline{32} \atop \overline{119 \text{ sec}}
$$

$$
\text{5-min handling capacity} \qquad = \frac{15 \times 300}{119} \times 5 \text{ elevators}
$$

$$
= 189 \text{ passenger}
$$

5-min outgoing capacity   18.9 per cent

Interval   23.8 sec. Excellent service

B. Given: School: 6 stories, 500 students on floors 2 through 6, 12-ft floor heights.

Determine: Size and speed of elevators to evacuate school in 20 min.

$$
\text{Procedure: Outgoing 5-min average traffic} = \frac{500 \text{ Students}}{4 \text{ (5-min periods)}} = 125
$$

Assume: two 3500 @ 350 fpm elevators, 5 upper-floor stops.

$$
\begin{aligned}
\text{Stop time: } (5 + 1) \times [7.5 + (4.4 - 3.6)] & \\
6 \times 8.3 &= 49.8 \text{ (A)} \\
\text{Transfer time } 2\left(\frac{19}{0.8} \times 0.6\right) &= 28.5 \text{ (B)} \\
\text{Inefficiency } 0.15 \text{ (A and B)} = 0.15 \,(78.3) &= 11.7 \\
\text{Running time} \quad \frac{(5 \times 12) \times 2 \times 60}{350} &= \underline{20.6} \atop \overline{110.6}
\end{aligned}
$$

$$
\text{HC} = \frac{24 \times 300}{111} \text{ (per elevator)} \qquad = 65
$$

Two elevators can perform evacuation

Interval $111\frac{1}{2}$ = 55 sec, which is reasonable.

C. Given: Four 3500 @ 500 fpm elevators in a 10-story office building, 12-ft floor heights.

Determine: Greatest number of people that can be moved out of building from all floors in a 5-min period.

Procedure: At least one trip to each floor must be made during each 5 min. Divide floors into zones to maximize service:

> Zone 1—floors 2, 3, 4   Zone 2—floors 5, 6
> Zone 3—floors 7, 8   Zone 4—floors 9, 10

Calculate: Zone 4:

Stops $7.5(2 + 1)$ $= 22.5$

Transfer $2(19\!\!/_{0.8} \times 0.6)$ $= 28.5$

Inefficiency $0.15(22.5 + 28.5) =\ \ 7.7$

$$\text{Run } \frac{(9 \times 12) \times 2 \times 60}{500} = \frac{25.9}{84.6}$$

$$HC = \frac{24 \times 300}{85} = 85 \text{ persons in 5 min}$$

Zone 3:

Stops   22.5

Transfer   28.5

Inefficiency   7.7

$$\text{Run } \frac{(7 \times 12) \times 2 \times 60}{500} = \frac{20.2}{78.9}$$

$$HC = \frac{24 \times 300}{79} = 91 \text{ persons in 5 min}$$

Zone 2:

Stops   22.5

Transfer   28.5

Inefficiency   7.7

$$\text{Run } \frac{(5 \times 12) \times 2 \times 60}{500} = \frac{14.4}{73.1}$$

$$HC = \frac{24 \times 300}{73} = 99 \text{ persons in 5 min}$$

Zone 1:

Stops $7.5(3 + 1)$ $= 30.0$

Transfer $= 28.5$

Inefficiency $=\ \ 8.8$

$$\text{Run } \frac{(3 \times 12) \times 2 \times 60}{500} = \frac{8.6}{75.9}$$

$$HC = \frac{24 \times 300}{76} = 94 \text{ persons in 5 min}$$

Therefore four elevators 3500 @ 500 serving floors 1 through 10 can serve approximately $(85 + 91 + 99 + 94) = 369$ in 5 min, outgoing. Average interval will be approximately

$$\frac{(84.6 + 78.9 + 73.1 + 75.9)}{4} = 78.1 \text{ sec,}$$

which may be considered long. To provide service within 60 sec, only two zones with two cars per zone should be used; capacity will be reduced.

SPECIAL OPERATIONS

Heavy outgoing traffic situations can occur in any building and from various floors. An excellent example is a hotel with a ballroom located two or three floors above the street entrance. Another example is a cafeteria on an upper floor of an office building, where on nice days many people will lunch and then seek the outdoors, creating a down peak of traffic from that floor. In such situations special considerations must be given to the capacity and operating procedure of elevators serving floors which generate heavy outgoing traffic.

The nature of the traffic must first be determined: are the passengers all expected to head for a building exit floor or to distribute themselves among many floors? Is the traffic from the floor in question all down (or up) with little or no traffic in the opposite direction? In the latter case the loading floor should be considered as an upper "lobby" with all elevators arranged to return to that floor. In addition, the system should be designed to load more than one elevator at that floor simultaneously and each entrance incorporate special direction signs. This raises the question whether building occupants will respond to hall lanterns or elevator signs. In many buildings such as hospitals or hotels, where the visitors are not used to elevators, traditional signs such as elevator hall lanterns and position indicators in the hall may be confusing and have little meaning. These signs should be augmented by verbal instructions, either personal or recorded, to encourage proper and prompt elevator loading.

Extra time for inefficiency must be included in situations where passenger discipline and familiarity with elevators is not great. In hotels, hospitals, department stores, and other public places 20 to 30 per cent inefficiency in transfer is to be expected This should be reflected in time considerations and in providing ample platform area as well as sufficient door size.

Escalators should be considered when outgoing traffic is expected to be as great as 250 or more persons in a 5-min period. An escalator traveling at 90 fpm with a nominal width of 32 in. can theoretically serve 425 persons in 5-min provided each step is filled with $1\frac{1}{4}$ persons (mother and child).

A speed of 120 fpm increases capacity to 566 persons in 5 min. Increasing the nominal width to 48 in. and retaining the speed at 90 fpm gives a theoretical capacity of 680 persons in 5 min. Increasing the width to 48 in. (two persons per step) and the speed to 120 fpm gives a 5-min theoretical capacity of 891 persons. These capacities are theoretical because every step is seldom used to its possible maximum. Maximum capacities have been approached in subway terminals, where the impact of an unloading train is so great that persons are forced to move. Average capacity is about 65 to 80 per cent of the theoretical maximum.

Escalators can be used effectively to funnel outgoing or incoming crowds to an area from which they can distribute themselves to other facilities such as check rooms, lounges, and refreshment stands. When paired escalators are provided to serve two-way traffic, both escalators can be operated in the direction of heavy traffic and other traffic diverted to stairs or elevators. Layout of escalators must be planned for this contingency. As with elevators, sufficient staging area and exits must be available for persons to leave the transportation facility. It is futile and dangerous to transport a stream of persons to an area faster than they can leave it. Measures of building design and operation should prevent such contingencies, but should they arise the simplest correction is to shut down temporarily or reduce the capacity of the transportation system and have people stay where they are.

GENERAL CONCLUSIONS

Active consideration should be given to the outgoing traffic in any building. Expected elevator performance should be calculated and checked against the expected outgoing traffic demand and necessary adjustment made in elevator number, size, or speed.

Outgoing traffic requirements are often effectively met by incorporating suitable control features in the elevator operating system. One of the most useful of these procedures is efficient load bypass operation of the elevators as well as means to minimize elevator unloading time at the lobby and to speed their return up into the building to continue the outgoing operation.

Additional operating features include dispatching means so that elevators provide equal service to all floors in the building or to areas of equal demand. To guard against long waits, spotting service should be provided if required by traffic intensity. As an alternative, an elevator system with provisions for future addition of these features should be considered. Such an approach is practical when the future tenancy of a building is unknown or when tenants are acquiring more than sufficient space initially and are planning future expansion within the building.

Escalators should be considered for outgoing traffic of substantial magnitude from a limited number of floors. Two-way escalator service allows both escalators to be operated down if their capacity is needed. Clearly understood direction of passengers to transportation as well as ample means to leave the exiting area is a necessity.

CHAPTER SEVEN

Elevator Operation and Control

CONTROL AND OPERATING SYSTEMS

Once the number, size, speed, and location of the elevators is determined for a particular building adequate control must be provided to insure that those elevators operate to serve expected traffic. This was alluded to in the previous chapters in discussing various types of traffic. Tied in with serving the predominant traffic period is the ability of the elevators to operate in the best manner to serve that traffic and to perform within the time limits prescribed. These terms must be translated into specifications so that the supplier of the elevator equipment knows what is expected.

Operating systems is our designation as an inclusive term for all the electrical decisions designed into an elevator system to control the sequence of movements an elevator or elevator group will make in response to calls for service. For ease of identification, operating systems have been given broad titles that are classified in the American Standard Safety Code for elevators and discussed later in this chapter. Individual manufacturers have added their own features and attractions to these operating systems, some providing more than others. The differences between various manufacturers are difficult to define in concise terms, hence we will state what should be provided. Various suppliers are more than willing to discuss their approaches to solving elevator problems, either by demonstration on previous installations or by verbal and written assurances.

Control systems is our designation for the equipment that determines individual performance characteristics of an elevator; how quickly it

can travel from floor to floor, its means and speed of door opening and closing, built-in time factors for passenger transfer, its ability to level swiftly and accurately, how the elevator displays hall lantern signals, are all functions of the control applied to an elevator. This control can and will be modified to a slight extent by the operating system but in general it is sufficiently distinct to be discussed separately.

POWER CONTROL

An important part of the control system is how power is applied to the elevator and the type of power that is used. As stated in the first chapter, ac resistance control and the variable voltage dc or generator field control are the two most prominent today.

Ac resistance control consists of starting the elevator machine directly across the ac line or through resistance steps. An induction-type motor is used and the full speed of the elevator depends on the operating speed and slip of the motor as well as the reduction of the elevator mechanical system (Figure 7.1a). While the elevator is getting up to speed it is being retarded by the inertia of the system (a heavily loaded elevator requiring more time to get up to speed than a lightly loaded system). Stopping is accomplished by applying the brake and cutting off power to the motor simultaneously, the final stop being a combination of the load, direction of travel, speed, and brake action. As can be imagined, the stop at a floor level will vary depending on the load in the car and the effectiveness of the brake system. Accuracy at a floor may vary from dead on to plus or minus 2 or 3 in. with a nominal car speed of 100 fpm. Such accuracy is tolerable in an apartment house but totally unacceptable in a hospital, where stretchers have to be wheeled in and out of the elevator. The operating time from floor to floor of such an elevator can be quite satisfactory. With a light load it is up to speed in a minimum time and, because a brake is used for stopping, it can be slowed down almost as quickly. Full running speed varies with load and motor slip. Regulation of plus or minus from 15 to 20 per cent is not uncommon. For example, if an elevator with a nominal speed of 100 fpm is specified, speed may vary from 90 to 110 fpm depending on load and direction of travel.

In view of these limitations, ac single-speed resistance is seldom used for speeds in excess of 100 fpm. If resistance elevators are used for higher speeds, a means to improve their stopping accuracy is essential.

Improved stopping accuracy of resistance elevators can be obtained by use of a two-speed motor. Such a motor should be designed so that the slow-speed winding will give an elevator operating speed of no more than 40 fpm. At that speed, cutting off power and applying the brake can give a stop within plus or minus an inch or better of the floor under all conditions of loading.

Common ratios between fast and slow speed windings are from 2 to 1 to 4 to 1. For example, with a four to one motor and a full operating speed of 100 fpm, leveling will be accomplished at 25 fpm. This is not without a time penalty. The elevator will get up to speed quickly but in stopping it is cut back from full speed to leveling speed and when it attains leveling speed the brake is applied and the car is stopped. Such action takes a second or two; for example, a 9-ft floor can be traveled by a single-speed elevator at 100 fpm in about 5 to 6 sec. With leveling at 25 fpm and good transitional control, the floor-to-floor run will take about 8 sec.

The economy of two-speed resistance operation is such that it is quite popular in low-rise buildings, is satisfactory for smaller hospitals, and fills the need for safe elevator convenience when a large investment is not economical.

Two-speed ac resistance is usually provided with leveling. We have described two-speed stopping. With leveling, the elevator will automatically level to within an inch of the floor if the car is stopped more than an inch from floor level. This should occur at any time. For example, if a large load is removed from the elevator and it rises above the floor due to release of tension on the ropes, the elevator should level back to within 1 in. of the floor.

Two-speed stopping with leveling allows the base speed of the elevator to be higher. At 150 fpm and with a 4:1 motor, the stopping speed is ¼ or about 37 fpm.

There are two types of two-speed motors common in elevator work. The two-winding type has two synchronous speeds and is available in ratios of three and four to one. The second type accomplishes two-speed operation by reconnecting motorcoil windings thereby changing poles and reducing synchronous speed. The 2:1 ratio is all that is available with that motor.

Hydraulic elevators use ac resistance control for a single-speed motor used to drive the pump supplying oil to the piston and pumping in the up direction only. Stopping is accomplished by throttling and then cutting off oil flow (Figure 7.1b). Leveling can be accomplished by restricting oil flow, bypassing a measured quantity of oil, or providing an auxiliary low-capacity pump. Down operation is accomplished by opening a down valve and allowing oil to return to the storage tank.

Hydraulic elevators are restricted in top operating speed to about

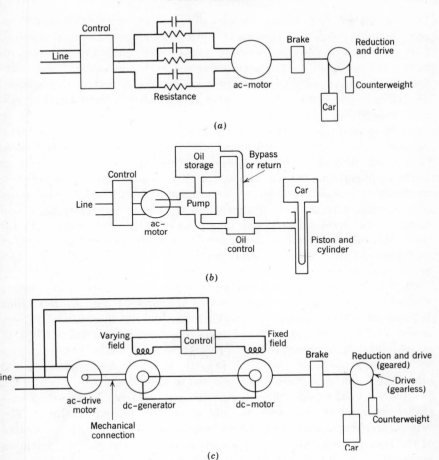

Figure 7.1 (*a*) ac resistance; (*b*) hydraulic resistance; (*c*) dc variable voltage.

150 fpm. Some units have been installed at 200 fpm but considerable refinement and development are needed to make higher speed possible. For higher speed and even for low speed the variable voltage generator field control type of electric elevator approach is so far superior that it has become the hallmark of elevator performance.

Variable voltage or generator field power control consists of providing a varying voltage to a dc elevator drive motor. The characteristics of the dc drive motor are that it has the torque to move the elevator load smoothly up to speed and can absorb the inertia of the moving load by regeneration to stop the elevator with smooth retardation. Stopping is independent of the brake with all the power being absorbed back through the electrical system. The system consists of the dc drive motor and the associated elevator drive reduction mechanism. The armature of the drive motor is directly connected to a source of controlled dc voltage such as the armature of a dc generator (Ward-Leonard system) (see Figure 7.1c).

As the voltage is increased on the drive motor armature, the elevator or load is accelerated up to speed. As the voltage is decreased speed is reduced until the elevator comes to a complete stop, and the brake is then applied to hold the car at the floor. Leveling requirements due to changing load at the floor are accomplished by lifting the brake and applying small voltages to the drive motor. Almost imperceptible movement can be accomplished. The most sophisticated system does not lift the brake fully and uses separate generator fields for leveling to restrict voltages and to avoid the possibility of the elevator moving too fast while passengers are transferring.

Operating speeds of variable voltage elevator control systems are available in any standard speed up to the present high of 1800 fpm. If faster elevators are built it is certain they will use this system. Performance is from about 4 to 5 sec for a one-floor run of from 10 to 12 ft and leveling accuracy under all conditions of loading is from plus or minus $\frac{1}{4}$ to $\frac{1}{2}$ in. No time penalty is incurred for leveling, and all variable voltage elevators are expected to have leveling.

Variable voltage control is used with both geared and gearless machines whereas ac resistance is only used with geared machines. The rate of acceleration and retardation possible on an elevator is a function of the horsepower available in the system. Because the gearless machines generally have higher horsepower ratings, they are capable of more rapid acceleration rates.

Acceleration is not constant but varies from instant to instant. Experience has shown that an average rate of between 3 and 5 fps/sec is comfortable for most people, the important consideration being to limit the severity of changing the rate of acceleration. Translated to practical terms, an elevator of 500 fpm capability should be able to get up to full speed and slowdown within 5.7 sec and in a distance not exceeding 23 ft within an acceleration range of from 3 to 5 fps/sec. Higher speeds will take correspondingly longer times (see Figure 7.2).

Speed regulation between no load and full load with a variable voltage system should be plus or minus 5 per cent. Any tendency to overspeed or underspeed should be governed and corrective measures such as motor field strengthening applied if the speed exceeds rated value. Safety codes

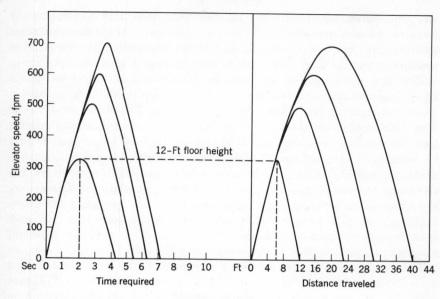

Figure 7.2

generally require the elevator to be stopped if its running speed exceeds its rated speed by about 10 per cent.

DOOR CONTROL

Operation from floor to floor or getting the elevator up to speed and stopping it is only one function of the control system. Other functions include giving the proper electrical signal to start opening the car door when the car is within a given distance of the floor. Like the elevator, the doors must be accelerated and retarded as well as stopped when they are fully opened. Passenger transfer time can be controlled by controlling the time the doors remain open. The simplest system will allow a fixed-door hold-open time. When this expires the doors start to close and may be reversed by someone actuating the safety edge on the car door or interrupting a photoelectric light device. The doors will then reopen and start to close again.

Additional features of elevator door control may include separate door hold-open times for car call stops and for hall call stops or a system whereby door hold-open time is cancelled or reduced if someone interrupts the photoelectric light beam by entering or exiting from the elevator. One advanced system has an electronic proximity device on the elevator doors which allows the doors to be closed within the minimum transfer time and will reverse them only far enough for the transferring passenger to get through, after which they immediately close.

The time the doors remain open on heavy-duty installations should be adjusted to the load in the elevator. Transfer to and from a lightly loaded car can be faster than from a filled car. The adjustment of the door hold-open time should permit this distinction. Similarly, transfer time for loading or unloading at the lobby will be longer and should be recognized. Any of the foregoing transfer times should be independently adjustable to suit the requirements of the building in which the elevators are installed as well as the characteristics of the traffic they are expected to serve. All the adjustments are not necessary for every building, but it is recommended that separate car stop and hall stop door hold-open times be specified for any building to match expected passenger transfer time with the operation of the elevator.

The combination of all the times discussed to this point adds up to a performance time for an elevator on a one-floor run or a trip (Figure 7.3). One of the means of insuring a quality elevator installation is to measure the operating and performance time of elevators installed by the supplier in question. The performance time or the time from the start of door closing at one floor until the doors are opened sufficiently to permit passenger transfer at another floor is a measure of quality and can easily be determined. The measurements should be consistent under all conditions of loading, from full load in the car to no load in the car and in either the up or down direction.

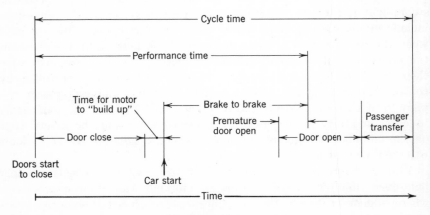

Figure 7.3

If hall lanterns are provided they should light in advance of a car's arrival at the floor and in the direction the car is expected to leave that floor. Adequate advance lighting will give prospective passengers a chance to approach the elevator and board it promptly, thus saving valuable seconds in transfer time.

There are many other things an individual elevator should do. They may be best summed up by requiring any elevator to be "honest" to the prospective passenger. If he obeys the lantern signals, boards the right elevator, and operates the car buttons it should take him swiftly and smoothly to his destination.

OPERATING SYSTEMS

The problem of causing an elevator to move in response to demands for service is solved by the operating system. With the first elevators, hydraulic or steam driven, the operating device was a continuous rope that ran the length of the hoistway and actuated a valve in the basement. To go up, the rope was pulled down to admit steam or water to the elevator driving means. To go down, the rope was pulled up and the driving machine was reversed. The pull in the opposite direction of travel had a distinct advantage; by sending the rope through a restricted hole in the car platform a stop ball on the rope could be placed at the extremes of elevator travel. The continued upward or downward movement of the car caused the rope to be pulled by the car and would stop the elevator (Figure 7.4).

Hand-rope operation, as it was called, had many advantages and continued in vogue for many years—some elevators still have it although it has been generally outlawed by local codes. Because in the early days hoistways were open or enclosed by waist-high gates, one could reach in, pull the rope, and summon the elevator—automatic albeit very unsafe operation.

Car Switch Operation

With the introduction of electric elevators, the natural step was to put a switch or lever in the car which when operated would electrically start the car in the up or down direction and if centered would stop the elevator. A means was therefore required to transmit the electric impulse to the motor room from the moving elevator and so the traveling cable was introduced. This is an electrical cable that hangs from some point near the middle of the hoistway and is attached to the underside

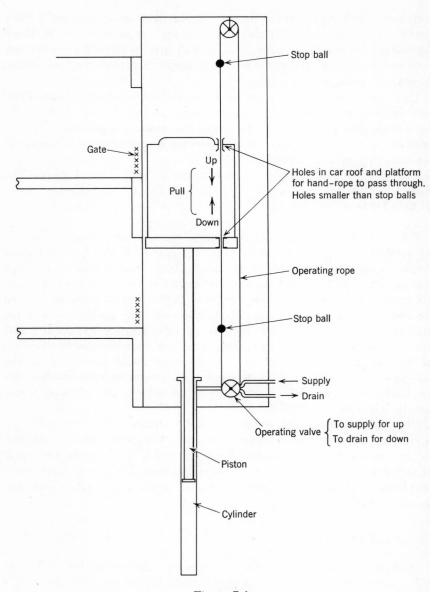

Stop ball

Gate

Up

Pull

Down

Holes in car roof and platform
for hand-rope to pass through.
Holes smaller than stop balls

Operating rope

Stop ball

Supply

Drain

Operating valve { To supply for up
To drain for down

Piston

Cylinder

Figure 7.4

120

of the car. With electric elevators and increased concentration on the safety of passengers, such things as hoistway door interlocks and car gates were introduced and required by law. The interlock prevents the elevator from being operated unless the door is closed and locked. Before that time, and until such interlocks became universally required many insurance companies had clauses in their policies excluding compensation for injuries or death incurred from elevators.

Car-switch operation as it is known, was the chief operating system available until the late 1920's. With its development came very elaborate signaling systems to inform the operator where he was to stop as well as buzzer systems so that the elevator starter at the main floor could direct the elevators. To aid the starter in this task lights were added to indicate where hall calls were waiting, as were either dials or lights to show the position of the elevators in the hoistways.

Automatic Operation

Parallel with the development and refinement of car-switch operation came the introduction of the simple automatic electrical operating system for single elevators. This was primarily intended to make the elevator acceptable to the residence or smaller apartment house where the traffic did not warrant a full-time elevator attendant. Safety was established by the use of interlocks on the hoistway doors and contacts on the car gate to insure both were closed before the elevator could be run. An automatic operating system known as the *single automatic push button* was introduced and became the accepted operating system for the period from about 1890 to 1920.

Single automatic push button operation or single automatic operation as it is presently known consists of single buttons at each landing and a button for each floor in a car operating panel. The car can be called from any floor provided the door and gate are closed and no one is operating the car. Once the car is intercepted, entering it and closing the hoistway door and car gate ensures the riding passenger exclusive use for that trip. It is a light service operation; the elevator can serve only one call at a time and the next passenger must wait until it is free before he can use it. To indicate availability, an "in use" light is generally placed in the hall call fixture. When the light is out the passenger can call the car. To make single automatic operation work properly, sequence switching and timing must be provided so that the passenger who enters will have a chance to register his call before another passenger can call the car from that floor.

Single automatic operation is still available as a standard operation. It is valuable in light traffic buildings where exclusive use of an elevator is desired. It is ideal for garages and factories where only one vehicle can fit on an elevator at one time.

Signal Operation

As elevator speeds were increased past 500 fpm, the skill of the elevator operator had to increase so that he knew the exact fraction of a second to drop his operating handle and make the next stop with fair accuracy. Various schemes to overcome this problem were tried.

A light would flash just before the next required stop and the operator would respond with split-second accuracy, provided he was looking at the light. Leveling devices were applied to eliminate jockeying at the floor. Younger operators were hired.

These approaches were satisfactory until the demand for speed was in excess of 700 fpm. No operator could recognize when to stop when floors were passing at about a second apart and even then he had to decide to stop at least 20 to 30 ft from the floor he wanted.

The need, then, for an improved operating system for fast elevators was apparent, and the system known as signal control was introduced. Signal control is a push button operating system in which the elevator operator registers the call for the floors at which the passengers wish to stop and operates a button or lever to start the car. Acceleration, response to floor stops, retardation, and leveling are all done automatically. Similarly, response to hall calls is in the same manner; in fact the operator does not know what hall calls he will respond to until he feels the car slow down.

Signal control, or signal operation as it is presently known, removed the speed limitation from elevators. Speeds of 1000, 1200, and 1400 fpm were attained and all the notable building of the late 1920's and the 1930's had signal control elevators. These include the Empire State and Chrysler buildings and most of Rockefeller Center as well as hundreds of others.

Technology also came to the aid of the elevator starter. In addition to indicator lights to show waiting hall passengers and the position or motion of each elevator, electrical scheduling systems were introduced. These systems attempted to operate cars on schedules maintained by the operator's response to signal lights in each elevator telling him when to start in relation to the car ahead of him.

The objective of spacing elevators throughout a building to render the best possible service to waiting passengers was only imperfectly realized. Elevator operators saw little point in rushing when traffic seemed light and could not resist the opportunity to stop at a floor and enjoy a smoke or conversation. The insistent buzzer of the starter generally superseded any electrical dispatching provided.

Collective Operations

While signal operation was being introduced for the larger building, the market was growing for automatic operation for apartments, hospitals, small office buildings, and any building that required elevators but had only limited traffic. The need for better service than the single automatic elevator could provide led to the introduction of the collective elevator and improved means of automatic elevator door operation.

Collective operation, as the name implies, is a means to collect and answer all the calls in one direction, reverse the elevator, and then "collect" and answer all the calls in the opposite direction.

The more common collective operations are the selective collective operations. With full selective collective, up and down hall call buttons are provided. The car will only stop for up calls in the up direction and down calls in the down direction, all calls being remembered until answered. A variation of selective collective is down collective when only down hall buttons are provided at each upper floor. This can be acceptable in an apartment house, in which most people want service up to their apartments from the lobby (up car call) and down to the lobby from their floors (down hall call).

Automatic operation of elevators is enhanced by the power operation of the doors and ample protection to keep the closing doors from striking the passengers. Earlier automatic elevators had manual doors and gates, usually equipped with spring or weighted closers. The passenger had to open both himself once he had called the car to his floor. With power operation the door opens automatically, remains open for a time interval (which should be adjustable and should be longer for a passenger to enter from the hall than for a passenger to exit from the car), and automatically closes.

If the leading edge of the door touches or is about to touch a person or object, some sensitive edge should actuate the reopening of the door and recycle the closing operation. If traffic is light and delay is tolerable, a light-ray device projecting across the entrance can be used in addition to the sensitive door edge to insure that the door will remain completely open until the entrance is clear.

At present, selective collective is the accepted operation for elevators in apartments and other light service buildings. Its utility has been enhanced by added features such as, with single-car operation, home landing when the car is always returned to a given floor on completion of any trip, load-weighing bypass, which prevents the car from stopping for additional hall calls if it is filled to a predetermined percentage of capacity, freight service bypass or independent service operation, wherein the car can be used to handle special loads and not respond to hall calls as long as the bypass switch is operated.

Two-car selective collective operation is accomplished by duplexing, hence the name duplex collective. This can be either full or down and consists of the following operations.

One of the two cars is designated as the home-landing car. It can be either car and may change after each trip. The other car is called "free" and may park at its last call or some designated landing (middle free car parking), or in a designated upper area of the building. The home-landing car is designated to respond to any hall call at the lobby or basement floor in the building. The free car is designated to respond to any call above the lobby or in a designated area.

If the home-landing car is taken to an upper floor by a car call, the free car becomes the home-landing car. If the free car is set in motion by a car or hall call, and a call occurs behind the free car (either an up or down hall call below an up traveling free car or an up or down hall call above a down traveling free car) the home-landing car can start to "help out" the free car. With a more sophisticated duplex collective system, the home-landing car will start if any hall call, behind or not, remains registered beyond a predetermined time or if the free car does not move within a predetermined time. This latter feature is known as the milkman circuit and was developed because the milkman would block the elevator with his carrying case while he delivered to the various apartments. Since tenants could be registering calls both ahead and behind the free car (the milkman's car) unless some release was provided, the home-landing car might never start.

Duplex collective can do a fine job of serving the normal expected traffic in an apartment house if the elevators have sufficient capacity to serve the needs of the building. Under heavier traffic operation and since duplex collective had no spacing means, cars will "bunch." The heavier traffic periods are usually of very short duration, however, and poor elevator operation for that period is generally tolerated. If heavier traffic persists for any period of time because of, say, an underelevatored situation, duplex collective generally is not a satisfactory operating scheme.

As we have stated, with duplex collective a call behind the free car starts the home landing car. With a busy situation, one or many calls behind may appear immediately. The former home-landing car is traveling right behind the free car and in the same direction. With many calls the elevators are "leapfrogging," that is, both will arrive at the lobby about the same time, will leave again, and start the cycle over—a condition known as "bunching." Instead of two-car coordinated operation, the operation is two cars bunched or not much better than a single large elevator.

A number of steps must be taken to improve two-car operation as well as any group operation for heavier traffic. Some of these steps have been described in the discussions of the various types of traffic in previous chapters. The application of various traffic handling features to elevators results in another class of operation known as *group automatic operation*.

Group Automatic Operation

At this stage of our discussion of the history of elevator operations we have seen the almost parallel development of signal operation with attendant for the larger, busier building and the duplex collective, non-attended operation for the residential and lighter traffic buildings. In about 1949, a number of developments occurred that started the rapid elimination of elevator attendants in any type of building.

At that time the completely automatic operatorless elevator was introduced. This innovation consisted of a number of steps such as the providing of an operating system that caused the elevators to respond to changing traffic demands, the refinement of the door protective devices, and the establishment of timing and scheduling systems circuits that maintained elevators on operating schedules, in response to traffic requirements and without the necessity of human interference.

The demand for good automatic operation for larger groups of elevators was apparent for some time. Various attempts to meet this demand were made using three- and four-car selective collective operations that were generally unsatisfactory for the heavier traffic situations. Their failure stemmed from the difficulty of putting elevators in proper position during periods of heavier traffic. With a collective system and with increased traffic, serious bunching can and does occur. However, their introduction plus the fact that persons had been operating elevators by themselves in various types of buildings for years allayed any fear that they would be unwilling to do so in a large office building.

All the developments came together when Otis Elevator Company introduced the first fully automatic elevator system for an office building. Otis provided the necessary scheduling system which made the decisions to start elevators on schedules, introduced the "electronic detector" system of door protection, and developed the various load weighing and protective devices to replace the other functions of an elevator attendant.

The electronic detector door protective system has a number of features. The edges of the door carry an electronic proximity field which, if disturbed, provides the electronic signal to reverse the doors. The doors do not have to touch a person or object. If the doors are held open for an excessive length of time, the closing power is reduced, the edge de-energized, and the doors close with a slow nudging force. In addition a buzzer sounds to indicate this closing action. The electronic detector was one of the initial features of the "operatorless elevator." It provided a competent electrical substitution for one of the jobs of the attendant. Once the introduction of automatic elevators was complete both the electronic detector and the conventional mechanical safety edges on the doors were found to be acceptable in busy buildings—the electronic detector more so since a door does not have to touch a person before reversing.

Another task of the operator was to count the number of people in an elevator and to leave the loading floor when sufficient passengers were on board. This function is replaced by load-weighing switches. To reduce the danger of overcrowding, loading restrictions were developed by limiting the area of the car in relation to its pounds of capacity. The other function of the attendant was to register the passenger calls, which they can easily do themselves.

The final task of the operator was to pay attention to the elevator starter or to an electrical signal. This was replaced by initiating door close by an electrical signal and relying on the door safety edges to protect the passengers.

The elevator starter generally provided the signals and the schedule of elevator operation in relation to the various demands for service he could note from a hall call and car position indicator in the lobby. Specialized electrical computers were developed to weigh all the factors a starter must plus many more that human limitation did not allow. Based on these factors, the various electrical signals for starting, stopping, and reversing elevators are given and the system operates completely unattended.

Various groups of operations were combined into programs for the various types of traffic. Names such as Otis' Autotronic, Westinghouse's Selectomatic, Haughton's Auto-Signamatic, and Montgomery's Measured Demand appeared as designations for individual manufacturer's concepts of what elevator operating systems should be. All represent some form of group automatic operation of elevators intended to serve heavily trafficked buildings.

Success of the initial efforts to gain public acceptance of automatic elevators in any type of building is evidenced by the fact that over 95 per cent of the elevators sold today are nonattendant.

A critical look at what group automatic operating systems must offer may be taken. We have discussed some of the details of the requirements to serve traffic as we discussed the various types of traffic. A definition of group automatic operation will help to clarify requirements.

Automatic Group Supervision

The American Standard Safety Code for Elevators (A17.1-1965) defines group automatic operation as follows:

"Automatic operation of two or more nonattendant elevators equipped with power operated car and hoistway doors. The operation of the cars is coordinated by a supervisory control system including automatic dispatching means whereby selected cars at designated dispatching points automatically close their doors and proceed on their trips in a *regulated* manner. It includes one button in each car for each floor served and up and down buttons at each landing (single buttons at the terminal landings). The stops set up by the momentary actuation of the car buttons are made automatically in succession as a car reaches the corresponding landing irrespective of its direction of travel or the sequence in which the buttons are actuated. The stops set up by the momentary actuation of the landing buttons may be accomplished by any elevator in the group, and are made automatically by the first available car that approaches the landing in the corresponding direction."

To make this definition more meaningful and to contrast a duplex collective operating system with a two-car group supervisory system, additional definition is needed. One approach is to qualify elevator operating systems either as "on call," which requires that a call for service be registered before an elevator will move, and "scheduled," which implies that the elevator will be operated in a regulated manner or on schedule without the necessity of a call being registered. In addition the total definition of group automatic operation, in our terms, should include the requirement for various patterns of elevator operation in response to various traffic requirements.

By our definition, collective, single-automatic, car switch, hand-rope, and so on, are "on-call" operations. Signal operation is on call unless signals are given by a dispatching system (or the elevator starter) and responded to by the elevator attendant to operate the elevators in search

of calls and without the necessity of a call being registered at the time
the elevator was signaled to start.

A true group automatic operating system, by our definition, has a
means to start elevators automatically and without the necessity of
a call being registered. It also incorporates features whereby the elevators
are operated in different patterns for various types of elevator traffic—
incoming, outgoing, two-way, and interfloor. It also includes provisions
for modifying these operations depending on the intensity of traffic—
light, moderate to heavy, and peak traffic. The group automatic operating
system may also include an on-call operation for periods of light traffic
or special situations.

A group automatic operating system should be capable of being engineered to suit the expected traffic activity in any type of building. For
example, if the number, speed, and duty of the elevators are chosen to
serve a specific type of peak traffic, the elevator operating system must
include the necessary operating features to serve that traffic. If the critical traffic, for example, is two way and is expected to be heavy the
group automatic operating system should have all the scheduling and
dispatching features to best handle that two-way traffic. If incoming
and outgoing traffic is not expected to be heavy the features required
for that type of traffic may be minimized. For example, there is very
little to be gained in giving priority service to an incoming group if
many people are required to travel between floors at the same time.

TRAFFIC AND OPERATION

In view of the foregoing the various operations described in the preceding chapters as well as the degree of traffic intensity expected may
be summarized as follows: It is up to the specifier of the elevator system
of a particular building to choose the features that best suit the traffic
requirements of the building and to see that at least the minimum is
furnished.

Intensity of Traffic

Light traffic is when the number of persons riding or requiring elevator
service at one time does not exceed the number of elevators in the group.
Traffic is light, for example, if there are four cars in a group and no
more than four calls, either car or hall, are expected to be registered
at one time.

Moderate to heavy traffic is when the number of persons riding or seeking elevator service at a given time is such that the available elevators in a group must be shared by more than one person and the average loading is not expected to fill any elevator beyond 50 to 80 per cent of its capacity.

Peak traffic is when the demands on the elevator system are such that the available capacity must be equalized among many passengers and priority of service may have to be given to passengers riding in one direction over those seeking to travel in the opposite direction.

Various traffic conditions require various operating features.

Incoming Traffic. *Light incoming traffic operations* require at least one elevator parked at the loading lobby to receive passengers. Operation is to the highest required call and immediate return if no other elevator is at the lobby to receive passengers.

Moderate to heavy incoming traffic operations require all the elevators at the loading lobby or returning to the lobby to receive passengers. The elevator travels to the highest required call and returns immediately to the lobby. More than one elevator can be loaded at the same time, and any filled car can then be dispatched.

Peak incoming traffic operations require all the foregoing operations plus a system to give priority to lobby traffic during designated periods of working days. Service to upper floor hall calls is temporarily denied if no car is available at the lobby for loading. For intense traffic a means should be provided to divide the group of elevators into subgroups and to restrict the number of floors and hall call traffic each subgroup will serve. This latter operation should be limited to groups of six or more cars or places in which a reasonable loading interval can be obtained.

Two-Way Traffic. *Light two-way traffic operations* require the elevators to be stationed throughout the building either at rest or in motion so that a car is either at or traveling toward the next expected call. Elevators should be stationed in various levels of the floors served and operated as individual units during periods of minimum demand.

Moderate to heavy two-way traffic operations require operation of all elevators on scheduled trips with time allowances for each trip matched with the intensity of traffic in each direction. A system should provide concentrated elevator service in the direction of heaviest traffic.

Peak two-way traffic operations require that in addition to time scheduled operation, some means be provided to separate the elevators in travel to equalize the time between each elevator and in each direction. There should be some way to move elevators from areas of light demand into areas of heavy directional demand. For intense situations a system to restrict number of stops each elevator will make and, in extreme cases, restrict the number of floors served by the group to the extent that only every second or third floor is served should be instituted.

Interfloor traffic operations include all the actions reuired for two-way traffic with concentration on elevators circulating between floors of heaviest demand. Trips to terminal floors should be restricted unless definite demands are registered for travel to those floors.

Outgoing Traffic. *Light outgoing traffic operations* call for minimal time spent by any elevator at the unloading terminal. Elevators should return up into the building to serve down demand with travel no higher than necessary.

Moderate to heavy outgoing traffic operations require spacing of elevators in the down direction, minimizing time spent at the unloading landing, and load bypassing of hall calls as well as some means to equalize service to all floors.

Peak outgoing traffic operations require all the foregoing plus a system to restrict up hall calls if down hall calls are being bypassed. In addition some means should be provided to divide groups of elevators into subgroups to minimize the possibility of lower floors being bypassed by cars filling at upper floors. Priority should be given to outgoing traffic limited to a predesignated time at the end of a working day. A system to automatically restrict up hall call service when passengers only wishing to go down operate both up and down hall calls is often required.

With any group automatic operating system it should be decided how the elevators will be operated during extended periods of intermittent traffic. Operation may then be a form of "on call" and allowed to take place at any time elevator demands are light.

Two major variations of intermittent operation are possible: (a) all the elevators are allowed to come to rest at the main floor and individual elevators are started as needed, or (b) the elevators are allowed to come to rest in various areas throughout the building and cars are started in the area of a call as required.

Providing for Contingencies

The total specification for a group automatic operating system should consider all contingencies. If, for example, a car is delayed at a floor beyond a predetermined period of time, some means to disengage that car from group operation should be provided. This will ensure that this elevator does not interfere with other elevators in the group or prevent other elevators from stopping at that floor in response to hall calls. A signal at some central location should be given to inform a responsible person of the delay or operating failure.

If for any reason the group operating system fails to function and elevators are not dispatched as intended, an auxiliary protective means of dispatching should be provided. This auxiliary means would at minimum operate the elevators in a random fashion, provide a signal to inform a responsible person of failure, and insure at least some service to passengers.

A third possible serious failure could occur if for any reason the hall buttons failed to function. Passengers would be stranded on floors, unable to summon elevator service. A means should be provided to detect such failure and take corrective action. If the failure is complete the elevators should be operated to make predetermined stops so that at least one car stops at each floor. A warning signal should occur in some central location so that necessary corrective action can be taken by responsible persons.

Elevators are complex combinations of electrical and mechanical elements. There may be as many as two or three thousand electrical contacts made or broken during the course of a single trip. In spite of this they are extremely reliable with no more than two or three shutdowns per year from failure to be expected on an average well-maintained elevator. In addition, the probability of a passenger being trapped is well below one out of ten shutdowns. If, even with this remote possibility of failure, a shutdown does occur with a passenger on board, adequate means to inform someone of that shutdown should be provided. Most important, passengers in the car must be protected. The common information system is an alarm bell button located in the car operating panel. Many buildings have two-way communication systems in each elevator or a telephone connected to the building office. Others have alarm systems connected to central protective agency offices.

A passenger in a stalled elevator is safest staying where he is. If he tries to get out without help, the elevator may move and he may be injured. To make his stay comfortable, the car lights and fan should continue to operate, by emergency power if necessary. Adequate switching should be provided because it is desirable to stop the fan and turn off the lights when the elevator is parked by normal means. In any event the fan and lights should have a separate power supply. The motor generator of the elevator can be started and stopped as elevator running requirements are apparent. The fan and lights can start and stop with the generator but if the generator is stopped because of abnormal action such as a blown fuse or failure the fan and lights can remain in operation provided their power supply is intact. Operation of elevators during a power failure and when emergency power is available will be discussed in a later chapter.

SPECIAL OPERATING FEATURES

Many of the operations and features described in the preceding pages may be applied to any type of operation and are not restricted solely to group automatic operation. Their application depends on the engineering acumen of the various elevator manufacturers and the purchaser's insistence. Many more features are necessary if an elevator system is to serve the traffic in a given building adequately and provide all the protective features required for passenger comfort, convenience, and safety.

It may be desired to take any elevator out of a group and use it for special service. This may be necessary in an office building during moving or in a hospital to transfer a patient. At that time it is desirable to have a system of operation from the car buttons only, bypassing all hall calls. A key switch or special switch can be located in the car operating panel, the actuation of which cancels all existing car calls and causes the car to bypass hall calls. Direction can be established by operating the car button for the desired floor and the car is started by operating an appropriate car start or door close button. A key switch is preferred to avoid abuse by unauthorized persons, and making the key removable only in the off position, ensures that the car will be restored to normal service when the special operation is complete. Such a system of operation is generally referred to as independent service, emergency service, or hospital service.

In some areas of the country and in certain buildings it is desired to summon an elevator to a particular floor to give priority service to an executive, fireman, or for other reasons. A key switch can be located at that floor that, when operated, will call a designated car to that floor. The question to be answered is, should the car be allowed to complete its existing calls or should the passengers who are on that car be made to travel to the priority call. For firemen or in a hospital the answer is obvious, but what would happen if a vice-president called the car and the president happened to be riding? Nevertheless, once the question about existing car calls is answered, the key switch will call the car to the floor of call and from that floor the car may be operated as described for independent service. Quite obviously such special service must be limited to one or two floors or insurmountable conflicts could arise.

A third form of special service is to operate one of the elevators in a group from a separate riser of hall buttons. When on this service the elevator responds only to the separate riser and the other cars respond only to the normal riser. This separate riser service is an economical approach to providing a separate service elevator where none exists. It can and often does lead to operational difficulty, as persons at a floor will push every button they can find, no matter how inconspicuous the architect may feel the separate riser's location is. The only satisfactory solution is to have the separate riser operate an annunciator so that an attendant on the separated car can decide that service is warranted at the floor. Stated otherwise, if the separate elevator is provided with an operating scheme by which it will operate automatically in response to calls from the separate riser, considerable inefficiency in operation and numerous false stops can be expected.

How to serve basements and special floors can often be a problem. As stated previously, extra time allowances must be made for special stops if they are to be served during any traffic situation. In addition, all the elevators in the group must serve the special floors or basements unless they are to be served only during independent service operations. Failure to do so impairs the accessibility of those floors.

With basements, assuming only one for the moment, the criteria is that less than 25 to 33 per cent of the critical traffic on the elevators is expected to originate from the basement. If that is the case the basement may be served only on call. Any car not selected for dispatching or a down traveling car should travel to the basement only if a car or hall call for basement service exists. If more than one basement is served the car should not travel any lower than the lowest hall call in the basement area.

If more than about 33 per cent of the critical traffic is expected from the basement consideration should be given to making the basement the lower dispatching terminal. If, for example, the basement is a cafeteria and only open at noon the dispatching or starting terminal for the group of elevators should then be switched from the lobby to the basement by either a clock-controlled switch or automatic means.

Floors above the main group of floors the elevators serve should be treated similarly, in effect like upsidedown basements. If there is a top floor restaurant, and it is only open at noon, the dispatching floor should be switched at that time.

Many other situations could arise in applying the proper control to a group of elevators, the foregoing being the most common. It is only necessary to state that the odd situations should be recognized early and sufficient control engineered into the group automatic operating system to meet the expected problems.

ADJUSTING OPERATION TO TRAFFIC

Initiating the proper operations of the elevators at the proper time is a task that should be accomplished automatically. In earlier systems an attendant was required to change the mode of operation or *program*, as it was known. Too often it was set on one operation and not changed so that when it was time to go home, the passengers had to fight elevators that had been left on "up peak" operation. Modern systems are or should be completely responsive to the traffic situation. They should, at minimum, be electrically conditioned to react to the difference between up hall or car calls and down hall calls. They should change their mode of operation if filled elevators appear in a particular direction. More sophisticated systems utilize computing circuits to determine where elevators can be directed to best serve the prevailing traffic at any time.

Responsible elevator manufacturers can demonstrate the extent of their data processing in dispatching elevators and should be called upon to do so. With the increasing availability of advanced computer circuitry and with the processing of more information, greater utilization of elevator capacity should become practicable and elevators will be able to provide service of even higher quality. In preceding chapters the basis of calculating required elevator capacity and quality of service was shown. The elevators chosen for a given building and the operating scheme specified should be capable of providing that required performance.

CHAPTER EIGHT

Space and
Physical Requirements

SPACE FOR ELEVATORS

Architects of successful buildings recognize that means of access to and from each floor of the building is more important than any other feature on a typical floor. Individual floor plans may readily be changed to suit individual requirements but means of access between floors affect everyone and are relatively permanent. Poor internal transportation can seriously impair the building that gives an outward appearance of being an architectural masterpiece.

Good internal transportation includes all aspects of the circulation within the building—the proper lobbies, the right-sized corridors, sufficient elevators of proper size, and adequate stairs. Elevator and escalator planning must consider both the space allocated for the equipment and the space provided for people to use that equipment.

In Chapter 2 elevator lobby space and its essential contribution to efficient elevator utilization are discussed. Traffic handling by elevators emphasizes the importance of sufficient elevators of specific size and speed as well as providing the proper width and door openings on those elevators. In this chapter building space to accommodate elevators is emphasized.

REQUIRED SPACE

To make an elevator platform travel up and down smoothly and safely certain structural requirements must be met. Each elevator must have

135

guides or rails that keep it in a true vertical path and provide the foundation from which it may be supported if, for any reason, its operation becomes unsafe. This latter consideration is called *safety application* and consists of a device below the elevator platform that will stop and hold it on the rails if it overspeeds in the down direction for any reason. As may be imagined, stopping an elevator that has a dead weight of three or four tons plus a passenger load of two to four or more thousand pounds and traveling at hundreds of feet per minute by clamping it on the building structure through the guide rails will require a sizable and rugged rail. Space for rails, therefore, is a necessity (Figure 8.1a).

Rail Support

In addition to the rails adequate rail supports or brackets must be provided. The brackets are fastened to the building steel by the elevator contractor or, in a concrete building, by means of inserts set in the concrete by the general contractor on advice from the elevator contractor (Figure 8-1b). The vertical space between brackets is critical and may affect the size of the rails required. Elevator rails are designed so that fastening at floor levels is generally sufficient provided floor levels are from about 8 to 12 ft apart. If longer spans are expected additional supporting beams should be provided in the structure or else there should be additional horizontal space to reinforce the elevator guides and provide the necessary stiffness. In some situations this may require 2 or 3 in. of additional hoistway width which should not be taken away from the platform size as it would result in a substandard elevator.

The maximum vertical distance between brackets, related to the size of elevator rails and the expected load on those rails, is given in a table in the American Standard Safety Code for elevators. That table is reproduced in Figure 8.2 because it is most important. The latest edition of the code should be checked for any changes.

Platform and Enclosure

The elevator must be enclosed. Because the interior should create a comfortable surrounding and is seen by everyone entering and leaving a building it merits the best architectural design and finest craftsmanship. This requires space and creates weight. In addition the enclosure, in the better elevators, is completely isolated, both for sound and vibration, from the structure that supports it. Such isolation, usually accomplished by rubber pads, requires space. The supporting structure, called the car frame, must be constructed to withstand the force of a safety application and the lifting forces on the elevator as well as the weight of the mechanism that will operate the doors (door operator), switches, cams, and so on. All this weight requires a structure that may become quite heavy and, again, requires space (Figure 8.1c).

Access to the elevator from each floor is guarded by a hoistway door. This door is required by local building codes to be of fire-resistant construction and to be able to withstand a blaze for a period of hours. In addition a mechanism must be provided to lock the door safely when the elevator is not at the floor and automatically open it when the car is leveling to the floor. Space for both the doors and its mechanism is required (Figure 8.1d).

In a traction-type elevator the dead load and part of the passenger load (usually about 40 per cent) is counterweighted, and the weights travel up or down in the opposite direction from the elevator. Counterweight guides are usually at the rear of the elevator, although some special installations have counterweights at the side. If the counterweight could be of unlimited height it could be very slim, but because the height of the counterweight cannot be much more than the height of the car horizontal space for the necessary cast-iron weight is required (Figure 8.1d).

Running Clearance

In addition to all the foregoing space requirements a small running clearance is required adjacent to the openings into the elevator. As you may note on an existing installation, the distance between the edge of the elevator door sill and the hoistway door sill is between ¾ and 1½ in. This is running clearance. Similarly, the space between the rear of the car and closest point on the counterweight is about 2 in and between the counterweight and its rail brackets supported from the back wall are another 2 in. These are necessary running clearances and must be maintained (Figure 8.1d).

An elevator must run up and down as plumb as possible. If it does not it will be leaning at the bottom and at the top with consequent extra wear on the elevator guide shoes and an uncomfortable swaying trip for the passenger. Buildings are often not plumb; tolerance will vary from a fraction of an inch for some trades to an inch or more for others such as concrete. Elevator contractors ask for an inch, plus or minus, plumbness in an elevator shaft, which means that a difference of 2 in. may exist between the top and bottom in either the front-to-back or side-to-side direction or both. Elevator layouts and space requirements must compensate for this by allowing an inch in both directions as a plumbness tolerance (Figure 8.1e).

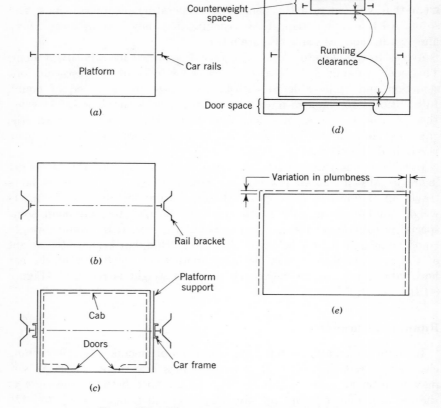

Figure 8.1 Elevator layout procedure—plan.

With all the foregoing specifications, the net usable platform area available in any elevator layout is about 60 per cent of the hoistway required for the elevator. Details of the steps in allocating this space are shown in Figure 8.3. Industrial effort to reduce this nonusable space is constant, including use of stronger steel, new approaches to door arrangement, and new fastenings. Since the safety operations of the elevator is utmost and most of the space required at present is for safety reasons, architects must provide the space.

Space can be achieved by making all the interior space as usable as possible. For example, handrails are of little value in present-day elevators and reduce interior space. Hanging panels reduce interior space since the rating of the floor area is independent of these panels. If such

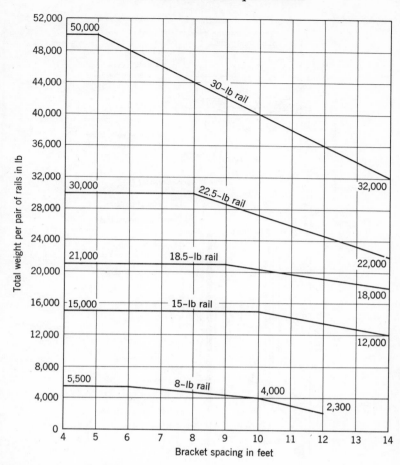

Figure 8.2 Maximum weight of car with rated load or of counterweight with safety for a pair of guide rails as specified in rule 200.4a.

is the desired architectural design, a higher-rated car which can accommodate the panels and produce the necessary net area should be specified.

OVERHEAD AND PIT REQUIREMENTS

Once the plan of the various elevators in the building is established, attention must be given to providing the necessary vertical space. We confine our discussion to conventional traction elevators, leaving until

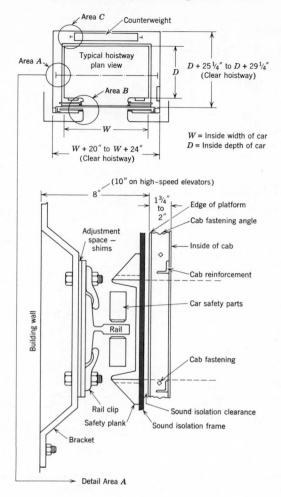

Figure 8.3

later details about hydraulics, basement machines, and underslung elevators.

Pit Space

When the elevator stops at a floor of a building certain parts of the structure of the elevator are either above or below the cab as it is seen at that floor. Below the cab floor is the platform, a structural base composed of either wood and angle iron or all steel. In the better elevators this platform is supported by rubber pads, on a sound isolation

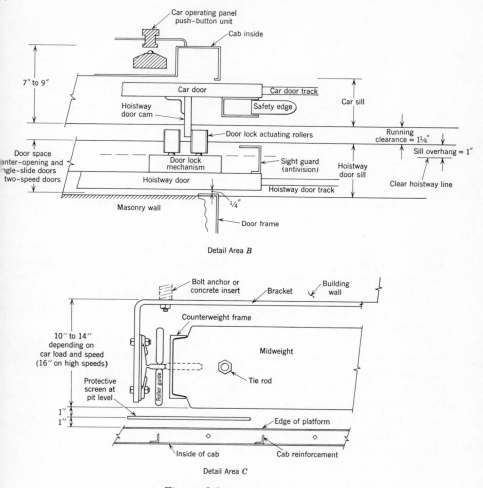

Detail Area *B*

Detail Area *C*

Figure 8.3 (*continued*)

frame. An accepted method of weighing the load in the elevator car is to measure the deflection of these rubber pads and actuate microswitches for the various degrees of loading in the car (Figure 8.4).

The combination of platform and sound isolation frame rests on the safety plank, which also supports the elevator safety device, clamps will stop and hold the elevator on the rails if it overspeeds in the down direction. The safety plank also must absorb the impact from the elevator buffers located in the pit (Figure 8.5a).

When the elevator is stopped at the lowest floor, there will be a few inches overtravel before it strikes the buffer. The buffer is designed to

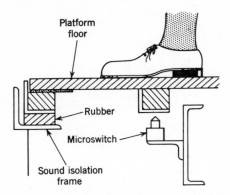

Figure 8.4 Load weighing by measuring platform deflection.

stop the elevator if, for some reason, it travels at its operating speed past the lowest floor. The buffer absorbs the kinetic energy of the moving car and brings it to a stop within the limit of the buffer stroke. The stop is not gentle but it is within safe limits. The buffer is not required to bring a free-falling elevator to a stop; this is the function of the car safety.

Pit depth therefore must consist of the platform and support space required for the elevator car (Figure 8.5b) plus operating clearance in addition to the buffer standing and stroke space (Figure 8.5c). For elevator speeds up to and including 200 fpm, spring buffers may be used. For speeds of 201 fpm and over, oil-type buffers must be used. The height and stroke of the buffer is a function of speed and is defined by the American Standard Safety Code for Elevators. The depths required for typical pits range from 5 to 16 ft or more for very high speed. Table 8.1 shows depths for the more common speeds.

For the higher-speed elevators of about 700 fpm and over the buffer stroke may be reduced if certain other precautions are taken. One of

Table 8.1. Pit depths. Traction elevators—overhead machines

	Speed (fpm)	100	200	300	400	500	600	700	800
Depth	With rope compensation				8′0	8′6	9′2	9′10	10′6
	With chain compensation	5′0	5′0	5′4″	7′10	8′4			
	Buffer type	Spring			Oil				

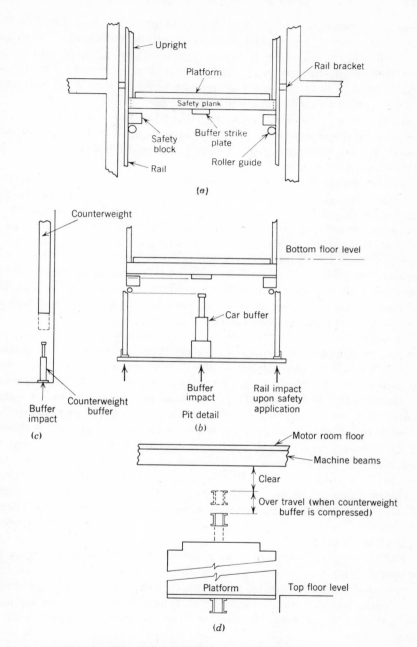

Figure 8.5   Elevator layout procedure—elevation.

143

these is a means to insure that the elevator brake is applied if the car is traveling at high speed when it is within a determined distance of the pit. If, for example, it normally takes about 20 ft to slow down and stop a 700-fpm elevator, and the elevator is traveling that fast within, say, 15 ft of the pit, applying the brake at that point will slow it down so that a shorter buffer will stop the car.

When the elevator car lands on the buffer and the buffer is fully compressed, the counterweight is at its highest point. Sufficient clearance above the counterweight must be maintained so that there is no danger of its striking the overhead.

To provide similarly for a possible counterweight landing in the pit, the counterweight, too, has a buffer of somewhat equal stroke to the car buffer. In addition space under the counterweight must be provided for normal running clearance (Figure 8.6*B*) plus sufficient additional space so that the normal stretching that is experienced with elevator ropes will not cause the counterweights to land and require shortening of the ropes (Figure 8.6*C*). This stretching can result from temperature changes, aging, or rope strands settling after manufacture because of the addition of load or various other causes. An inch or two per hundred feet of rope length is a nominal allowance for this contingency.

In addition to the buffers, the pit must often contain provisions for guiding of compensating ropes. These are ropes, attached to the bottom of the car and to the bottom of the counterweight, whose function is to compensate for the weight of the hoist ropes moving from the car to the counterweight side of the machine as the car travels up and down. In taller buildings this compensating rope guide may consist of a weighted sheave riding on short tracks in the pit. In very tall buildings or higher-speed elevators the guiding mechanism may be arranged to link the car and counterweight together in such a way that when the car safety applies it acts on the entire mass of the system. This avoids excessive jump of the up-traveling weights when the high kinetic energy of the down-traveling elevator is arrested. Such a system is known as *tied-down compensation* or *monomass* safety and creates a tremendous up-pull in the pit.

For slower-speed elevators, chain interwoven with sash cord may be substituted for guided rope as compensation. The sash cord is used to overcome the normal rattling noise a moving chain makes. This approach is usually confined to elevators of 350 fpm or less; it may be used at 500 fpm if economy is desired and an increased noise level is acceptable.

In determining the pit depth consideration of other equipment is necessary. The electrical cables that hang from the bottom of the elevator to a point near the middle of the hoistway and carry all the power and signals to the elevator car must travel into the pit without coming in contact with equipment that would cause premature wear and failure. A tensioning device for the elevator governor or safety rope, which controls the application of the car safety, must also be located in the pit.

The total design of the pit (Figure 8.6) must include provisions for all the necessary elevator equipment, sufficient depth for the possible run-by of the elevator, as well as sufficient support for the various impacts that may occur. These impacts include those of the rail on safety application, those on the buffers if they are called on to perform, and the up-pulls on the compensating arrangement in the event of safety application. All these reactions are shown on the elevator layout provided by the consulting engineer or the elevator manufacturer. It is up to the architect to provide for them in his total plan.

Overhead Space

Overhead space, required by the elevator when it is stopped at the top landing, must be allocated in a manner similar to pit space. On top of the elevator car is the mechanism that operates the elevator doors and the elevator lifting beam or crosshead. In addition space must be allocated for the car fan or blower, the elevator leveling device, plus sufficient clearance to the next higher point in the hoistway. This next higher point may be the bottom of the beams that support the elevator machinery or a sheave used to deflect the hoisting ropes back toward the counterweight.

If the elevator passes the top landing a number of events occur. First the counterweight lands and starts to compress the counterweight buffer. If the elevator is traveling at any speed the car will have a slight jump. If someone is working on top of the car, he will require a safe clearance to crouch—safety codes require a minimum of two feet. All this adds up to the space required for run-by. The space required from the top landing to the top of the motor room floor may be 20 to 30 or more feet.

Figure 8.6 shows this space and how it is allocated. Considerable variation may be expected with various speeds, sizes, and arrangements of elevator equipment.

Motor Room Space

The usual location for the elevator machinery is above the elevator hoistway itself. For some electric elevator applications this location **can**

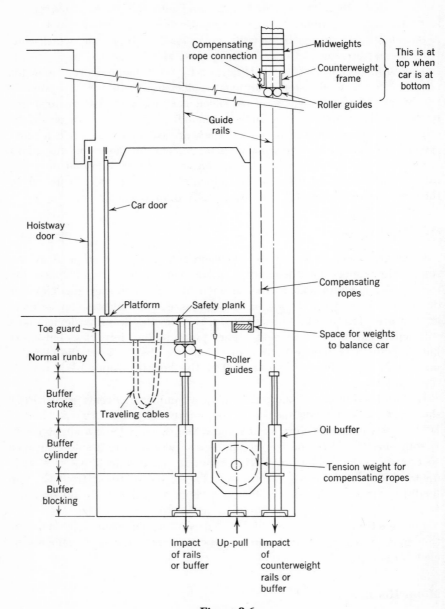

Figure 8.6

146

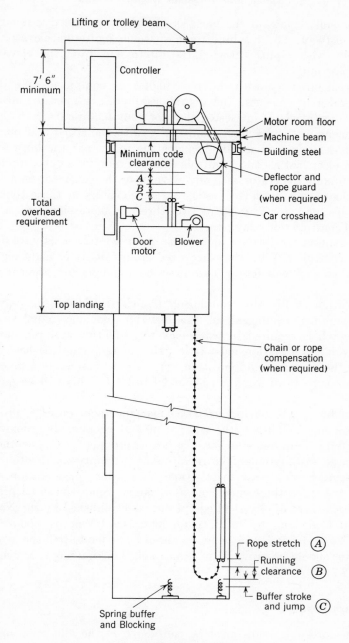

Figure 8.6 (*continued*)

147

be at the side, below, at the back, or elsewhere, provided it is adjacent to the hoistway. The machine room space in hydraulic elevators may be remote, with piping carrying the oil to and from the elevator to the pumping unit.

Requirements vary with different makes of equipment. We discuss the general requirements; the actual requirements must be discussed with representatives of interested elevator manufacturers.

Equipment in the machine room varies with the speed and operation of the elevator but essentially includes the following: the hoisting machine, an electrical elevator controller, a governor for safety application control, a motor generator with any elevator of the generator field control type, a floor-selecting device on the larger elevators or those that serve many stops, and, for a group of two, three, or more elevators, a group electrical controller or relay panel.

Some manufacturers may mount the group controller as part of each elevator controller. With the office-sized groups of six or eight elevators an extra control cabinet or two may be required for efficient group control.

In addition to elevator equipment (which should be the only part of the building equipment in the elevator machine room) a main power switch is required for each elevator. Lighting and ventilation is necessary, the ventilation must be capable of removing the heat generated by the elevator equipment to maintain a reasonable temperature in the motor room of less than about 90 to 95°F. This will be qualified later.

Reasonable access to and from the machine room must be provided. Mechanics must maintain the equipment and occasionally remove and replace parts. Trap doors and trolley beams provide for this contingency in the large installations. The repairman's ingenuity must often suffice in the smaller, single-car installations, but prior consideration to the problem will save the owner time and money. Space must be provided around each piece of electrical equipment, as established by the National Electrical Code and by local codes, and usually means about 30 in. in front, 24 in. behind, and 18 in. on one side. Space to pull the armature of a motor should be provided in front of the hoisting motor or generator (Figure 8.7).

Secondary Levels

All the foregoing items must be considered in the allocation of space for the machine room. On the average, the motor room for each elevator requires the space necessary for the elevator hoistway plus that space

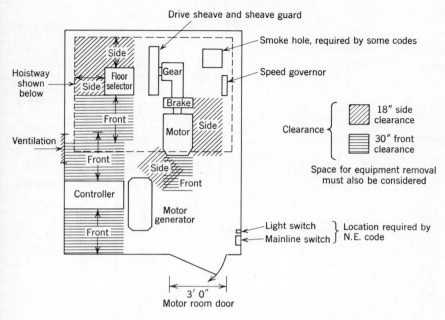

Figure 8.7

again. In the larger installations, elevator equipment may advantageously be placed on two levels.

With smaller or slower installations all equipment may be located on one level so that no space for secondary equipment is necessary. With the larger installation a secondary sheave, located below the driving machine, is often necessary, and because there must be access to this sheave, a sub-machine room or secondary level is created. This level can be half a floor below the elevator machine room floor and be provided with suitable access for personnel (Figure 8.8).

ELEVATOR REACTIONS

Concurrent with the space allocations in the machine room are the loads that the equipment creates. The primary force is due to the elevator hanging load which is transmitted through the driving machine sheave shaft to the elevator machine beams. These beams are supplied by the elevator contractor and the building must provide the supports for them. A series of two or three beams is placed across the hoistway and the

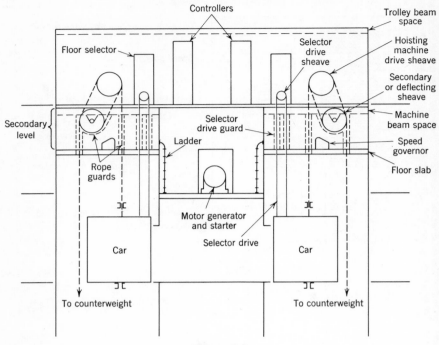

Figure 8.8

reactions at the end or support point of each beam indicated on the elevator layout. This load includes the dead weights and an allowance for impact on the structure. In addition the weight and location of each piece of elevator equipment is provided and the floor or supporting structure must be designed to accommodate these loads. Connecting conduits for electrical wiring can be buried in the floor or the wiring installed in overhead troughs. Trolley beams for moving equipment should be provided and the maximum expected load on the trolley is provided by the equipment manufacturer. Typical machine room layouts are shown in Figures 8.9*a* and *b*. Figure 8.9*a* is for a single-car, resistance control elevator; Figure 8.9*b* shows a total of four elevators and the allocation of space for the necessary equipment.

Typical Layouts

Every elevator manufacturer as well as the National Elevator Manufacturers Institute and the National Association of Elevator Contractors provide typical layouts for standard elevators on request. The most economical and often the best elevator installation for any building results from using these layouts for the speed and duty required. The typical layout contains all the necessary information to enable the architect to provide the necessary space, the structural engineer to design the structure, and the electrical engineer to provide for necessary power.

For the larger or special installation, the architect or consulting engineer may work with the elevator manufacturers to establish the best layout of the equipment.

Changing a typical layout to suit some particular situation should be attempted only with expert advice. As may be seen from the earlier discussion of space requirements, an assumed minor change in any dimension may have a chain effect and render the entire layout useless. In many countries, such as Italy and France, where elevators are completely standardized, any deviation may double the cost of the installation. In the United States such changes can usually be accomplished with minor price penalty.

Sample typical layouts are shown on pages 154 to 157. Note that all the necessary dimensions are provided with a minimum of detail. Each layout plus a page or two of description could form the entire specification of an elevator.

ADDITIONAL MACHINE ROOM CONSIDERATIONS

We mentioned power and ventilation requirements in discussing machine room requirements. Because these items concern the efficient operation of the elevators, additional discussion is required.

Power

Electrical power is primarily required to start and stop an elevator (traction type) and only partially to lift the load. Except for power consumed in opening and closing the doors, and in control, much of the power a traction elevator requires to lift loads is returned to the line when such load is lowered. Stated otherwise, the elevators require power to lift the uncounterbalanced portion of the load when people come to work and those same people, as they leave, thus theoretically cause the elevator to pump back an equal amount of power. In practice, friction, impedance, and other factors introduce losses and some power will always be required.

Efficiency of traction elevator machinery runs from 50 to 70 per cent for the geared-type elevator with rolling guides and from **75** to **85** per cent for gearless elevators. Losses are generally changed to heat and must be dissipated by the building ventilation system.

The power required by any fully or partly loaded elevator may be readily derived from the following formula:

$$\text{horsepower} = \frac{\text{load in car} \times \text{velocity (fpm)} \times \text{per cent unbalanced load}}{33,000 \times \text{efficiency of the hoisting machine}}.$$

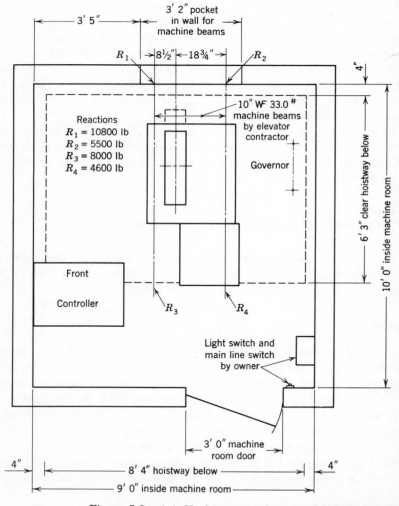

Figure 8.9   (*a*) **Machine room layout—2500 @ 100 fpm;**

Example: Traction elevator, 2500 lb, 500 fpm, gearless machine, 40 per cent counterbalance.

$$\text{hp} = \frac{2500 \times 500 \times 0.60}{33000 \times 0.80} = 28 \text{ hp approximate.}$$

The energy consumption of a group of elevators operating over a period of time requires a number of calculations, including the determi-

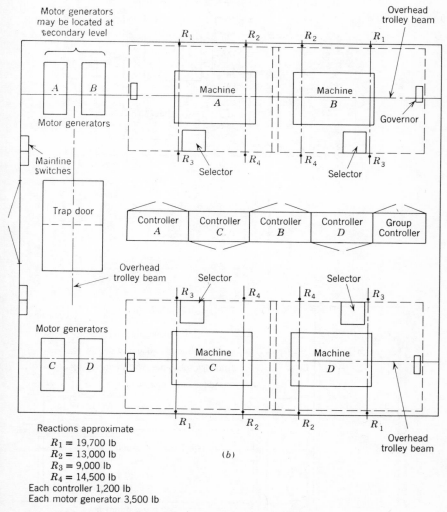

Reactions approximate
R_1 = 19,700 lb
R_2 = 13,000 lb
R_3 = 9,000 lb
R_4 = 14,500 lb
Each controller 1,200 lb
Each motor generator 3,500 lb

(*b*)

(*b*) machine room layout—four elevators 3500 @ 700 fpm.

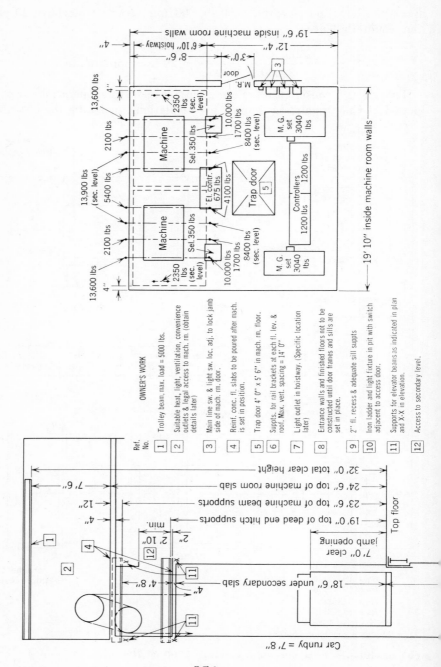

OWNER'S WORK

Ref. No.	
1	Trolley beam, max. load = 5000 lbs.
2	Suitable heat, light, ventilation, convenience outlets & legal access to mach. rm. (obtain details later)
3	Main line sw. & light sw. loc. adj. to lock jamb side of mach. rm. door.
4	Reinf. conc. fl. slabs to be poured after mach. is set in position.
5	Trap door 4' 0" x 5' 6" in mach. rm. floor.
6	Supports. for rail brackets at each fl. lev. & roof. Max. vert. spacing = 14' 0"
7	Light outlet in hoistway. (Specific location later)
8	Entrance walls and finished floors not to be constructed until door frames and sills are set in place.
9	2" fl. recess & adequate sill supts
10	Iron ladder and light fixture in pit with switch adjacent to access door.
11	Supports for elevator beams as indicated in plan and X-X in elevation.
12	Access to secondary level.

154

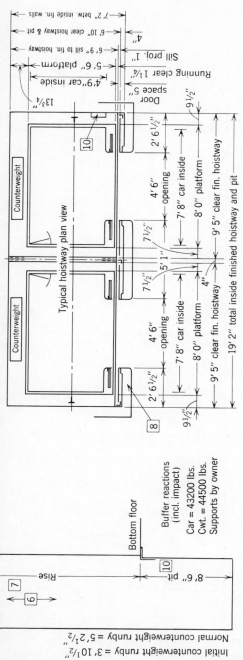

Typical layout. Variable voltage gearless elevator. 3500 lb @ 500 fpm (wide platform and doors).

Typical hoistway plan view

Counterweight

Counterweight

7'2" betw. inside fin. walls
6'10" clear hoistway & pit
4"
6'9" sill to fin. hoistway
Sill proj. 1"
5'6" platform
Running clear 1¼"
4'9" car inside
Door space 5"
13¾"

10

8

2'6½"
4'6" opening
7½"
7'8" car inside
8'0" platform
9'5" clear fin. hoistway
9½"

5'1"

7½"
4"
4'6" opening
2'6½"
7'8" car inside
8'0" platform
9'5" clear fin. hoistway
9½"
19'2" total inside finished hoistway and pit

Bottom floor

Buffer reactions
(incl. impact)
Car = 43200 lbs.
Cwt. = 44500 lbs.
Supports by owner

Rise

7

6

10

8'6" pit

Initial counterweight runby = 3'10½"
Normal counterweight runby = 5'2½"

155

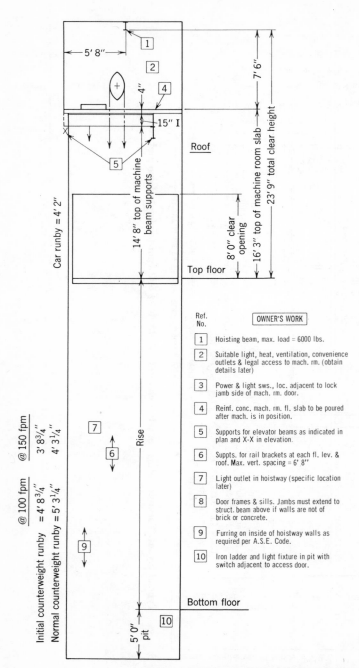

← 5'8" →

[1]

[2]

+ 4" [4]

15" I

Roof

[5]

Car runby = 4'2"

14'8" top of machine beam supports

7'6"

23'9" total clear height

8'0" clear opening

16'3" top of machine room slab

Top floor

Rise

[7]

[6]

[9]

@ 150 fpm 3'8¾" 4'3¼"

@ 100 fpm = 4'8¾" = 5'3¼"

Initial counterweight runby
Normal counterweight runby

Bottom floor

5'0" pit

[10]

Ref. No.	OWNER'S WORK
1	Hoisting beam, max. load = 6000 lbs.
2	Suitable light, heat, ventilation, convenience outlets & legal access to mach. rm. (obtain details later)
3	Power & light sws., loc. adjacent to lock jamb side of mach. rm. door.
4	Reinf. conc. mach. rm. fl. slab to be poured after mach. is in position.
5	Supports for elevator beams as indicated in plan and X-X in elevation.
6	Suppts. for rail brackets at each fl. lev. & roof. Max. vert. spacing = 6'8"
7	Light outlet in hoistway (specific location later)
8	Door frames & sills. Jambs must extend to struct. beam above if walls are not of brick or concrete.
9	Furring on inside of hoistway walls as required per A.S.E. Code.
10	Iron ladder and light fixture in pit with switch adjacent to access door.

Typical layout. Geared, variable-voltage freight

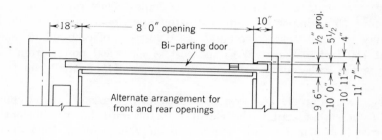

18″ — 8′ 0″ opening — 10″

Bi-parting door

Alternate arrangement for
front and rear openings

½″ proj.
5½″
4″
11′ 7″
10′ 0″
9′ 6″

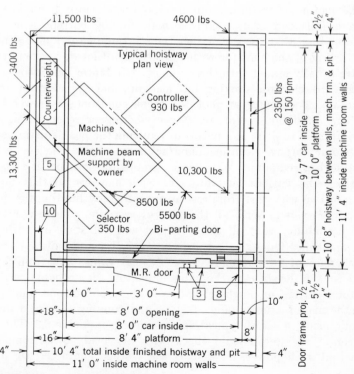

11,500 lbs   4600 lbs

3400 lbs

Typical hoistway
plan view

Counterweight

Controller
930 lbs

Machine

Machine beam
support by
owner

5

10,300 lbs

13,300 lbs

10

8500 lbs
5500 lbs

Selector
350 lbs

Bi-parting door

M.R. door

3   8

2½″
4″

2350 lbs
@ 150 fpm

9′ 7″ car inside
10′ 0″ platform

10′ 8″ hoistway between walls, mach. rm. & pit

11′ 4″ inside machine room walls

Door frame proj. ½″
5½″
4″

4′ 0″ — 3′ 0″

10″

18″ — 8′ 0″ opening
8′ 0″ car inside
16″ — 8′ 4″ platform — 8″
4″ — 10′ 4″ total inside finished hoistway and pit — 4″
11′ 0″ inside machine room walls

elevator, 6000 lb @ 100 or 150 fpm.

157

nation of full-, partial-, and no-load trips, direction, and number of car stops. The task would be almost impossible for any building without the help of a specially programmed computer.

Sufficient to say, the average power required by an automatic elevator varies with its size and speed. It must be determined by a recording watt-hour meter after the building is completed and in operation.

Estimates can be based on known examples. They range from values of about 10 kwh per day for a 10-stop apartment house to 100 kwh per day for a 10-story office building. A 20-story office building requires about 150 kwh per day. With the cost of electrical power from 0.5 to 4 cents per kwh, power consumption is generally of small concern for traction elevators.

The demand an elevator system creates for power is of greater concern. The feeders that supply the elevator motor must be of sufficient size to serve that demand with a minimum of voltage drop. Because most elevator motor generators are driven by ac induction motors of about 10 to 75 or more horsepower, starting the motor from rest usually creates the greatest power demand. An equal or higher-power demand may occur when the motor generator is running and the elevator itself is started up with a full load in the car. Normal running current is generally much lower than that used for either the starting of the motor generator or the starting of the elevator with full load up. Elevator power requirements are usually stated with three values: (a) Motor generator starting from rest, (b) elevator starting full load up, and (c) elevator running full load up. The motor current for other conditions is lower.

With any induction motor, resistance starting or reconnecting motor windings from Y to delta is a means of reducing the peak starting current of the motor. Many elevator manufacturers employ various schemes to effect such a reduction. With larger groups of elevators it is possible to interlock the various generators of each elevator so that no more than one or two will start from rest at once, thereby limiting the demand on the power system. With all the generators running there is a mathematical probability that all the elevators will not start up with a full load at one time. This is called a diversity factor and can be calculated for any group of two or more cars. Typical values run from 0.87 for two cars to 0.75 for six cars, the value indicating the probable percentage of the total current of all the elevators in the group at one time.

Elevator manufacturers offer starting and running current values for their equipment; a set of typical values appears in Table 8.2. The building owner or architect should check with his local power company to confirm that such power, as well as the voltage characteristic of such

Table 8.2. Starting and running current; typical generator field control elevators @ 208 volts, 3φ, 60 cycles

Geared	2500 @ 200	3000 @ 300	3500 @ 350
M.G.[a] starting from rest	84 amp	113 amp	164 amp
Elevator start full load up	96 amp	184 amp	248 amp
Elevator run full load up	60 amp	115 amp	155 amp

Gearless	2500 @ 500	3000 @ 700	3500 @ 800
M.G. starting from rest	113 amp	258 amp	413 amp
Elevator start full load up	129 amp	322 amp	407 amp
Elevator run full load up	81 amp	184 amp	233 amp

[a] M.G. = Motor generator.

power, is available before the elevator manufacturer undertakes the production of equipment.

Electric current requirements for single-speed traction and for hydraulic elevators are easier to calculate. The elevator is either running or stopped, unlike generator field control where a generator is running whether or not the elevator is. With a single-speed elevator, starting is either across the line or through a resistance step. The horsepower of the elevator motor establishes the electrical power required.

Ventilation

The heat generated by a single-speed or hydraulic elevator is also relatively easy to figure. Most of the power supplied to the motor will be changed to heat through braking when stops are made. Since the elevator can run up much less than half the time, and since most-single speed or hydraulic elevators are found in low-rise buildings, it is fair to estimate a maximum of 25 to 30 per cent of time spent will be spent running full load, the worst condition. Converting this percentage of the elevator motor horsepower to Btu's gives a good approximation of the heating expected in the elevator machine room. (Horsepower per hour equals 2544 Btu's.) This heat must be dissipated for efficient elevator operation.

Dissipation of machine room heat is important in any elevator installation. If the motor room gets too hot electrical insulation deteriorates, oil loses its viscosity, and erratic operation such as poor leveling, jerky starts, and poor brake action can be experienced.

Heat generated by the elevator may be considerable during certain periods of the day. For example, during the morning inrush in an office building, elevators are expected to be leaving the lobby with full loads, so that power demands will be at their maximum for a half hour or so. At that time a typical office building elevator may generate from 25,000 to 35,000 or more Btu's per hour—about the rating of a small furnace! At the same time, the maintenance man is expected to be on duty and check operation and oil levels. Without ventilation the machine room temperature may soar to 100 or 120°F.

Adequate ventilation is required in any elevator machine room to dissipate the heat and provide a reasonable temperature of no more than 90° or no less than 50° no matter what the outside temperature may be. In the smaller, single-car installations a thermostatically controlled exhaust fan may accomplish this. In the larger installations the spill air of the air conditioning system may be sufficient. No matter what the approach, it must be provided for. Table 8.3 shows a sample of typical heat generated by elevator equipment. If the generator is remote from the elevator drive motor and control this must be taken into consideration because about two-thirds of the heat is emanates from the generator and one-third from the drive motor.

An accurate estimate of machine room heating can be given by the elevator equipment manufacturer. This estimate can be calculated from the number of floors an elevator serves, its rise, the speed, and the duty load, plus information as to its expected use. The percentage of full load running time is then calculated from probable stop data and the heating losses expressed in Btu's. Approximations for larger elevators

Table 8.3. Sample heating; typical gearless installations under busy conditions

1. 2000 @ 500 fpm   30-story apartment (250 ft rise)
                                        18,000 Btu/hr/elevator
2. 3000 @ 500   10-story office bldg. (100-ft rise)
                                        22,000 Btu/hr/elevator
3. 3500 @ 700   Serving floors 1, 10–20 in an office building (240-ft rise)
                                        35,000 Btu/hr/elevator
4. 4000 @ 500   10-story hospital (100-ft rise)
                                        25,000 Btu/hr/elevator

can be made using the same approach as suggested for the hydraulic and single-speed elevator, that is converting to Btu's about 25 to 35 per cent of the required elevator horsepower for full load over a period of an hour.

Emergency Operation

In most hospitals and in areas where power failures are frequent it is desirable to provide an emergency power supply to operate the elevators. In any building it is desirable to have a separate power source for the car lights and fan so that passengers will be comfortable no matter why the car shuts down. When elevators are essential they should be capable of operation during a power failure.

The amount of emergency power available determines how elevators can be operated. If the supply is limited the elevator equipment manufacturer can arrange the installation so that only one elevator operates at one time, the choice being made manually by a selecting switch. When passengers are released from all the elevators, one car can remain in service. The building owner provides the wiring and switchover to provide power at the machine room. The elevator manufacturer provides a switch on each elevator controller to insure that only one elevator is operated at one time. He also provides the selecting switch to determine which elevator will operate.

The building's emergency power system should supply sufficient power to operate any one elevator (or more if the emergency plant is large enough) as well as sufficient provisions to absorb the current generated by the elevator if it should travel down with a full load. This absorption of regenerated power is essential to prevent possible overspeeding of the elevator or damage to the emergency generator. The value of absorption needed is given by the elevator equipment manufacturer and must be designed into the emergency power system. If fixed emergency lighting is sufficient, it may provide sufficient capacity to take care of regenerated power. Each situation, however, must be individually calculated.

If only very limited emergency power is available reduced-speed operation of the elevators is possible to minimize power requirements, provided they are the generator field control type. Hydraulic elevators generally have a manual lowering valve that can be used to move a car to a next lower floor. Smaller geared elevators can be cranked to a landing. Any elevator that stops for other than normal reasons is potentially dangerous. No attempt to move the car or remove the passengers in that car should be made without adequate professional precautions.

Requirements for emergency power operations should be discussed with elevator manufacturers' representatives or consulting engineers.

ELEVATOR LAYOUTS

We have discussed establishing space, ventilation, and power requirements of elevators, particularly passenger overhead traction elevators. Layouts for hydraulic elevators, elevators with basement machines, freight elevators, sidewalk elevators, dumbwaiters, self-supporting elevators, and other types follow, in general, the steps that have been outlined. Based on the car size, the hoistway plan is established, the pit and overhead determined, the machine room laid out, supports for equipment and impacts determined, and power and ventilation established. For other than overhead traction elevators, additional considerations must be made.

Hydraulic Elevators

Hydraulic elevators require a hoistway space for the car but not for a counterweight. No overhead machine room is required but space must be provided for the pump, control equipment, and piping to and from the elevator shaft. Adequate pit space for the plunger and cylinder supports are necessary and impacts on buffers must be considered. In areas where there is ground water consideration must be given to tying down the cylinder and well casing lest it float up. In the elevator hoistway adequate run-by space above the top landing as well as sufficient support for fastening rail brackets at established distances (usually at floor levels) must be provided (see Figure 1.11).

Freight Elevators

For both electric and hydraulic heavy-duty freight elevators, adequate rail supports must be provided, usually at shorter distances than at floor levels. These supports can be building steel at each floor and at intermediate levels or a solid concrete hoistway into which the elevator contractor places bracket supporting inserts. For elevators loaded by trucks or carrying trucks, fabricated steel supports must be erected at each side of the hoistway (Figure 8.10).

These steel supports for elevator guides and brackets must be designed to absorb the impact of the truck as it loads on the elevator. The impacts consist of the braking load on the truck wheels, the twisting motion

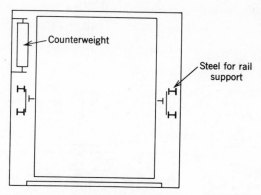

Figure 8.10   Heavy-duty freight elevator.

of unbalanced loading, and opposing forces on the top and bottom elevator guide shoes transmitted to the rails. Figure 8.11 shows the directions
some of these forces will take.

If an elevator is to be loaded by an industrial truck it must be designed
to hold both its capacity load and some of the weight of the truck.
Depending on the type of load, either all or part of the truck may be
on the elevator as the last portion of the load is deposited. The elevator
machine, brake, car frame, and platform must all be designed to withstand this extra "static" load. The elevator need not lift this load but
must be able to level, that is, move the platform level with the floor
with the extra load on board.

Basement Traction Machines

It is often desirable to install an elevator without a rooftop penthouse.
The hydraulic elevator needs no penthouse but is limited in speed and
performance. It also has high power demands that may not be desirable
in a small building. Another approach is to install an electric traction
machine in the basement or adjacent to the hoistway at an upper floor,
thus taking advantage of the counterweighted elevator with its lower
power demands and higher speeds. These arrangements are called, simply, *machine below*.

This class of traction machine can be of two types, underslung or
direct pickup. The underslung arrangement consists of lifting sheaves
located under the car platform and requires somewhat more pit depth
and hoistway space than the direct pickup (Figure 8.12). The direct
pickup is lifted at the crosshead like any conventional traction elevator

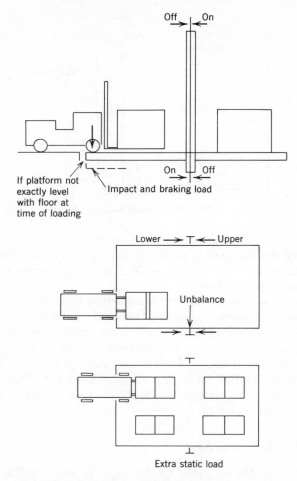

Figue 8.11   Loads produced by industrial trucks.

(Figure 8.13). Either arrangement requires overhead space for rope sheaves and a machine room located either in back of or beside the shaft. With more than one elevator in a line, the back location is preferred and with three or more elevators in a line is mandatory (Figure 8.14).

With any machine-below arrangement, up-thrust forces equal to the entire weight of the elevator and counterweight plus impact allowances require sufficient tie-down, which can be in the form of building steel or a concrete foundation block.

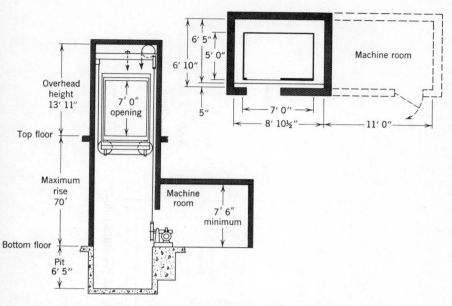

Figure 8.12   Dimensions shown are for 2500 lb @ 200 fpm elevator.

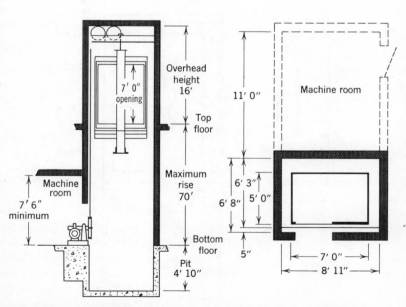

Figure 8.13   Dimensions shown are for 2500 lb @ 200 fpm elevator.

165

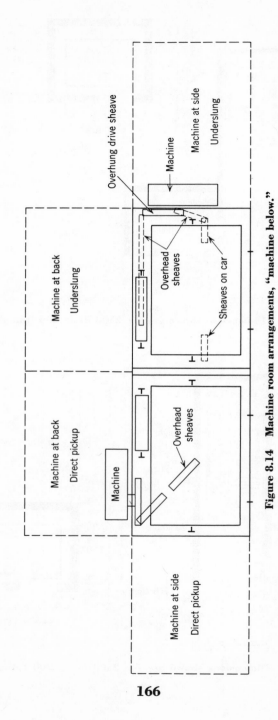

Figure 8.14 Machine room arrangements, "machine below."

Standard typical layouts are available from elevator manufacturers for underslung or direct pickup elevators of 2000- to 4000-lb capacity and speeds from 75 to 350 fpm. Larger duties and higher speeds become somewhat critical and are special. Also note that any consideration of front and rear or front and side entrances on an elevator is extremely critical with a machine-below arrangement.

Sidewalk Elevators

Sidewalk elevators are those that rise to a top level by opening hatch doors located in the floor. The term sidewalk is a carryover from earlier days; most municipal codes forbid raising an elevator in the sidewalk area; they must be located inside a building line.

The typical sidewalk elevator can be electric or hydraulic. The electric sidewalk elevator consists of a drum-type machine with an underslung car. The machine must lift the full load of both the car and the duty plus part of the weight of the sidewalk hatch (Figure 8.15).

A variation of the sidewalk elevator is the self-supporting freight elevator, also a drum-type arrangement. With the self supporting car, the load is transferred to the rail structure, conventional freight-type doors are provided, and a convenient elevator for light freight service can be provided (Figure 8.16). Safety codes generally forbid the use of winding drum-type elevators for passenger use since the required additional maintenance of the hoist ropes is difficult to enforce.

Dumbwaiters

Dumbwaiters are either traction or drum type. The size of a dumbwaiter is limited to 9 ft² of platform area (any combination of dimensions within reason) and no more than 4 ft high. Anything over that size must be classified as a freight elevator to comply with safety codes.

Dumbwaiters are operated from the hall and must be equipped with doors and electrical locks or contacts to prevent their operation if a door is opened. Typical operations are (a) call and send for a two-stop dumbwaiter; (b) multifloor buttons at one floor to send the dumbwaiter to a designated floor with return or call or both buttons at the other floors; (c) multifloor button stations at all floors and complete flexibility. Loading can be at waist height, under-counter, or at the floor. The latter requires automatic leveling and carts with wheels of sufficient diameter to bridge the running clearance and any leveling inaccuracies.

Dumbwaiters can be manual loading and unloading, automatic unloading, or both automatic loading and unloading. Sufficient protected unload-

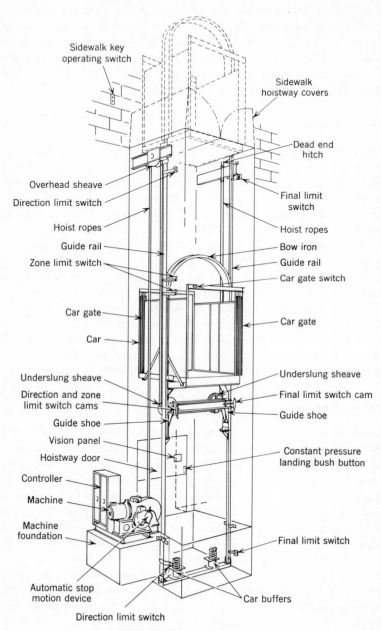

Figure 8.15   Sidewalk elevator.

Sidewalk key operating switch

Sidewalk hoistway covers

Dead end hitch

Overhead sheave

Direction limit switch

Final limit switch

Hoist ropes

Hoist ropes

Guide rail

Bow iron

Zone limit switch

Guide rail

Car gate switch

Car gate

Car gate

Car

Underslung sheave

Underslung sheave

Direction and zone limit switch cams

Final limit switch cam

Guide shoe

Guide shoe

Vision panel

Hoistway door

Constant pressure landing bush button

Controller

Machine

Machine foundation

Final limit switch

Automatic stop motion device

Car buffers

Direction limit switch

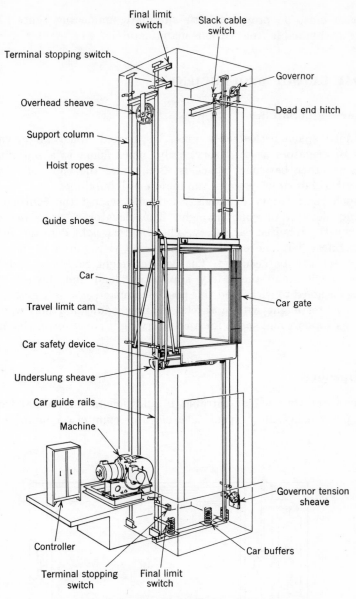

Figure 8.16 "Self supporting" freight elevator.

169

ing space must be provided with automatic unloading types. Typical layouts are available from various manufacturers.

SPECIAL LAYOUT REQUIREMENTS

Counterweight Safeties

Occupied space occasionally must be located under an elevator or groups of elevators as they serve only upper floors in a building or if garage or other basement space is used under the elevators. In some cities railroad or subway trains run underneath buildings.

In such cases safety demands provisions against the contingency of a falling elevator or counterweight. The elevator is protected against falling by the required car safety. The counterweight does not normally have a safety but one can be installed and is required if space below the elevator can be occupied. The counterweight rails are made heavy enough to withstand the safety application load and the elevator pit must be designed to withstand this possible impact.

The counterweight with a safety requires additional hoistway space as well as support and space for a counterweight governor in the machine room.

Rear Openings

An elevator with a rear entrance in addition to the normal front entrance poses a layout problem. The elevator counterweight must be lo-

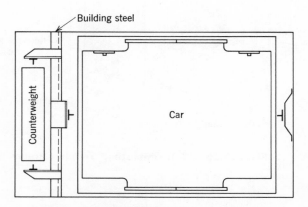

Figure 8.17   "No. 4" construction.

cated at the side rather than in the rear, the machine room must be redesigned, and special supports may be required for both car and counterweight rails. A common hoistway arrangement for front and rear openings is known in the elevator trade as "no. 4" construction from an early standard layout. This arrangement consists of a support beam for the car rails across the shaft, with counterweight space behind it (Figure 8.17). These provisions require extra hoistway space for front and rear entrances, which can be calculated similarly to conventional front-only entrances. Another use for no. 4 construction is to provide a deeper car if front-to-back space is limited and additional space is available at the side.

Corner-Post Arrangement

Another variation with additional entrances on an elevator is front and side entrances, which requires a corner-post arrangement. The car frame is specially built, the rails are placed in opposite corners of the hoistway, the counterweight is properly located, and the machine room is completely rearranged. Space is usually enough only for two-speed doors on both the front and side openings (Figure 8.18).

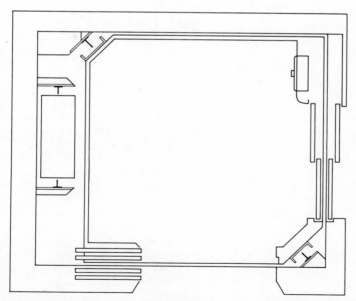

Figure 8.18   Corner-post arrangement (note necessity to use two-speed doors).

A corner-post elevator is difficult to lay out, can create impossible situations, and should be avoided by the novice.

Many other possible elevator layouts include elevators on the outside of buildings—wall climbers; explosion-proof elevators in chemical processing plants; shipboard elevators; special elevators to automatically load and unload rolls of paper or pallets; and elevators with revolving platforms. These all require some special considerations and early collaboration with elevator consultants and manufacturers. These specialists may already have solved a similar problem and can apply their background and ingenuity to new situations and needs.

CHAPTER NINE

Escalators and Moving Ramps

ESCALATORS VERSUS MOVING RAMPS

In this chapter we emphasize the moving stairway and moving walkway types of vertical to horizontal transportation. Of the two, the escalator is the more important since it is used more frequently and has been in use for over 60 years. The moving ramp, either inclined or horizontal, is a relatively newcomer. Numerous devices of the ramp nature have been installed but few have proved completely satisfactory. For vertical transportation along an incline the escalator is unsurpassed in requiring the least amount of horizontal space and providing the safest service at lowest cost. For horizontal travel a moving walk, once its development is complete and public acceptance extended, should prove to be an effective means of directing and transporting passengers.

To date, interest in providing ramps is at a minimum. The installations have accounted for about 1 to 2 per cent of the total escalator–ramp installations in the United States. Interest is growing, however, and although this chapter emphasizes escalators, the rules and suggestions for escalator application can be extended to include moving ramps.

THE IMPORTANCE OF ESCALATORS

There is no better way to steer people in a given path in a building than by providing an escalator. Department store owners discovered this years ago and the most successful stores have their escalators as centers of attraction. The most desirable space is located in line with or next to the escalators. World's fairs and other major expositions have used escalators to direct people to desirable sights and to keep people moving past exhibits to gain maximum exposure.

Transportation terminals, subway stations, and other areas in which large groups of persons are moving at one time have used escalators to speed circulation and avoid congestion. Everyone is moved at a constant speed and persons are carried efficiently from one place to another. When people are walking, some are slow, others are fast; some have baggage, others are accompanied by children, so that, with large groups, walking is slowed to the speed of the slowest pedestrian.

Escalators provide an effective means to make the second floor or basement space as attractive as street floor space. In a commercial building this increases revenue. In an institutional building service performance is enhanced, horizontal walking distance is shortened, and a greater concentration of production is attained.

Escalators are found in many places besides their initial field of applications in stores and transportation facilities. Today, schools, hospitals, factories, office buildings, and restaurants have escalators. So do hotels, motels, museums, theaters, convention halls, sport arenas, and other buildings that must accommodate large groups of people in a minimum time.

EFFECTIVE APPLICATION

Escalators can be advantageously applied to any building if certain requirements are met. Equipment should be located so that most persons entering the building can see it. Access to the escalator must be attractive and in the path of the heaviest expected traffic. Traffic should be sufficient so that frequent and loaded use of the equipment occurs. Evaluation of expected traffic volume, which could range from a few people continuously to hundreds in a peak 5-min period, depends on the type of building facility and its use.

An escalator is a continuously running, unidirectional vehicle. It cannot be effectively started and stopped on demand, nor can it be run in one direction for one trip and reversed for the next. Starting, stopping, or reversal should be done only by an attendant and with the assurance that no one is riding at the time. Pairs of escalators are necessary for two-way service.

Ample space for people must be provided at the entry and exit landings of an escalator. The escalator can feed people into an area much more rapidly than they can climb a stairway or walk through a restricted opening to leave that area. If an unloading area is restricted persons could be crowded into it with possibly dangerous results. Such restrictions as door or gates should be interlocked with the escalator or ramp to insure that the restriction is removed before the escalator can be run.

In many localities a building can have fewer stairs if fire protective enclosures are provided around the escalator. This enclosure must be equipped with sufficient doors and space at the landings for the doors to swing with the traffic and not impede prompt passenger transfer. When escalator traffic of any magnitude is expected its volume may reach the capacity limit of the unit and ample loading area must be provided.

One of the attractions of an escalator is its continuous motion, providing service with zero interval in elevator terms. Normally people need not wait but may enjoy service the moment they reach the landing. If the capacity of the escalator is exceeded, however, a wait may be necessary; however, its length is readily apparent. If more people arrive than the escalator can handle, additional facilities, higher speed, or adequate alternative routes should be offered. Escalator handling capacity is discussed later in this chapter.

If escalators are the primary means of vertical transportation they should be supplemented by one or more elevators. Handicapped persons can usually negotiate an escalator but it is almost impossible for a person in a wheelchair to do so. Similarly, a blind person would have difficulty picking a proper tread to step on as would many older persons with poor eyesight.

Mothers with baby carriages or strollers should be encouraged to use elevators rather than escalators or moving ramps. Escalators are almost impossible to negotiate with a carriage and the incline of a ramp may make a loaded carriage difficult to hold back. A loaded food cart, which may weigh from 50 to 100 lb, is dangerous on an inclined ramp unless the wheels are locked. Locking must be done automatically since the building owner assumes the responsibility in allowing the vehicle on the ramp in the first place.

TRAFFIC HANDLING ABILITY

Escalators and ramps are rated in two ways, by nominal width at approximate hip level, and by speed in feet per minute. Because escalators and ramps are usually driven by ac induction motors, operating speed is constant under load conditions and rating is at a single speed. The generally recognized escalator speeds are either 90 fpm or 120 fpm along the incline. Faster escalators have been provided in some areas but their use is not common and a factor of diminishing return sets in; the steps move too fast for people to use them. Many escalators are equipped for two-speed operation by manual switching; these escalator can be run at 120 fpm for the rush period and at 90 fpm during the rest of the day with the consequent reduction in operating mileage. The normal angle of incline of an escalator is 30 degrees, give or take a few degrees for particular building conditions.

Because ramps can be installed at any angle from 0° (a moving walkway) to 15° (inclined ramp), operating speed varies with the angle of inclination. At any speed with an inclined ramp, the entering and exiting area should move horizontally for boarding or leaving and make a smooth transition to inclined motion. This is not always done but is considered essential for complete safety protection. If level boarding and exiting are provided operating speed can be higher. If the passenger must board at an incline a lower operating speed is necessary. Operating speeds, angles, and ramp widths are established by the American Standard Safety Code for Elevators, ASA17.1, and is briefly shown in Tables 9.1, 9.2, and 9.3. Latest editions of the code and local codes should be consulted.

The nominal widths of escalators are either 32 or 48 in., the first is wide enough for a parent and child on the same step and the second

Table 9.1. Escalator capacities (30° incline)

Width	Speed	Maximum Capacity	Nominal Capacity (75 per cent)
32″ (1.25 persons/step)	90 fpm	425/5 min, 5000/hr	319/5 min, 3750/hr
	120 fpm	566/5 min, 6700/hr	425/5 min, 5025/hr
48″ (2 persons/step)	90 fpm	680/5 min, 8000/hr	510/5 min, 6000/hr
	120 fpm	891/5 min, 10,700/hr	668/5 min, 8025/hr

Table 9.2. Operating speeds of moving ramps (based on 40-in. nominal width[a])

Incline of Ramp on Slope	Maximum Speed with Level Entrance and Exit	Maximum Speed with Sloping Entrance and Exit
0–3°	180 fpm	180 fpm
Over 3°–5°	180 fpm	160 fpm
Over 5°–8°	180 fpm	140 fpm
Over 8°–12°	140 fpm	130 fpm
Over 12°–15°	140 fpm	125 fpm

[a] Speed, angles, and capacities will vary with width. See ASA 17.1(code).

Table 9.3. Moving ramp capacities, 40-in. nominal width[a] **(2 persons per 1.5 ft of treadway)**

	Treadway Speed	Maximum Capacity	Nominal Capacity
0° incline	180 fpm	1200/5 min, 14,400/hr	900/5 min, 10,000/hr
5° incline	140 fpm	932/5 min, 11,180/hr	700/5 min, 8400/hr
10° incline	130 fpm	867/5 min, 10,400/hr	650/5 min, 7800/hr
15° incline	125 fpm	833/5 min, 10,000/hr	625/5 min, 7500/hr

[a] Speed, angles, and capacities will vary with width. See ASA 17.1 (Code).

allows two adults to ride side by side. A further advantage of the 48-in. escalator is that persons in a hurry can pass a standing rider. In fact capacities of escalators and ramps could be almost doubled if all riders would also walk along the moving treadway, for the combination of walking and riding speeds almost doubles the passenger output at the exit.

Escalator capacities are generally expressed in passengers per hour. These capacities are optimum and assume that each step carries either $1\frac{1}{4}$ or 2 passengers, depending on the width. Such output is possible for about 5 min at a time. A reasonable estimate of actual output would be from 65 to 85 per cent of optimum output, as in Table 9.1.

Ramps are rated in much the same way. Nominal width is expressed as the width at hip height and limited by the incline of the ramp. Escalators and ramps should have moving handrails at both sides of the steps; however, the American Standard Safety code allows a moving ramp to have only one handrail if the slope is 3° or less, if speed is 70 fpm or less, or if the width is no more than 21 in. A table of nominal inclines and ratings is shown in Table 9.2.

ARRANGEMENT AND LOCATION

Two general arrangements of escalators are descriptively named *parallel* and *crisscross*. Both arrangements may have up and down equipment side by side or separated by a distance. A third possible arrangement, which could be called *multiple parallel*, consists of a number of escalators side by side between the same exiting and entering levels, primarily to serve more traffic than a single escalator could handle. Flexibility is provided by operating all the units but one in the direction of heavy traffic.

The various arrangements are sketched in Figure 9.1. The crisscross arrangement is the most popular in department stores because it uses minimum floor space and structural requirements and achieves maximum exposure of passengers to merchandise on the various floors. Separating crisscross escalators increases exposure to the various floors and eases the intermingling of riding passengers and persons wishing to board. The separated crisscross arrangement is considered the safest by many users because only one escalator is presented to the riding passenger and there is minimum confusion about whether it is going up or down.

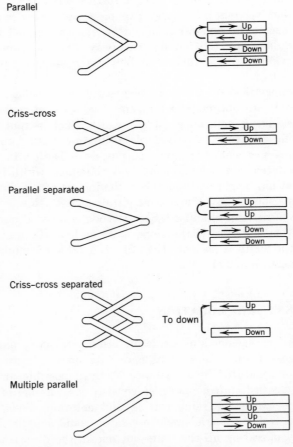

Figure 9.1   Escalator or moving ramp arrangements.

The parallel arrangement provides the most impressive appearance to the prospective passenger. Massing the escalator or ramp entrances immediately attracts persons to that area. The open appearance at upper landings provides space for decoration or high-traffic selling area as well as additional open space for intermingling traffic.

The multiple parallel arrangement is provided when many persons must be transported to another level in minimum time, such as in a busy commuter terminal. Passenger demands could be served by three of a four-unit installation, operated with the traffic morning and evening and reversed to two units in each direction during the rest of the day. Frequent applications are in buildings where the main lobby must be located above the street because of a subway or railroad underneath the building. Here, again, direction of operation is changed to conform with traffic. Units would also be reversed in sports arenas, exhibit halls, and theaters at the start and end of performances.

SPACE REQUIREMENTS

An escalator or moving ramp can be thought of as three component units: an upper and lower portion and a midsection.

The lower unit includes the newel (where the handrail is reversed), the lower step return and step tensioning device, and the landing plate and step entry. The upper unit consists of the upper newel, the upper landing, and the driving mechanism (motor and control) for steps and handrail. The midsection can be of indefinite length (within limits, of course) and consists of balustrading, steps, step tracks, supports, and so on.

Normal support points for escalators and short-run inclined ramps are at the top and bottom and are established by working points. A working point is approximately where the beginning and end of the incline occur; all distances to escalator supports are measured from these points.

Escalator or ramp layout procedure begins with determination of the vertical rise and approximate location of the escalator and the upper or lower access space, to establish the upper (or lower) working point. The opposite working point is then established based on the angle of the vertical path of the steps or ramp. Since escalators are generally inclined at 30° the distance between working points is 1.732 times the rise (Figure 9.2). Once both working points are established the particular manufacturer's standard space requirements must be met to locate the necessary support that must be built into the building structure. The

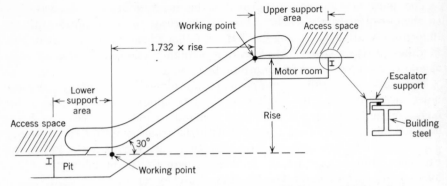

Figure 9.2   Escalator space requirements. W. P. = working point.

reactions on those supports depends on the length and width of the escalator.

For an average 32-in. wide escalator serving a 12-ft rise, the lower end of the truss imposes a load of about 12,400 lb and the upper end about 15,900 lb. These loads include plaster facing on the sides of the escalator and normal balustrade treatment. The loads are, for the most part, uniformly distributed over the width of the escalator and allowance should be made for the dynamic stresses due to the passenger load which alter the actual points of load application so that one side may be loaded up to 35 per cent more than the other. Escalators are mounted on the building steel by means of an angle so the load given is not centered on a beam (Figure 9.2a). Rises over about 18 ft for the 48-in. and over 23 ft for the 32-in. escalators as well as for most moving ramps usually require intermediate supports. A table of average loads for escalators is given in Table 9.4.

The loads of moving ramps vary considerably with the angle of incline and the length of the ramp. When a desired application of a ramp is

Table 9.4. Average loads of escalators on building structure

	Rise	10 ft	12 ft	14 ft	16 ft	18 ft	20 ft	22 ft
32 in.	Upper	14,900	15,900	16,900	18,000	19,000	20,100	21,100
	Lower	11,400	12,400	13,400	14,500	15,500	16,600	17,600
48 in.	Upper	17,450	18,700	20,000	21,300	Consult Manufacturer		
	Lower	13,950	15,300	16,500	17,800			

established, it is best to work with a manufacturer's representative or consulting engineer to determine necessary space requirements and the loads imposed on the structure.

The railing around an escalator or ramp wellway is the responsibility of the architect and can either be a continuation of the escalator or ramp balustrading or part of the building design. Much work has been done in perfecting compatible rails and the experience of the supplier should be sought.

Many local fire regulations and the American Standard Safety Code require that the escalator or ramp wellway be closed in the event of fire. One of the accepted ways of accomplishing this is by utilizing a rolling shutter that is extended over the escalator or ramp and its newel once the escalator is stopped. A specially designed, fire-rated shutter is used and it is the responsibility of the building owner, hence the architect, to provide the space for the shutter and the shutter itself. The American Standard Safety Code describes alternate methods of fire protection.

The plan of an escalator includes the width of the steps, the width of the balustrading plus space for the truss support and external decoration. A 32-in escalator has an over-all width of about 4 ft 4 in.; a 48-in. escalator, about 5 ft 8 in. (Figure 9.3). Widths for moving ramps vary with the width of the tread and, to some degree, with the angle of incline. The greater the incline the greater the requirement for truss support.

The over-all length of an escalator is much shorter than a moving ramp for the same rise because of the greater angle of inclination of

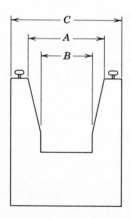

	48″	32″	Escalators
	A = 48″	A = 32″	
	B = 40″	B = 24″	
	C = 68″	C = 52″	

Figure 9.3

the escalator. An average 32-in. escalator for a 12-ft rise requires about 37 ft 6 in. between supports, excluding upper and lower access area. A 10° ramp serving the same rise will require about 82 ft, excluding upper and lower access areas. An average escalator truss depth is about 2 ft 8 in., whereas the truss for a ramp can be of very limited depth, depending on the rise. Escalator trusses are deeper because they must provide space for the returning steps whereas the ramp truss need accommodate only a returning belt or pallets.

ADDITIONAL REQUIREMENTS

Properly servicing an escalator or ramp requires certain access points. The normal approach to access is the removal of the top and bottom landing plates. The bottom landing plate covers the step or belt tensioning device and the top landing plate covers the escalator or ramp machine and upper drive.

Power must be supplied to the escalator or ramp controller. This is the responsibility of the builder and the power supply must meet the requirements of the particular manufacturer. For escalators this is usually about 44 amp starting and 32 amp running at 208 volts, three phase, 60 cycle for the 48-in. escalator. The respective motor horsepowers of escalators are 10 hp for the 32-in. and 15 hp for the 48-in. for rises up to about 23-ft. Moving ramp power requirements vary with different widths and angles of incline again, the equipment supplier should be consulted.

To dissipate the heat generated when an escalator or ramp is operated for long periods under load conditions, ample ventilation for the motor area should be provided. This can be grillwork if the machine room is in an open area or forced ventilation if the machine room is confined. The approximate heating effect of escalators will be about 10,000 Btu's/hr for the 10-hp, 32-in. escalator and 15,000 Btu's/hr for the 15-hp, 48-in. escalator. The heating effect of moving-ramp machinery will vary correspondingly with the horsepower required.

FEATURES OF ESCALATORS AND RAMPS

Because escalators and ramps must serve people of all ages and abilities, they must be inherently safe. It has been determined that escalators are generally safer than stairs but comparable statistics for moving ramps are not yet available. Escalator safety has been the result of much research and development. Early escalators, for example, had wide step cleats, but well-designed modern escalators have cleats of no more than ¼ in. wide and not less than ⅜ in. deep. These cleats are "combed" as they enter the top or lower landing to dislodge soft shoe soles and avoid accidents (Figure 9.4).

The American Standard Safety Code requires the same type of combing on moving ramps. The face of escalator step risers is cleated so that persons who ride with their toes against the riser will not have their soft shoe soles drawn between the steps as they straighten out (Figure 9.5). This is another combing action. Ramps, in general, do not have risers between pallets so this precaution is not necessary.

Some persons ride with their feet pressed against the side of an escalator. As the steps straighten out there is a possibility of a soft shoe sole being drawn between the step and the side. If this occurs, a switch

Figure 9.4

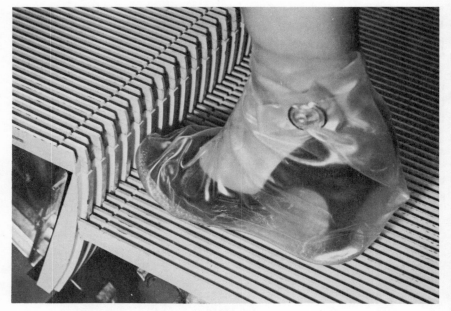

Figure 9.5

actuated by the deflection of the side will stop the escalator (Figure 9.6). Escalator and ramp brakes must be designed to stop the fully loaded treadway without jarring the passengers. On many escalators these brakes are double acting with a smooth slowdown and stop for nonemergency braking and a quick stop in the event of an emergency.

All escalators and ramps should be reversible so that their capacity can be utilized in either direction. Reversing switches are key operated and generally located at the top or bottom landing in the newel. An emergency stop switch is required for escalators and ramps and can be located on a nearby wall at adult height to discourage juvenile mischief.

The landing and exiting levels of escalators and ramps should be extended so that passengers can grasp the handrail and become adjusted to the speed of the steps before they board. At least a one- or two-level step area should be provided before the incline begins.

Balustrade treatments have undergone radical changes since the early days of escalators. A wide variety of materials is available for the balustrading of both escalators and ramps, including stainless steel, vitreous enamel, glass (often called crystal balustrading), lighted glass panels,

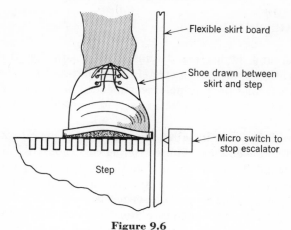

Flexible skirt board

Shoe drawn between
skirt and step

Micro switch to
stop escalator

Step

Figure 9.6

and fiberglass material. Handrails are now being made of vinyl in a variety of colors. The basic oval section of the handrail is unchanged, however, as this shape provides the firmest and most comfortable gripping surface. The entry of the handrail into the newel is made as inaccessible as possible to minimize hazard (Figure 9.7).

Figure 9.7

SPECIAL APPLICATIONS

Escalators and ramps can be installed practically anywhere. Outdoor applications can be completely weatherproofed. Their operation under exposed conditions is not recommended since wet or icy steps or ramps are extremely hazardous. Instead suitable shelter should be provided.

Escalators have been installed aboard ships to operate while the ship is in motion and even under limited rolling conditions. Shipboard applications have included access to and from the flight deck on aircraft carriers, between the restaurant and the kitchen on cruise liners (for waiters carrying trays), and for general passenger use.

Many industrial plants have escalators to serve their employees during shift changes and in the normal course of their duties. Subway stations have the highest and fastest escalators in the world. Such escalators in London have a vertical rise of 85 ft and operate at 180 fpm.

ESCALATORS VERSUS ELEVATORS

Many office buildings and schools have escalators as the primary means of vertical transportation. Escalators can often be more economical than elevators for a given building condition or to solve a particular vertical transportation problem.

One of the best examples is a high school or college in a single building. The major transportation demand occurs when classes change and can be as high as 40 to 50 per cent of the student population moving during a 5-min period. For a six-story school of about 2500 students, eight to ten elevators would be required to give everyone floor-to-floor service. The usual approach would be to have elevators stop only at every other floor and have about half the students walk a floor. With the skip-stop arrangements, only about six elevators are required. With up and down escalators everyone can ride and the average trip requires no more time than the average elevator trip. In addition, the cost of the escalator arrangement plus two elevators for handicapped and freight service could amount to about the same or less than equivalent elevator service depending on prevalent equipment costs.

Another example of the economy of escalators is an eight-story industrial research building with a population of about 2150 persons. Parking is in four areas with good access to main highways so the arrival rate at the building can amount to about 25 per cent of the population in a 5-min period. To provide sufficient vertical transportation would require a group of seven elevators with the elevators operated spotted, that is, one car designated per floor.

A pair of 32-in. escalators, both operated in the same direction during the incoming and outgoing periods would provide the necessary capacity and at lower cost when all the comparative cost factors are calculated. These factors include the usable space required by the elevators versus the escalators, capital investment, maintenance cost, cost of elevator pit and penthouse structure.

Escalators in combination with elevators can provide the answer to some intricate vertical transportation problems. A good example is a merchandise mart where buyers converge during show times once or twice a year. Various suppliers hire space to display their products on the various floors. The average buyers will start at the top of the building and move down from floor to floor. For this traffic elevators can travel solely between the top and bottom and escalators in the down direction only, to take the buyers from floor to floor. Since it may take more than a half day to travel the entire building, elevators could stop at some middle floor, in addition to the top, to serve persons who want to go out for a rest.

Escalators are the answer to extra heavy incoming, outgoing, and two-way traffic problems. Their limitation may be the length of time a person bound from the bottom to the top would have to travel. Based on average floor heights of 12 ft and an escalator speed of 120 fpm, each floor would take about 22 sec to traverse including time to turn around and board the next up escalator. If we arbitrarily limit riding time to about 3 min, effective application of escalators would be limited to buildings of no more than nine floors high. If a system of escalators traveling two floors at a rise were installed, this effective height could be raised to eleven floors since the turn-around and boarding time would be halved.

If some attraction is created about halfway up, the escalator passenger would be relieved for the moment and the long trip would be broken up. The effective height could be raised by this factor of relief. In a school the relief could be the cafeteria or locker room. In an office building a coffee shop is a good place for a break. Whatever the approach, the problem of the long ride must be contended with and the combination of elevators and escalators may be the best solution.

CALCULATING ESCALATOR OR RAMP REQUIREMENTS

The examples on pp. 189 and 190 give typical situations where escalators may be applied. Examples 9.1 and 9.2 could be an office building with escalators as the primary means of getting people to and from work. Here the problem is to provide sufficient capacity to fill the building during the incoming period and to utilize that capacity to expedite evacuation. A building that can provide space for 500 persons per floor will cover an area of at least 60 to 75,000 ft² based on a density of 100 ft² of net area per person. If only a single pair of escalators is provided they should be in the center of a square building so that internal walking distance is minimized. If the building is long and narrow a number of groups of escalators are necessary at points that limit maximum walking distance to about 150 to 200 ft. This latter consideration may change the entire economic aspect of the problem to favor elevators. With any vertical transportation arrangement where more than one group of elevators or escalators serve the same floors, each group must have about 20 per cent excess capacity to compensate for unequal demand.

Example 9.3 is a typical store situation in which the interest is in providing transportation to turn over the customer attendance on each floor within some given time period. We have chosen a customer density of 20 ft² of net selling area per person. This will, of course, vary with different types of stores and for different floors within the same store. More expensive shops have lower densities and bargain basements much greater densities. The problem remains the same, that is, to provide sufficient vertical transportation so that persons can be carried to a floor to replace those already there, who must have transportation to leave. This constant replacing of patrons is called turnover.

The complete vertical transportation system of any store must include passenger elevators for the one-stop shoppers and for handicapped persons. In fact any building with escalators as its primary means of vertical transportation should have an elevator for this contingency. Stocking the various floors usually requires freight elevators; these elevators can combine passenger and freight functions.

Further discussion of stores are given in the chapter on commercial buildings.

APPLICATION OF ESCALATORS AND RAMPS

Proper application of escalators or ramps requires knowledge of the expected demand on the system. This is true of any vertical transportation system and must be part of the research undertaken when the facility is planned. Decision as to how many persons will be seeking vertical transportation in a period of time must be made. This is an operational problem and may depend on many external considerations. In a sports arena the rate at which tickets can be sold or collected influences vertical transportation requirements. In a store the availability of parking space, whether mass transportation is a factor, the nature of the business, and the price of the merchandise must all be considered.

Location is all-important in the application of escalators and ramps. They have a known output of passengers, and suitable provisions must be made to accommodate that output. By proper location the use of the facility may be controlled. If the entrance area is restricted fewer persons will be able to use the escalator or ramp than if the entrance is wide open. Convenience is another factor; if the facility will save people walking or climbing they will go out of their way to use it. If a building is on a hillside and the escalator provides ready transportation from one level to the other, all the persons in the neighborhood will use that escalator if allowed to do so. Providing community transportation has contributed to the success of at least one store; its escalators provide access to municipal parking located on a hill about 30 ft above the main street. The store gains patrons and patrons save a difficult climb.

Application opportunities vary with each location and each building. The foregoing discussion is designed to create the awareness of what a ramp or escalator will do. Its success will depend on how well it is placed and used.

EXAMPLES OF ESCALATOR APPLICATIONS

Example 9.1. Incoming Traffic

Given: 5-story building, 500 persons per floor, arrival rate 25 per cent of population in 5 min.

Assume: Equal attraction per floor, therefore 125 persons must be carried to each floor.

Floor	Population	5-min Demand	Escalator Must Carry
5	500	125	125
4	500	125	250
3	500	125	375
2	500	125	500
1	500	125	0

Choose escalator to carry 500 persons in 5 min from Table 9.1, page 176

Floors 1–2   48″ @ 90 fpm   Nominal capacity 510/5 min vs 500 demand
Floors 2–3   48″ @ 90 fpm   Nominal capacity 510/5 min vs 375 demand
Floors 3–4   32″ @ 90 fpm   Nominal capacity 319/5 min vs 250 demand
Floors 4–5   32″ @ 90 fpm   Nominal capacity 319/5 min vs 125 demand

Example 9.2. Outgoing Traffic

Floors 4–5   32″ @ 120 fpm   Nominal capacity 425/5 min
Floors 3–4   32″ @ 120 fpm   Nominal capacity 425/5 min
Floors 2–3   48″ @ 120 fpm   Nominal capacity 668/5 min
Floors 1–2   48″ @ 120 fpm   Nominal capacity 668/5 min

500 persons on fifth floor will require
$\qquad$ 5.9 min + 1.3 min (riding time at 22 sec/floor = 7.2 min
500 persons on fourth floor will require
$\qquad$ 5.9 min + 1 min (riding time at 22 sec/floor) = 6.9 min
500 persons on third floor will require
$\qquad$ 3.7 min + .6 min (riding time at 22 sec/floor) = 4.3 min
500 persons on second floor will require
$\qquad$ 3.7 min + .3 min (riding time at 22 sec/floor) = $\underline{4.0\text{ min}}$
$\qquad\qquad\qquad$ Maximum time to evacuate = 22.4 min

If it is quitting time, full capacity will probably be used plus walking, so time will probably be less than 15 min. If up and down escalators are available and both are operated down at 120 fpm, time will be less than 10 min.

Example 9.3. Two-Way Traffic

Given: 6-story building, 20,000 ft² net selling area per floor, turnover 1 person/20 ft²/floor/hour.

Demand: each floor $\dfrac{20,000}{20}$ = 1000 persons/floor/hr × 2 (up and down)

$\qquad\qquad\qquad$ = 2000/floor/hr.

Floor	Demand	Demand on Escalators/hr		Equipment Required	Capacity
		Up	Down		
6	2000	1000	1000		
				5–6: pair 32″ @ 90 fpm	3750/hr/escalator
5	2000	2000	2000		
				4–5: pair 32″ @ 90 fpm	3750/hr/escalator
4	2000	3000	3000		
				3–4: pair 32″ @ 90 fpm	3750/hr/escalator
3	2000	4000	4000		
				2–3: pair 48″ @ 90 fpm	6000/hr/escalator
2	2000	5000	5000		
				1–2: pair 48″ @ 90 fpm	6000/hr/escalator
1	2000	—	—		

CHAPTER TEN

Elevatoring
Commercial Buildings

DEFINITION

Commercial buildings, by our definition, are those wherein space is rented or used for a definite commercial purpose. This would include all types of business and professional office buildings, stores, industrial buildings, self-parking garages, and so forth. Apartments and hotels will be considered as residential buildings and schools and hospitals as institutional buildings.

Commercial buildings are somewhat critical from a vertical transportation aspect since arrival and departure of population is concentrated within certain periods of the working day. This traffic pattern varies with the use of the building and the major variations will be shown.

Although commercial buildings can be located anywhere and a trend to decentralization has been evident, most of them are still in the central business districts of our cities, areas with reasonably good horizontal transportation. The efficiency of transportation to and from buildings will greatly influence circulation patterns within any building and hence its elevator traffic.

High-density horizontal transportation may be provided by a subway station right at the building. As the trains arrive, waves of people enter the building, most persons timing their subway trip to arrive almost at the time they must start to work. Needless to say, with a train capable of discharging a thousand or so persons in a short time, the building's vertical transportation system could be subject to severe peak demands.

The other extreme of horizontal traffic affecting a building's elevators is a suburban office building with inefficient parking. Demand on the

191

building's elevators may be directly related to the time required for people to park their cars and walk to the building. If there are local coffee shops, the potential elevator passenger may arrive early, have breakfast, then enter the building. With enough coffee shops, the morning rush may approach that of a local subway system. Similarly, with adequate, well-designed parking facilities, the ability to park and arrive at the building coincident with starting time may again approach the subway system arrival rate.

How persons will arrive, when they go to lunch, what they do when they are at work, and how they leave are all factors in elevatoring any commercial building. A systematic consideration of these factors will follow.

POPULATION

As important as the arrival rate of traffic is the number of persons who will occupy the building. To some extent, tradition governs allocating space within a building. To perform his job a person requires a certain minimum space, which can be as low as 10 or 15 ft^2. He must get to and from his desk, which requires another 10 ft^2. If he uses files or records, about another 10 ft^2 must be allocated for that function. The minimum space therefore is about 30 to 40 ft^2. If the person must deal with outsiders he requires additional room to transact his business so another 25 ft^2 is alloted. These were the common office specifications during the times when office space was at a premium and office work itself held high status. Today, size is status and even the most menial office worker expects and gets about 100 ft^2 to perform his tasks. The average manager gets about 200 ft^2, and the executive may have over 300 ft^2.

The nature of the task to be performed greatly influences commercial building population. A law office, with its necessary reference files and library, requires more square feet per occupant than a drafting office, in which total working area is within reach of the drawing board. Bookkeeping departments with their large business machines must have more space per occupant than the typing pool, where a typist can operate at a single desk and typewriter.

In professional buildings the examining room may require specialized equipment and an area of 200 ft^2 or more. Technician's shops—eyeglass fitting, denture making, photo laboratories, and so on—are compact and may average less than 50 ft^2.

Where there are many tenants on a single floor, a considerable amount of space is required to provide the necessary anterooms and passageways. With single large tenants, more of the space is usable since passageways can be minimized and public space is often nonexistent.

Office buildings are classed as diversified or single-purpose or some degree in between. The completely diversified office building is one in which no more than one tenant occupies more than a single floor and less than 25 per cent of the tenants are in a similar line of work. This last qualification is important because if all tenants are in the same business competition will cause them to start work at the same time, have the same luncheon habits, and have similar patterns of visitor traffic. The tenants may be diversified but their impact on the building will be the same as that of one large firm. We shall refer to this as single-purpose diversified occupancy.

The single-purpose building is exactly that, one firm occupying the entire building. The notable difference between a pure single-purpose building and a single-purpose diversified building is that the first provides opportunities to control traffic by staggering employee working times.

In determining how many elevators are required for a given building it is necessary to quantify and qualify its population. Because we seldom know at the time the building is planned exactly who will occupy each floor, the quantity of population must be averaged for each floor based on the type of tenancy expected. Table 10.1 gives typical values

Table 10.1. Population factors, commercial buildings

Diversified	120 to 150 ft² net area/person
Diversified single-purpose	110 to 135 ft² net area/person
Single-purpose	100 to 120 ft² net area/person

Net area = gross area less elevator shaft and lobby space, air conditioning, janitorial, columns, toilets, corridor around core, and convector space.

of population related to the net square feet in each building. This net square feet can be the rentable area if it excludes columns, toilets, elevator lobbies, radiator or convector space, etc. If rentable area includes these factors as in some definitions, an allowance must be made. This allowance varies with building height, as in Table 10.3 on page 194.

The thoroughness with which the building program is planned has a great influence on the population of the building. If a building is being built on an investment basis, tenant rental to follow, population must be established conservatively, based on the experience of com-

Table 10.2. Net area, various height buildings (15 to 20,000 gross ft²/floor)

0–10 floors	Approximately 85 per cent gross
0–20 floors	Floors 1–10 approximately 80 per cent gross
	11–20 approximately 85 per cent gross
0–30 floors	Floors 1–10 approximately 75 per cent gross
	11–20 approximately 80 per cent gross
	21–30 approximately 85 per cent gross
0–40 floors	Floors 1–10 approximately 75 per cent gross
	11–20 approximately 80 per cent gross
	21–30 approximately 85 per cent gross
	31–40 approximately 90 per cent gross

Net area based on New York real estate net rentable area—approximately 88 per cent NRA.

Table 10.3. Building population density related to building height

0–10 floors	100–125 ft² per person
0–20 floors	Floors 1–10 100–125 ft² per person
	11–20 115–130 ft² per person
0–30 floors	Floors 1–10 100–125 ft² per person
	11–20 115–130 ft² per person
	21–30 125–140 ft² per person
0–40 floors	Floors 1–10 100–125 ft² per person
	11–20 115–130 ft² per person
	21–30 125–140 ft² per person
	31–40 130–150 ft² per person

Other commercial space
Professional buildings   200 ft² per doctor's office
Self-parking garages   300 ft² per auto, 1.4 to 3.5 persons per auto
Stores   Customer density of 10 to 40 ft² of net selling area.
Industrial buildings
Factories   Depends on manufacturing layout and product
Drafting   60–80 ft² per draftman

parable buildings. If the building is built for a specific tenant or group of tenants investigation as to tenant plans should be undertaken and documented. If the building is for a specific tenant who has planned and allocated his space requirements, advantage should be taken of that planning in establishing population, with allowance for expansion.

Because elevators will be planned to serve the need of the building population, the importance of correctly estimating population cannot be overemphasized. It can be costly to underestimate population or make undue allowances for absent employees. These variables depend on current business conditions which may change and affect the entire basis of elevatoring. The essential consideration is space that can be used by personnel whether or not it is occupied at any particular time.

ELEVATOR TRAFFIC IN COMMERCIAL BUILDINGS

Once the population that requires vertical transportation is established, the next step is to determine the quantity and quality of such transportation. As discussed in the chapter on elevator traffic, we are seeking a critical 5-min traffic period on which to base handling capacity and against which to check all other active traffic periods.

The up-peak or start-to-work period is usually the basis for establishing the size and quantity of elevators for an office building. This is a critical period as surface transportation and subways discharge passengers at the building. It is essential to clear the lobby and get people to their desks so they can begin work.

The traffic will peak during a 5-min period before the time most persons start work. The intensity of this peak, stated as a percentage of building population, forms a means of relating one building to another and the basis of establishing the elevatoring of each (Figure 10.1).

The other periods of the day when elevator traffic may be critical are at lunchtime and quitting time. Because it is general practice to stagger lunchtimes, these traffic peaks are usually not as severe as the incoming peak. Quitting time is an intense period of elevator traffic;

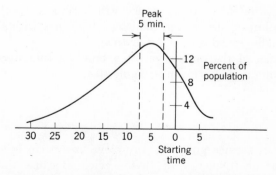

Figure 10.1   Typical arrival rate, office building.

Table 10.4. Expected peak traffic periods—various commercial buildings

Per cent of Population in a 5-min Period

	Up-Peak	Noontime
Diversified offices	11–12.5 per cent	10–12 per cent
Diversified single-purpose	12.5–15 per cent	12–15 per cent
Single-purpose[a]	15–20 per cent	15–20 per cent
Professional buildings	Peak traffic	Two-way, based on 1–2 visitors per doctor/15 min coming + going
Garages—self-parking, (assume sufficient ramps to fill or empty garage in 1 hr).	Peak traffic, commuter garage	10–15 per cent of parking capacity, one-way traffic
	Peak traffic, store garage	10–15 per cent of parking capacity, two-way traffic
Stores	Population density per floor to be turned over, i.e., up and down (two-way) in 1 hr.	
Industrial buildings	Peak traffic, 15–20 per cent (up-peak or two-way).	

[a] Note: Some companies give bonuses for on-time arrival. If so, 20–25 per cent up-peak expected.

however, elevator efficiency is greater during an outgoing rush. People will crowd elevators more since they are usually more anxious to leave work than they are to get to work. With this crowding, and because the passengers are distributed over many floors rather than waiting in the lobby as during up-peak, the elevators tend to make fewer stops— hence more trips in a given period of time. The net result is that, for a given number of elevators, the outgoing capacity is a substantial percentage greater than for incoming capacity.

If good horizontal transportation exists, the incoming peak traffic will remain the critical traffic period. If an extended arrival rate is expected, the noontime period of two-way traffic will become critical. In professional office buildings, stores, and industrial buildings with shift changes the two-way traffic period is the most critical.

The percentage of the population of a building that must be served in a critical 5-min period is given in Table 10.4.

INTERVAL

The quality of service given by any elevator system is also reflected by the interval or frequency of that service. Because the reputation of commercial buildings and the rentals they can command are based on the quality of service the building offers, the best quality of elevator service is a necessity. Stated otherwise, a building may have the most beautiful facade and decoration and may offer the best space layout and services, but if persons must wait too long for elevator service the value of other advantages can be lost.

Proper waits for elevator service have been a subject of much controversy and discussion. Excessive waiting times have been arrived at in a somewhat negative way, by analyzing service in buildings where complaints were minimal.

Experience has shown that a loading interval of between 25 and 30 sec produces generally acceptable elevator service in office buildings. Intervals of from 30 to 35 sec are considered fair in noncritical, invest-

Table 10.5. Suggested intervals

Office Buildings	Up-Peak	Two-Way
Prestige	25–30 sec	30–40 sec
Investment	25–35 sec	30–50 sec
Professional buildings	—	30–50 sec
Self-parking garages	40–50 sec	40–60 sec
Stores	—	30–50 sec
Industrial buildings	25–30 sec	30–40 sec

ment-type buildings, but may be unacceptable in the prestige or single-purpose building. Loading intervals of over 35 sec are certain to lead to complaints in office buildings of any type and should be avoided.

Two-way traffic intervals of from 30 to 40 sec are generally acceptable provided the elevator control system is designed to maintain that range or better. With a designed two-way interval of 40 sec and poor elevator control, waits over 40 sec will be frequent and complaints will be received. In general 30 sec is the maximum wait an average person will tolerate in a busy commercial atmosphere.

In professional buildings, stores, or industrial buildings the maximum two-way interval should never exceed 50 sec. The preferable safe maximum should be 40 sec for quality service. Again the elevator control system should be designed to maintain that maximum or better.

The use of Table 10.5, on suggested intervals, is predicated on providing sufficient traffic handling capacity as shown in Table 10.4. Multiple entrances to the building, upper-floor cafeterias, roof or basements stops on the elevators, and necessary odd openings must be considered before any interval can be calculated.

CAPACITY AND SPEED

The combination of capacity and speed (known as duty) of elevators for commercial buildings should be selected to provide service of the highest quality. The typical office building tenant is continually using elevators in his own and other buildings and soon learns what to expect in the way of service standards.

Table 10.6. Recommended elevator sizes—commercial buildings

Minimum Sizes	Class of Building		
Type of Building	Small	Average	Large or Prestige
Offices, suburban	2500	2500–3000	3500
Service elevator	3000	3500	4000
Offices, downtown	3000	3500	4000
Service elevator	3500	4000	4000–6000
Professional offices			
Passenger[a]	2500	3000–3500	3500–4000
Service[b]	3500	4000	4000
Stores			
Passenger[c]	2500	3000–3500	3500–4000
Service[d]	4000	4000–6000	6000–8000
Garages	2000	2500–3000	3500
Industrial[e]	3500	4000	4000

[a] If many wheelchairs or mobile stretchers are expected, 4-ft center-opening doors on a 3500-lb car should be provided to allow stretcher to enter.
[b] A hospital-shaped car should be provided.
[c] Wide, shallow cars with widest possible center-opening door desirable.
[d] Capacity is primarily to get largest size elevator possible.
[e] Consideration should be given to combination passenger-freight elevators.

For the smallest office building the minimum recommended size of elevator is the 2500-lb, 6 ft 8 in. $\times$ 4 ft 5 in. car inside. This size allows the architect to take advantage of superior inside decoration not possible in a smaller car and allows the use of the 3 ft 6 in. center-opening door.

For most office buildings the 3000-lb car should be the minimum. Office buildings that are prominent and heavily traveled should have 3500- and 4000-lb elevators and a monumental building such as the headquarters of large corporations should have 4000-lb elevators.

For commercial buildings other than offices the minimum recommended size of the elevator varies with the traffic demand and use of the building as shown in Table 10.6.

Elevator speeds in commercial buildings should be fast enough to contribute to a feeling of prompt, efficient service. Automatic leveling of the elevators is necessary from both a service and safety aspect. Because floor-to-floor operation should be prompt and smooth, the generator field type elevator control is categorically recommended. Speed will vary with the type and height of commercial buildings, the accepted minimum being no less than 200 fpm for a building with from two to five stops and in any office building; 350 fpm for between five and ten stops in suburban areas; and 400 to 500 fpm for buildings of between five and twelve stops in downtown areas. Table 10.7 shows recommended elevator speeds for various types of commercial buildings.

The faster, gearless elevator is favored not because its top speed is necessary but for its superior floor-to-floor performance and its exceptionally long life as opposed to worm and gear elevators. Because a

Table 10.7. Recommended elevator speeds

Minimum Speeds		Class of Building			
		Small	Average	Large or Prestige	Service
Office buildings (including professional offices)					
2–5	floors	200–250 fpm	300–350 fpm	350–400 fpm	200 fpm
5–10	floors	300–350 fpm	350–500 fpm	500 fpm	300 fpm
10–15	floors	500 fpm	500–700 fpm	700 fpm	350–500 fpm
15–25	floors	700 fpm	800 fpm	800 fpm	500 fpm
25–35	floors	—	1000 fpm	1000 fpm	500 fpm
35–45	floors	—	1000–1200 fpm	1200 fpm	700–800 fpm
45–60	floors	—	1200–1400 fpm	1400–1600 fpm	800–1000 fpm
over 60	floors	—	—	1800 fpm	1000 fpm
Stores					
2–5	floors	200–250 fpm	250 fpm	300 fpm	200 fpm
5–10	floors	350 fpm	350–500 fpm	500 fpm	350 fpm
10–15	floors	500 fpm	500 fpm	500–700 fpm	500 fpm
Garages					
2–5	floors	100–200 fpm	200–300 fpm	200–300 fpm	
5–10	floors	250–300 fpm	350–500 fpm	350–500 fpm	
10–15	floors	350–500 fpm	500–700 fpm	500–700 fpm	
Industrial—same as offices					

Table 10.8. Time and distance required to get up to speed or to slow down from full speed (approximate)

Ultimate Elevator Speed (feet per minute)	Time (seconds)	Distance (feet)	Minimum Number of Floors[a] Required for Express Run
500	2.9	12	2
700	3.6	20	4
1000	4.7	38	6
1200	5.5	53	10
1400	6.2	70	12
1600	6.9	80	14

[a] Based on 12-ft floor heights

commercial building is expected to last for 40 years or longer, the simplicity of the gearless elevator makes possible a machine life as long as that of the building and is well worth the additional initial investment.

When buildings have high- and low-rise elevators the high-speed elevators are required to traverse the express run in the shortest possible time. Because an elevator can not be accelerated faster than persons can adjust to the change in speed, a certain minimum number of floors are required for the express run with various speeds of elevators. This variation is shown in Table 10.8.

LAYOUT AND GROUPING OF ELEVATORS

In any multistory commercial building the vertical transportation system should visually dominate the lobby. Since the system is, in effect, the main entrance to the upper floors, persons should be directed to the elevators or escalators both physically and visually. Signs, clearly visible from each building entrance, should plainly indicate each system and the floors it serves.

Vertical transportation should be grouped in one area, either the central "utility core" of the building or a service tower along one wall. Long corridors from the main entrance to the elevator lobbies should be avoided. The main entrance, no matter where the architect plans it, will be the one closest to the main horizontal transportation. No one can expect persons to take an indirect route to a "main" entrance if there is an entrance next to the subway station.

Making a building's entrances too attractive may have drawbacks. Entrances of hillside buildings that have elevator stops at both the lower and upper levels will encourage everyone in the neighborhood to use that building's elevators to get to the upper street level. Either public use of this kind should be restricted or enough escalators should be provided to take care of the expected public use.

Elevators in office buildings are commonly installed in groups of either 4, 6 or 8 cars. Four-car groups are generally used for the low-rise section and groups of either six or eight for the high-rise portions of the building. In many buildings the architect will try to conserve high-rise shaft space for air conditioning or fire tower requirements. If expedient and in conformity with elevator requirements, the highest-rise elevators may be in a six-car group. As an alternative, shaft space adjacent to the service elevators may prove the best location for a fire tower or for air conditioning risers.

As pointed out in the chapter on grouping of elevators, the six- and eight-car groups should have open-ended lobbies to leave space for people to wait before they board elevators. The space adjacent to the elevator lobby is a necessary reservoir for persons entering at the main entrance and its extent is based on the ability of the elevators to serve the incoming traffic. It should be equal, as a minimum, to the elevator lobby area.

Accepted elevator groupings are sketched in Figure 10.2. Buildings comparable in size and nature to the building being planned should be studied before actual layout of a new building begins. Also, as a prerequisite to a new building plan, an approximate grouping and space allocation of elevators must be made. Once determined for a particular building size, the layout and space requirements of elevators is inflexible. The building must proceed from the elevators out and never the other way if a satisfactory elevator plant is expected and if the cost of redesigning is to be avoided if sufficient space is not allocated. This problem must be resolved early because most other aspects of the building design depend on the initial elevator design.

TRANSFER FLOORS

Local and express elevators in a building raise the question of providing a transfer floor. The answer depends on the ultimate use of the building and the nature of its tenancy. If a tenant is expected to occupy floors served by more than one group of elevators a transfer floor can be considered necessary. Otherwise, persons would have to travel to the lobby and change to the next group of elevators. At the transfer floor he will also have to change elevators but will not be backtracking. The time saved is questionable and depends on the relative interval in each group of elevators and the traffic at that moment. Certainly, a passenger

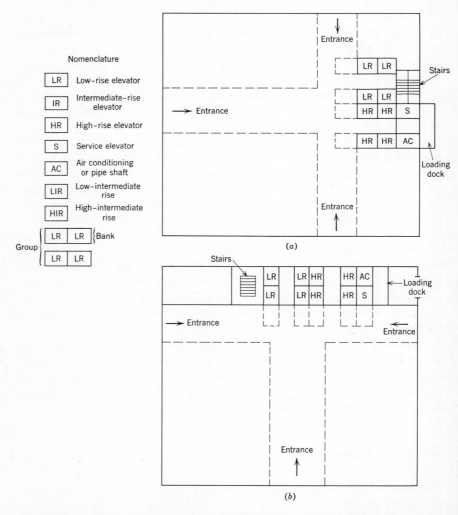

Figure 10.2   High-rise office building elevator layouts: (a) and (b) two groups of four (or six) elevators, approximately 20–25-story buildings;

wishing to go to a higher floor by transferring to a higher group of elevators during the outgoing period time is better off going to the lobby.

The elevator control system at the transfer floor should be arranged to allow the higher-rise elevator to stop only for an up hall call or down car call. This avoids the necessity of persons at the ground floor deciding which group of elevators to take to the common floor. It also avoids the possibility of a tenant using the high-rise group to reach

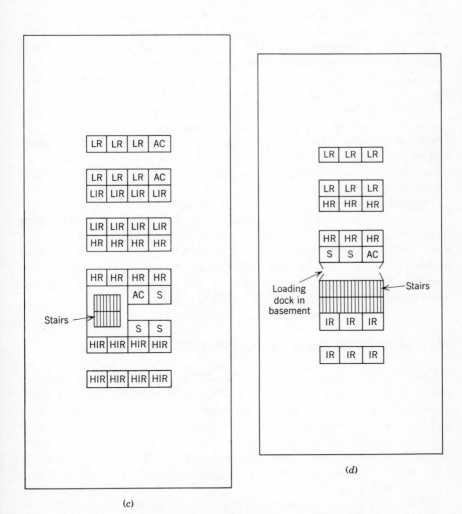

(*c*) one group of six, three groups of eight elevators, approximately 35–45 story building; (*d*) three groups of six elevators, approximately 25–32-story building.

the transfer floor in the morning, when it is the first stop after the express run, so his employees do not have to wait for intermediate stops, and the lower-rise elevators in the evening, when his floor is the first stop in the down direction. If his employees fill the car they get priority down service. Response only to up hall calls and down car calls at the high-rise transfer stop avoids this possibility.

A transfer floor can also be used to provide flexibility in the elevator system. If the lower rise is made to travel one floor higher than necessary and that floor is temporarily used as a transfer floor, and, for some reason, the service demand on the low rise is not so great as expected, a stop may be removed from the high rise and service to the building improved. The reverse is also true. If the low rise has a heavier demand than anticipated, the high rise can be made to serve an additional floor. Proper control adjustment will have to be made.

A third alternative to transfer floor and elevator flexibility requirements is to provide for future entrances on the high-rise elevators at overlapping floors. The entrances could be masonry closed door frames, and as the building matures and changes in elevator requirements are apparent, these entrances could be put into use and necessary adjustments made to the elevator control.

Transfer between high- and low-rise elevators can present some problems in single-purpose office buildings. Normally a single transfer floor should be sufficient; however, if the nature of the business is such that a great deal of interfloor traffic will take place, openings can be installed in the high-rise elevator hoistway at all floors. The openings that overlap the low rise can be designed to operate only in response to an up hall call or down car call.

ELEVATOR OPERATION IN COMMERCIAL BUILDINGS

Based on knowledge of expected traffic in a building, the elevators proposed, and the handling capacity and interval expected during various periods of the day, a traffic flow chart can be prepared. This flow chart will indicate the complexity of the elevator traffic problem and the degree of elevator control required to handle that problem. A rough chart can be used as a start and additional refinements added as requirements are analyzed in greater detail. An example of such planning is shown in Figure 10.3.

Figure 10.3 shows the expected traffic in a typical diversified office building, a pattern characteristic of most such buildings. The intensity will, of course, vary inversely with the degree of tenant diversity.

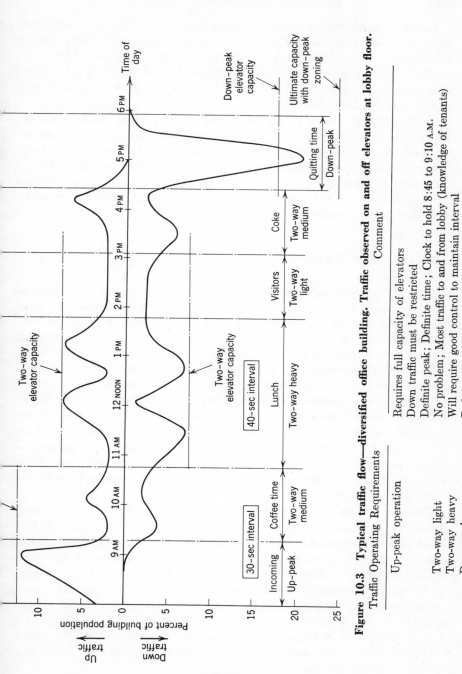

Figure 10.3 Typical traffic flow—diversified office building. Traffic observed on and off elevators at lobby floor.

Traffic Operating Requirements   Comment

Up-peak operation   Requires full capacity of elevators
                                     Down traffic must be restricted
                                     Definite peak; Definite time; Clock to hold 8:45 to 9:10 A.M.
Two-way light   No problem; Most traffic to and from lobby (knowledge of tenants)
Two-way heavy   Will require good control to maintain interval
Down-peak   Definite time; Slight crackup without zoning
                                     Use zoning and clock to hold 4:45 to 5:20 P.M.

205

In planning elevator control the service expected of the elevators must be considered. As an example, if much visitor traffic is expected during the day, the system may have to provide for varying degrees of two-way traffic in the heavier up, heavier down, and balanced directions. If considerable traffic between floors is expected, additional provisions for traffic of that nature may be needed.

Each building has its unique requirements depending on location, expected tenancy, the nature of the tenants' business, and visitors traffic, as well as external transportation to and from the building. Typical traffic flow diagrams for other types of commercial buildings as in Figure 10.4 may be used as a guide for a particular building, supplemented by information on control and operation given in Chapter 7 to select a suitable control system.

SPECIAL REQUIREMENTS

Commercial buildings are in general public buildings and are expected to have many visitors. The elevator layout and design should be such that it will attract the visitor and offer him service. Tenants, as well as visitors, appreciate attractive elevator design in addition to prompt and efficient service with minimum effort.

To fulfill this requirement the architect must employ an informational system that is clear and distinct. Signs that indicate the floors served by each elevator group must be clearly visible from the building lobby. Hall lanterns for each elevator should be easily discerned from every point in the elevator lobby. The elevator call button likewise must be plainly identifiable and readily accessible from routes of passenger approach and located so that passengers will wait near the elevators. Floor numerals applied to the edge of hoistway doors at each floor help the rider identify his floor.

Communication between elevator passengers and building staff through a central telephone system or intercom is most valuable. If the building has a receptionist or lobby floor attendant, he should be able to communicate with the elevators so that he can take action if needed. In many buildings a lobby indicator panel shows the lobby attendant the position of the various elevators and can be equipped with flickering indicators to call attention to a car delayed beyond a predetermined time. Communication by intercom can establish the reason and necessary help can be summoned. Building personnel can also observe any other elevator system failure at the lobby station by means of indicator lights and take appropriate action.

If no attendant is stationed at the lobby the indication and communication equipment can be located in the building office or at any place where surveillance is available. In smaller buildings the required emergency call bell in the elevator is used to summon help. In many situations when only part-time help is in attendance an emergency call system to a central protective agency is provided.

Controls to call a particular car to the lobby for cleaning or some other purpose are desirable. One such arrangement is a number of key switches, one for each car, in a lobby panel. Operating the switch can call the car so it may be placed on special service such as operating from its car buttons independently of the group or so it may be shut down for necessary cleaning or maintenance. The lobby switch should also serve to close elevator doors when a car is locked out of service for, say, nighttime security.

Service Elevators

A separate service elevator or elevators is a necessity in any building of over 250,000 ft^2 of usable area or where the passenger elevators are in full use during the entire day. Normally in smaller buildings the need for freight service is so slight that one of the passenger elevators may be diverted to this purpose during off-peak periods. If this is not feasible because much visitor traffic is expected, a separate service elevator is a necessity.

Transportation of myriad items used for tenant activities and building operation requires service elevators. These items may range from mail and office supplies to new furniture, soft drinks, coffee carts, lunch wagons, wall partitions during renovations, or masonry supplies. Increasing cost of service personnel make it economical to schedule repairs during the day and, for tenant convenience, management wants to avoid passage of replacement machinery or maintenance men through the passenger lobby.

In many buildings simple freight traffic can attain volumes amounting, in the form of mail, trash, office supplies, and drawings, to about 150 to 200 lb per employee per week. A 250,000-ft^2 building with as many as 2000 to 2500 employees will require about 250 tons of material to be moved in and out each week. With a service elevator of 4000-lb capacity, and averaging about a trip every 10 min at half capacity, handling 250 tons is a week's work!

Most organizations depend on mail and insist on its prompt delivery. Too often, concurrent mail and passenger peaks pose a dilemma for management. An unsatisfactory solution is to spread the mail on the

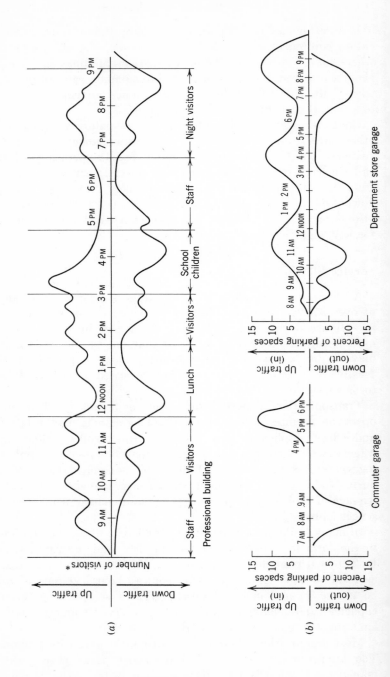

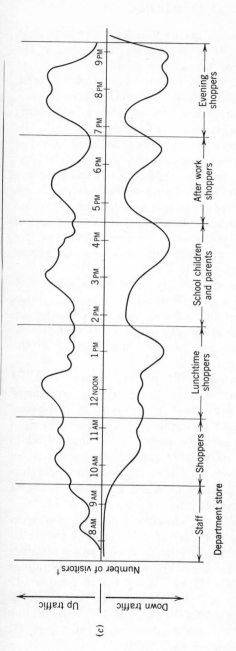

Figure 10.4 (a) Professional buildings (elevator traffic in and out at lobby); (b) garages (elevator traffic in and out at main entrance). "In" or "up" are people driving out of garage, "out" or "down" are people who have just parked; (c) Department stores (downtown) (elevator traffic in and out at main floor, weekday).

* Relative scale, depends on facility.
† Relative scale, depends on escalator-elevator arrangement.

209

lobby floor to be picked up by tenants as they enter the building. A separate service elevator can expedite mail delivery and provide the additional handling capacity required for service needs during the rest of the day. Various schemes of mail distribution have been proposed, utilizing automatic unloading dumbwaiters or conveyors. These specialized systems can supplement the required service elevator in a building of substantial size or housing a single tenant.

Sizes recommended for service elevators vary with building use. The 3500- and 4000-lb standard platform sizes are the most satisfactory. Dimensions of the opening depend on the largest-sized equipment expected to be in the building and the normal size of the building doors. If wider elevator openings are required, two-speed sliding or two-speed center-opening doors should be provided. If a great deal of freight is expected and the elevator is used exclusively for freight and not for personnel, use of vertical biparting entrances will allow openings almost as wide as the elevator.

Larger elevators with capacities of 5000 and 6000 lb or more may be required in larger buildings when air conditioning pumps, transformers, and so on, are of that weight and size. A serious breakdown of equipment impractical to rebuild on the site may require replacement of the entire unit. A larger elevator can expedite the handling of the replacement.

When single large loads must occasionally be moved in a building an elevator can be equipped with a "safelift" operation. The equipment is designed to handle 33 per cent more than its capacity by provisions for attaching additional counterweight during the safelift operation. Special lugs on the rails permit the car to be loaded and unloaded while it is locked in place independent of the hoist ropes. Operation is by remote control from the machine room level with the operator communicating by telephone to the loading and unloading floors. All parts of the elevator structure must be designed for the extra load.

In professional buildings, especially medical office buildings where persons may arrive on stretchers, a service elevator is required to handle the unusual loads. The size and shape of the unusual load determines the size and shape of the service elevator. For medical office buildings of any size the 4000-lb hospital-shaped car, discussed in Chapter 12 on institutional buildings, is usually the most satisfactory service elevator. For a smaller medical building a 2500-lb car with 3 ft 6 in. sliding doors may be used for mobile stretchers as described in Chapter 11, on residential buildings, under Housing for the Elderly.

Easy access to the service elevator at the loading dock and at the upper floors is of prime importance in locating this elevator. If one of the passenger elevators is to be used for part-time service, traffic flow between that elevator and the building service entrance must be considered. A rear entrance on an elevator may solve the access problem. If a rear entrance is used it should be operative only during special service periods and preferably under the control of an attendant.

Cafeterias and Restaurants

A club, restaurant, cafeteria, or any eating facility in a commercial building requires a separate service elevator. It is almost impossible to carry foodstuff, carts, garbage, or bottles on an elevator without damaging the sides, spilling, or leaving an odor. Protective pads can be used, but strict management control is required to insure their use. A feeding facility of any size requires considerable time to transfer its supplies, which often arrive at the height of the morning rush.

Eating facilities in a building also place extra demands on the passenger elevators. The size of the facility, its expected turnover, and its mode of operation must be considered in the initial elevatoring of the building. In general any facility designed to serve about 300 persons requires an additional passenger elevator, plus use of the building's service elevator, over the normal requirements of the building. An additional elevator would be required for each multiple of 300. Because restaurants are often located on the top floor and generally cater to persons outside of the building, the extra elevator(s) should be of the shuttle type and travel only between the restaurant and the ground floor. Many successful top-floor restaurants use outside, glass-enclosed elevators to attract and accommodate their clientele. This type of equipment is discussed in a later chapter.

Cafeterias are preferably located in the basement or at the second floor with escalators between the cafeteria and street. The main building elevators should not stop at the cafeteria floor, which should be served separately. Cloakrooms at the cafeteria floor reduce elevator use by employees who eat and leave the building. Reducing this traffic lessens interference with the next group of employees going to lunch. Separate kitchen-supply elevators located near a loading dock are desirable for the basement or second-floor cafeteria.

TYPICAL OFFICE BUILDING ELEVATORING

We must presume that before he starts planning an office building of any size the architect or builder has investigated existing buildings of a similar size and nature. The architectural magazines, building hand-books, various building services, and real estate boards can suggest com-parable examples. A concurrent requirement is that some idea of the size and height of the building should be established. Initial elevatoring may be based on very meager information that includes the expected height and approximate floor area of the building and its intended use. With more specific information a better-elevatored building will result.

Sample calculations for elevatoring a diversified office building appears in Example 10.1, on page 213, where the type and size of building is indicated and its elevatoring is developed. Introduction of a garage facility in the basement markedly affects what may be done with four elevators. Alternatively, the maximum amount of upper-floor space may be gained by providing a separate shuttle elevator between the lobby and garage floor. In addition to enabling the main elevators to serve one more floor, the second approach facilitates use of the garage. The shuttle elevator allows the garage to be operated independently of the main elevators and possibly used as a public facility weekends and evenings without impairing the security of the building.

Solving elevatoring problems often takes the form of considerable com-promise between the optimum size of the building and the number of elevators to be provided. Each elevator represents a cost factor in both initial equipment investment and rentable area sacrificed. With land selling as high as $500 to $800 per ft^2 in some areas of large cities the greatest return on total investment is necessary. Commanding rents to yield an adequate return requires the best possible elevator service. Space is necessary, however, so for tall buildings the initial cost of eleva-tors relative to all the other aspects of a building is generally from 10 to 12 per cent of total construction cost. The difference between the best and poorest elevators from speed and capacity standpoint is only about 10 or 15 per cent of their cost—less than 2 per cent of the entire project—but the return in terms of satisfied tenants can be far greater.

Rules of thumb for evaluating the elevatoring of a planned office build-ing quickly are helpful if requirements are relatively clear-cut and eleva-tors need *not* serve more than one entrance, a garage or a cafeteria, or as parttime service elevators. In other words the rules are only valid when the elevators serve direct traffic between the office floors and the lobby.

One such rule of thumb is one elevator per 35,000 ft^2 of net area. It is only valid if the building area is at least 10,000 ft^2 per floor and less than 20 floors. The elevators must be in groups of at least four for the lower 9 floors of the building and in groups of at least six for the floors between the tenth and the twentieth to provide reasonable

Example 10.1

A. Given: Diversified offices, suburban location, investment-type building; 12,000 ft² gross per floor, 10–12 floors, 12-ft floor-to-floor height. Population: 12,000 × 0.85 = 10,200 net/floor @ 120 ft²/person = 85/persons/floor.
Assume: Four 2500 @ 500 elevators, 11 stops.

From table: probable stops — 12 passenger, 10 upper floors = 7

Incoming 7 × 9.5	=	66.5 sec
Lobby:	=	20.0 sec

$$\text{Run:}\ \frac{10 \times 12 \times 2 \times 60}{500} \qquad = \underline{\ 28.0 \text{ sec}}$$

$$114.5 \text{ sec}$$

$$\text{HC:}\ \frac{12 \times 300}{114.5} \times 4 \text{ elevators} \qquad = 125 \text{ persons}$$

Population: 10 × 85 = 850 persons
Per cent HC: $^{125}\!/_{850}$ = 14.7 per cent

$$\text{Interval:}\ \frac{114.5}{4} \qquad = 28.6 \text{ sec O.K.}$$

Suggest: Four–2500 @ 500 elevators, floors 1–12 for 12,000 ft² gross, diversified, investment-type building.

B. If basement garage for 200 cars is added: 200 automobiles at 1.5 persons/auto = 300 persons = about 30 per cent of building population. Therefore it is likely elevators will travel to basement every trip.
Recalculate round-trip time: Building B, 1–11

7 × 9.5	=	66.5 sec
Lobby:	=	20.0 sec
Basement:	=	10.0 sec
Rise:	=	32.0 sec

$$128.5 \text{ sec}$$

$$\text{HC:}\ \frac{12 \times 300}{128.5} \qquad = 111 \text{ persons}$$

Population: 10 × 85 = 850 persons
Per cent HC: $^{111}\!/_{850}$ = 13 per cent

$$\text{Interval:}\ \frac{128.5}{4} \qquad = 32 \text{ sec O.K.}$$

Building could have slightly larger floor area, but height should be limited to 11 floors with 4–2500 @ 500 elevators serving B, 1–11.

intervals of service. The rule becomes inapplicable for higher buildings because of the necessary time consumed by an express run.

Another rule of thumb is to provide at least one elevator for each 250 to 300 building occupants. This rule is related to the 35,000-ft² rule on the basis of population density of 100 to 125 ft² per person.

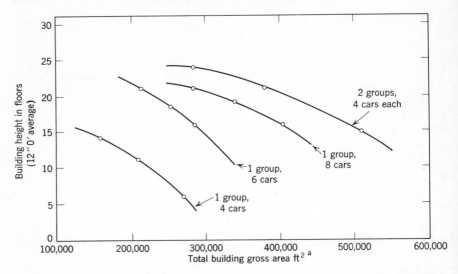

**Figure 10.5   Office building elevatoring: requirements for diversified buildings
(no basements, no upper-floor garages or eating facilities). Based on:**
30-sec maximum loading interval
180-sec maximum round-trip time
120 ft²/ person net
75 per cent usable area net
12.5 per cent up-peak handling capacity

(a) Includes first floor, excludes basements and mechanical floors.

Again, the rule fails for buildings over 20 floors or with floor areas
of less than about 10,000 ft².

A better guide is given in Figure 10.5. By reference to the chart,
the approximate elevatoring may be established for a diversified office
building requiring the percentage of handling capacity and having the
density of population shown. This chart is based on simple elevatoring
without a garage floor, no double lobbies, no odd stops, no other complex-
ities. The size and speed of the elevators to be used must, be established
from the guides shown earlier in this chapter.

MAXIMUM ELEVATOR SIZE IN OFFICE BUILDINGS

Elevators of more than 4000-lb capacity should not be used in office
buildings without special provisions for loading and operation. The
4000-lb car is about the maximum that people will fill to capacity when
left on their own. Its nominal capacity is 22 persons, which is quite

a large group and will make the elevator appear crowded even though it is not. Other persons will usually wait for the next car. In addition, if a 4000-lb car serves more than 12 to 14 stops, the trip becomes too long, people are irritated, and building reputation suffers.

If there is ample lobby space for queuing and a spotting operation of the elevators, larger elevators may be used. Spotting operation assigns each individual elevator to serve only a floor or two during peak traffic operations. For example, during the up peak, car *A* is assigned to serve the lobby and floors 2 and 3 only, car *B* to the lobby and floors 4 and 5 only, car *C* to the lobby and floors 6 and 7 only, and so forth. Because persons must line up in front of their respective cars to get service, there must be ample lobby space. When a car arrives, a large group of persons will enter quickly with minimum persuasion to avoid waiting for the car to return.

Large organizations such as insurance companies successfully use spotting. When it can be used elevators of 5000- or 6000-lb capacities can be provided and the lobby necessarily arranged to accommodate the queue.

ELEVATORING STORES

As noted in the chapter on escalators and ramps, escalators are usually the preferred vertical transportation in stores. Stores depend on people visiting each floor to shop and the best way to turn over the patronage on each floor is by escalator. The escalator is a center of attraction, is constantly operating, and requires very little decision or patience on the part of the user.

Demands on the vertical transportation in a store vary with selling space (net selling area) on each floor, the density at which customers are expected to occupy that space, and the rate the per floor customer population must be "turned over," that is, carried up and down to and from that floor.

Nominal densities in selling area vary from 10 ft^2 per person on the "bargain" floors to 40 to 50 ft^2 or more in exclusive departments. The normal time of turnover expected is an hour, about the time a person will spend if she is a serious shopper and seeking a particular item of any consequence. In some downtown specialty shops, where much patronage comes from office workers during lunch time, a half-hour turnover may be more realistic.

Escalators should provide transportation for about 90 per cent of the shoppers, leaving the other 10 per cent to elevators. The elevators should also be capable of serving about 10 to 15 per cent of the staff during working hours to provide for lunchtime or shift changes. If the store's offices are above the selling levels the entire population of the office floors needs elevator service similar to a single-purpose office building. Store elevators should be located so that the view from the elevator encompasses prime selling area. When a store is large enough to require a group of four or more elevators, multiple groups of four elevators located in different quadrants of a large floor are suggested. The elevators should be in a line but, a line of no more than four avoid unnecessary holding of an elevator at a floor. With more than four, the distance between the first and last car would be too great and prospective passengers would ignore the end cars if they were not waiting near them.

A department store elevator should be shallower than an office building elevator and have wider doors. A 3500-lb capacity elevator with a special platform 8 ft 0 in. wide (7 ft 8 in. car inside) by 5 ft 6 in. deep (4 ft 9 in. inside) is recommended as an optimum size. The doors should be of the center-opening type and no less than 4 ft 0 in. wide, 4 ft 6 in. preferred (see layout pp. 154, 155). Ample hall lantern signals should be provided because many persons in department stores are unfamiliar with elevator operation. An announcing device is recommended in each car to automatically announce the various floors, the direction of car travel, and, possibly, the attraction at each floor.

Hall call buttons should be prominent so that passengers will note that they must summon the elevators themselves. The location of the buttons should be central so that persons waiting near the buttons can move easily to either extreme elevator.

Sufficient service or freight elevators must be provided in a store for stock handling. A complete department store may require elevators of sufficient size to handle 12-ft rolls of carpet, for which a special 5000-lb freight elevator can be provided (Figure 10.6). The more usual requirement is for racks of dresses or coats which may be from 5 to 8 ft long. In general an 8000-lb passenger-type elevator with a platform approximately 8 ft × 8 ft is recommended. This arrangement allows automatic operation and use by both passengers and freight. Providing two-speed doors from 5 to 6 ft wide will allow any large packages to pass with ease. If the elevator is to be used for freight only and an attendant employed, a freight elevator of lesser capacity may be provided, but with a similar size platform (pp. 156, 157). The attendant is required to restrict loading and operate the vertical biparting doors. The differences in platform sizes and restrictions are American Safety Code requirements. Easy access from loading docks to the service or freight elevator is a necessity.

Restaurants and cafeterias in department stores require the same considerations as in office buildings. If the escalators do not serve the cafeteria floor ample elevator service must be provided.

PASSENGER ELEVATORS IN GARAGES

How many passenger elevators are required for a self-parking garage depends largely on the efficiency of the garage design. That efficiency in turn depends on how quickly the city streets can deliver or absorb autos from the garage.

If we assume that a well-designed garage has sufficient ramps to allow all its spaces to be filled (or emptied) within an hour, we will have some basis for elevator calculations. The nature of the garage is also important. Is it to be used by commuters who will park in the morning, leave their cars all day and drive away in the evening, or by transients who will come and go during the course of a day, parking while they shop or attend to business? The commuter garage has the simplest elevator traffic to serve, all out in the morning and all in in the evening. The transient garage presents a two-way elevator traffic pattern; shoppers with children comprise the greatest traffic volume.

Actual demand on elevators varies with the two types of traffic and is a function of the number of automobile passengers. The commuter may or may not have a partner with him and, on the average, each car has about 1.4 occupants. The shopper usually has someone with her, for an average of about 3.5 occupants. This of course varies with the type of parking facility, its location, as well as the area of the country.

If the garage can be filled, emptied, or turned over in an hour's time, the number of cars that can be parked times the average number of occupants divided by 12 (for 12 5-min periods) gives the expected demand for elevator service.

Example 10.2 gives two typical situations. Similar calculations would be used for basement or upper-floor garages in buildings where separate garage elevators are provided.

It is reasonable to expect some patrons to use stairs in a garage if they are conveniently located and well marked. With large garages connected with sports arenas or theaters the impact of the crowd exiting from an event is such that escalators may be warranted. For general convenience, in any large multilevel garage, escalators are recommended. If the garage covers a large area multiple locations are necessary. Economics and required capacity can dictate the advisibility of elevators

OWNER'S WORK

Ref. No.	
1	Hoisting beam, max. load = 6000 lbs.
2	Suitable light, heat, ventilation, convenience outlets & legal access to mach. rm. (obtain details later)
3	Power & light sws., loc. adjacent to lock jamb side of mach. rm. door
4	Reinf. conc. mach. rm. fl. slab to be poured after mach. is in position.
5	Supports for elevator beams as indicated in plan and X-X in elevation.
6	Suppts. for rail brackets at each fl. lev. & roof. Max. vert. spacing = 7'-0".
7	Light outlet in hoistway (specific location later)
8	Door frames & sills. Jambs must extend to struct. beam above if walls are not of brick or concrete.
9	Iron ladder and light fixture in pit with switch adjacent to access door.

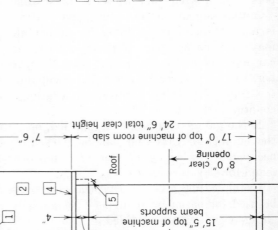

218

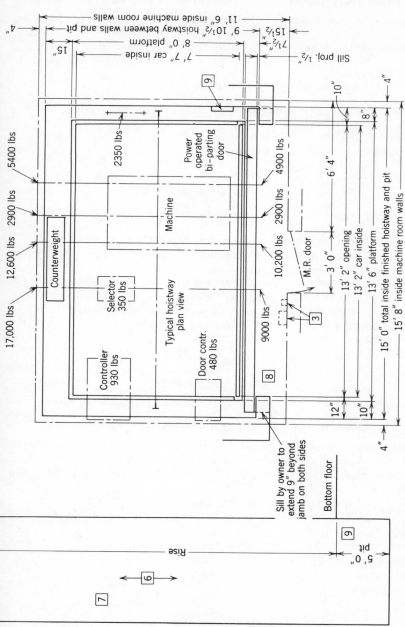

Figure 10.6 Geared, variable-voltage, department-store freight elevator, 5000 lb @ 200 fpm.

219

Example 10.2. Garages—Self-parking—Passenger Elevators

A. Commuter garage: 6 levels, 8-ft floor heights, 200 automobiles per parking level. Expected elevator demand:

5 (upper levels) $\times$ 200 = 1000 automobiles $\times$ 1.4 persons/auto

$$= 1400 \text{ persons}$$

$\dfrac{1400}{12} = 117$ persons (all up or all down) in 5 min

Assume: 2500 @ 250 fpm elevators, 3-ft, 6-in., center-opening doors, 12 passengers/trip, incoming traffic.

Stops: 5 $\times$ 10.3	= 51.5 sec
Lobby:	= 20.0 sec
Run: $\dfrac{40 \text{ ft} \times 2 \times 60}{250}$	= 19.2 sec
	90.7 say 90 sec

HC/elevator: $\dfrac{12 \times 300}{90} = 40$ persons; $^{117}\!/_{40} = 3$ elevators required.

If 3 elevators in same location, interval = 30 sec. Good.

Because of size of floor for 200 automobiles (60,000 ft^2 approximately), at least two locations are required.

Recalculate: demand = 117 + 20 per cent (split-location inefficiency) = 140 or 70 persons elevator demand per location

Assume: 2500 @ 200 fpm elevators, 12 passengers/trip, incoming traffic

Stops: 5 $\times$ 10.3	= 51.5 sec
Lobby:	= 20.0 sec
Run: $\dfrac{40 \times 2 \times 60}{200}$	= 24.0 sec
	95.5, say 96 sec

HC/elevator: $\dfrac{12 \times 300}{96} = 37.5 \times 2 = 75$ persons vs 70. Good.

Interval: $^{96}\!/_2$ = 48.0 sec. O.K.

B. Store garage: 7 levels, 8-ft floor heights, Bridge at fourth level, 50 cars/level. Expected elevator demand, turnover entire garage in 1 hr.

5 (upper levels, exclude bridge floor) $\times$ 50 = 250 automobiles $\times$ 3.5 = 875 persons.

875 $\times$ 2 (up and down/hr) $\div$ 12 = 146 up and down/5 min.

Assume: 2500 @ 350 fpm elevators, 12 passengers up, 12 passengers down/trip, two-way traffic

Stops: (floors 2,3,5,6,7) 10 $\times$ 12	= 120 sec
Lobbies: (1 and 4) 2(12 + 24 $\times$ 1)	= 72 sec
Extra transfer 2(1 $\times$ 6)	= 12 sec
Run: $\dfrac{48 \times 2 \times 60}{350}$	= 16 sec
	220 sec

HC/elevator: $\dfrac{(12 \times 2) \times 300}{220}$ = 33 persons, $^{146}\!/_{33} = 4.4$ elevators

Interval: $^{220}\!/_4$ = 55 sec, OK. Four 3000 @ 350 fpm elevators with 3 ft 6 in. center-opening doors should be used.

220

that can be installed singly to provide up and down service, compared with a pair of escalators.

For the one- or two-level garage, the hydraulic-type elevator gives the convenience of elevator service at a minimum investment when speed and performance are not the prime considerations.

A note of caution: it is recommended and many municipal codes require that the elevator lobby in underground garages be totally enclosed to avoid the possibility of gasoline fumes, which are heavier than air, accumulating in the elevator pit. It is also a good safety practice to isolate the elevator lobby from the traffic by a suitable enclosure on any garage floor.

Not all garages operate as intended. A classic example is the parking facility of the Moulton Airport near Toronto, Canada, an imposing eight-story, 3000-automobile facility commanding a superior view of the airport and its operations. Although it was primarily designed for the airborne commuter, families take it over on weekends and vie for choice picnic spots on each floor's periphery. The elevators seem to be for the children's amusement and the place is overwhelmed every fine Sunday.

PROFESSIONAL BUILDINGS

Professional buildings are specialized office buildings generally devoted to medical and dental use. Their success depends on services offered and accessibility to a large populace. It is not unusual to find 200 or more doctors, dentists, optometrists, X-ray labs, and other services concentrated in one downtown building.

Traffic in such buildings consists of patients visiting these professions, and its volume is a function of the normal turnover of visitors. The average doctor may take care of about three to four visitors per hour, each visitor usually coming with a companion. Based on the number of professional offices, the elevator traffic will amount to about eight persons in and eight persons out per office per hour.

As an example, if the building has 200 offices the critical elevator traffic would be about 16 persons times 200 offices divided by 12 5-min periods or about 267 persons in and out of the building in a 5-min period. Peak elevator traffic usually occurs between 2 and 4 in the afternoon (see Fig. 10.4).

If the number of offices is not known at the time the building is being planned it may be estimated on the basis of 200 ft^2 of net area per office. A further estimate of two persons per office and a 5-min elevator peak traffic of 20 per cent of this population, two-way traffic, leads to an approximate solution of the elevatoring problem.

The suggested speed, capacity, and interval may be found in tables 10.5, 10.6, and 10.7. In addition, consideration should be given to the possible need in some professional buildings for stretcher service on the elevator. A hospital-shaped service elevator or special provisions such as a wider passenger-shaped platform with wide doors should be considered. The 3500-lb passenger car as shown for department stores will accommodate a standard 76 $\times$ 22-ft mobile stretcher, or any size wheelchair, as well as a number of passengers. For the smaller medical building, a 2500-lb car, specially arranged, can carry stretchers as noted in the section on service elevators.

MERCHANDISE MARTS

Success of a merchandise mart depends in part on the speed with which exhibits of wares can be set up and how well the excitement of a show can be maintained. It is the modern equivalent of the medieval fair, but caters to persons interested only in a restricted line of merchandise. Shows will run from one to three days, the usual buyer trying to visit each display in the building the first day and negotiating with a limited number of sellers on succeeding days.

A common pattern for buyers is to start at the top and work their way down, using the elevators, stairs, or escalators if available. A crowded atmosphere contributes to the excitement and the standard of vertical transportation need not be as high as in a comparable department store.

Escalators or elevators on approximately the same basis as a diversified office building of the same area will provide approximately the vertical transportation needed for passengers. Large-size, 3500 to 4000-lb elevators are recommended. Ample, large freight elevators are necessary to accommodate the merchandise that must be moved in for the show. The number and size of such elevators will depend on the requirements of the building and the time allowed to set up for the show, and must be determined for each facility.

INDUSTRIAL BUILDINGS

Elevatoring of industrial buildings depends on their general function, the specific type of work to be performed, and the personnel practices of the occupying firm. There are no general rules and the extent of each specific traffic problem must be determined and treated accordingly.

In larger plants escalators have proved advantageous in that they can accommodate large numbers of people in a short time and are ideal for shift changes. Elevators have the advantage of being able to double as freight elevators during working hours and to serve the employees at incoming, luncheon, and quitting times. Employee demand for service is usually established by strict working rules, and because everyone usually starts or finishes at the same time the impact is high.

Elevator spotting operations, as described earlier in this chapter, are usually advantageous for industrial buildings. Special considerations must be given to providing ample space for persons to line up and wait.

It is obviously impossible to cover all the vertical transportation situations that may arise in the elevatoring of commercial and industrial buildings. Particular attention must be paid to avoiding situations that will reduce the efficiency of the elevator plant, such as two entrances to the building, odd floors served, unnecessary special operations, too many priority services, and upper-floor cafeterias. The best elevator or escalator installation is usually the simplest and most direct, with one clear, unobstructed path for everyone.

CHAPTER ELEVEN

Elevatoring
Residential Buildings

Any building in which a number of people live is, by our definition, a residential building. This includes hotels, motels, apartments, senior citizen housing, dormitories, and other residence halls. Elevator traffic in such buildings is generally not so severe as in commercial or institutional buildings.

POPULATION

Each occupant is alloted a certain minimum space to live and sleep, as little as 100 ft² in some low-cost housing projects and considerably higher in luxury apartments. The average, when the layout and room utilization of a residential floor is unknown, is about 200 ft² of net area per person. Design and use of a building will alter this average. For example, in hotels and motels average occupancy per room is relevant. In apartments, because room count is distorted by assigning half and quarter room values to such areas as foyers and closets, the number of bedrooms and the average occupancy per bedroom is the criteria. In dormitories, which may start as large single suites and change to two- or three-person bedrooms, the 200 ft² per person average is best to use.

In most apartments and residences persons have a more relaxed attitude toward vertical transportation than in commercial buildings and will tolerate a longer average wait for service and a longer trip time.

In hotels and motels, because persons are paying for service, they expect more prompt and efficient vertical transportation. There is a paradox, however; during a convention or gathering when crowds are coming and going, the average patron is tolerant of delays and accepts them in the carnival atmosphere that prevails. But how long he will wait is problematical.

CHARACTERISTIC TRAFFIC

Vertical traffic in residential buildings is predominately two-way. In downtown apartment buildings and hotels substantial down peaks occur at the start of the working day and up peaks as business people arrive home. In in-town and suburban apartments the peak traffic occurs in the early evening when persons are leaving for evening activities and others are returning after shopping or other activities. In a hotel the late afternoon is marked by a check-in, check-out peak, meetings breaking up, and people returning to rooms as others leave to seek refreshment.

In dormitories and residential halls the two-way peak may be in the evening when residents are going to and returning from dinner. This peak is also influenced by whether the dining facilities are cafeterias or dining rooms. In housing for the elderly recreational periods cause the greatest elevator activity.

Traffic Intensity

The percentage of a building's population the elevators must serve during the critical traffic periods varies with the facility. For a hotel that hosts frequent conventions equipment must be able to serve from 10 to 15 per cent of the population during a critical 5-min period. In a luxury apartment where the number of children is expected to be low, the percentage of the population served during a critical 5-min period may be as low as 5 per cent. Required capacity for other building types varies between those extremes. Information about recommended handling capacities, intervals, and population criteria appears in Table 11.1.

CALCULATING ELEVATOR REQUIREMENTS

Elevatoring a residential building can proceed as with any other type of building. The population is determined and the number, speed, and capacity of elevators are assumed and verified for handling capacity

Table 11.1. Residential buildings

Type of Building	Population Criteria	Recommended 5-Min Capacity	Maximum Interval
Hotel	1.5–1.9 persons/room	10–15 per cent	40–60 sec
Motel	1.5–1.9 persons/room	10–12 per cent	40–60 sec
Apartments			
Downtown	1.5–1.75 persons/bedroom	5–7 per cent	50–70 sec
Development	1.75–2 persons/bedroom	6–7 per cent	50–90 sec
Dormitories			
Cafeteria feeding	200 ft^2 net/person	10 per cent	50–70 sec
Dining room feeding	200 ft^2 net/person	15 per cent	50–70 sec
Residence Halls	Same as dormitories		
Senior Citizen Housing Housing for Elderly	1.25–1.5 persons/bedroom	6 per cent	50–90 sec

Recommended Elevator Size

Type of Building	Passenger Elevators Size; Door Type and Size	Service Elevators Size; Door Type and Size
Hotel	3000–3500 lb 3′6″ center-opening	3500–4000 lb 4′0″ center-opening
Motel	2500–3000 lb 3′6″ center-opening	3500 lb 4′0″ center-opening
Apartments	2000–2500 lb 3′0″ single slide	2500 lb 3′6″ 2 speed
Dormitories Residence halls	2500–3000 lb 3′6″ center-opening	Use passenger elevators at off peak times.
Senior Citizen Housing, Housing for Elderly	2000 lb 3′0″ single slide	Arrange 1 passenger car 2500 lb 3′6″ 2 speed doors.

Recommended Elevator Speed (in fpm)

Building Height	Hotels-Motels	Apartments and Housing for Elderly	Dormitories and Residence Halls	
2–6 floors	200	100	200	
6–12 floors	250	200	250	
12–20 floors	350–500	250–350	250–500	
20–25 floors	500	350–500	350–500	For buildings of this height, local and express elevators should be considered.
25–30 floors	700	500	500–700	
30–40 floors	800–1000	500–700	700–1000	
40–50 floors	1000–1200	1000–1200	1000–1200	

and interval. Double entrances to the building, garage stops above or below the main entrance floor, and other services or facilities such as rooftop swimming pools, restaurants, and lounges all require additional elevator service. The extent, use, and capacity of such facilities must be determined and the impact on the elevator situation calculated.

Service requirements may be quite stringent in residential buildings. In hotels and motels there is always someone moving in and out, chamber maids at work, and, in the higher-class establishments, considerable room service for refreshments and food.

Luxury apartments hardly deserve that appellation without a separate service elevator. In a large apartment building the frequency of moves in and out may require use of a service elevator 4 to 6 hr daily just for moving.

Each major type of residential structure is reviewed here to show the impact of expected activity on the vertical transportation.

ELEVATOR EQUIPMENT AND LAYOUT

Rules of elevator location and grouping introduced in Chapter 2 apply to residential as well as other buildings. Elevators should be a center of attraction in the lobby and readily accessible on each floor. In hotels and dormitories, where many people come and go at the same time, ample elevator lobby space must be provided at the entrance and on other floors where people are expected to gather.

Service elevators should be located in separate alcoves with ample lobby space at each floor to turn any carts to be carried as well as to accommodate waiting or stored vehicles. This is especially important in hotels, where the room service tables and carts with their dirty dishes may be stored until picked up by service personnel.

Elevator hoistways should be isolated from sleeping rooms by lobbies, mechanical shaft space, or stairwells. Although elevators are relatively quiet, air noises of an elevator traveling through a shaftway are noticeable when other building noise is low. In addition such mechanical noises as the opening of doors on a floor or the passing of the counterweight within an inch or two of a wall are unavoidable. If a sleeping person's head is on the other side of the wall within 10 or 12 in. of the passing car or counterweight (assuming an 8-in. wall), he will hear the noise and complain. If sleeping rooms must be placed next to the elevator space, ample sound insulation should be provided in the form of dead air space or a mineral wool blanket inside the finished wall.

Similarly, sleeping spaces should not be located next to elevator machine rooms. Electric motors starting and stopping can be objectionable in the middle of the night.

HOTELS AND MOTELS

From an operational point of view the distinction between motels and hotels is not always sharp. From the vertical transportation aspect we define a motel as a lodging in which room service demands are minimum and a hotel as one in which considerable service is expected. A difference then, is in the number of service elevators required.

A further distinction is necessary. If the establishment has considerable convention facilities, large dining or meeting rooms, or a ball room, it is more a hotel than a motel.

Parking

Today, hotels and motels are expected to have ample parking facilities within or near the structure. Even if there are in-building facilities they should be separated from guest rooms in the interest of security. This may require either attendant parking or checking in and checking out at the entrance to the garage. With self-parking one of the best security arrangements is a separate shuttle elevator for the garage area. Not only can the desk clerk see who is coming and going, but this eliminates garage floor stops for the main elevators, improves their efficiency, and may minimize the number required.

In spite of impaired security and the inefficiency created by garage stops many hotel and motel operators insist that the main elevators serve both the garage and guest floors. In this case a constant lobby stop plus additional stops both up and down in the garage area must be considered in elevator calculations. In any event elevators must be of ample size to accommodate guests and luggage.

Meeting Rooms

Another critical area in elevatoring a hotel or motel is the meeting room or ballroom floors. When meetings are starting and breaking up these floors are constant elevator stops so that adequate allowance in elevator trip time must be made. A good alternative is to locate the meeting floors where an escalator can connect them to the street or lobby floor. (We presume the lobby floor is at street level or connected with it by escalators.) Separate escalator service to the meeting room floor permits public use of the facility with minimum interference with the hotel guests. If large meetings are breaking up the elevators will be overwhelmed by many persons wishing to get back to their rooms. With an escalator they can be guided to a lounge area where refreshments can make the wait more pleasant.

Kitchens

Kitchen facilities should be at the lower levels. A kitchen service elevator should connect the kitchen to the loading dock and possibly to the restaurant level or ballroom level. Dumbwaiters can be used to connect the kitchen to the various food shops usually located at the main level. The kitchen service elevator may be a freight elevator with vertical biparting doors or a service-type with sliding doors. The advantage of the service-type elevator is that it can be operated automatically because the doors will close unattended.

SERVICE ELEVATORS

Elevators for room service should be large enough to handle carts or portable tables. A 3500-lb car with 4-ft wide center-opening doors is recommended. The number of service elevators depends on many factors, and experience has shown that a minimum of one service elevator for each 200 to 300 rooms in a hotel is necessary. This minimum number requires that schedules, deliveries, and movement of linen and other supplies to each floor be restricted to other than peak dining hours and that special functions be held to a minimum. If a number of special facilities such as rooftop restaurants or lounges must be serviced, or if there are a considerable number of hospitality rooms, additional service elevators are necessary.

A complete study of service requirements can be made by determining the average time per delivery and relating that to the number of deliveries in a given period of time and the average time required per elevator. Such factors as the number of room-service meals the kitchen can prepare in a given time, the number of service employees who must be transported, their shift changes or local labor requirements, and frequency of special parties must be considered.

During the 1920's the era of luxury hotel room service, when many larger hotels were built, the rule of thumb for service elevators was one for each passenger elevator. Today, with swifter intercity transportation and a greater turnover in hotel guests plus considerably less room service, an approximate ratio of service elevators to passenger elevators should be from 50 to 60 per cent.

SAMPLE HOTEL ELEVATORING

Sample calculations for elevatoring a typical hotel or motel are shown in Example 11.1, using factors from Table 11.1. Note the impact of the garage, although minimum use was assumed. Also note that a restaurant on the top floor of a hotel or any other building requires considerable additional service. This impact cannot be minimized because the restaurant will be used concurrently with other activities; the traffic restaurant patrons create will be opposed to other traffic in the hotel.

Example 11.1. Hotel–Motel

Given: 25-story + 3-basement motel; first and second floors 20-ft, typical floors 10-ft; self-parking for 300 cars in basements; first floor, lobby and restaurants (kitchen in basement); second floor, meeting rooms and 1200-person ballroom; floors 3–25 guest rooms, 15 rooms per floor; located near college football stadium; will be used for conventions, may have 300-person restaurant on twenty-sixth floor.

Required: Number of passenger elevators and service elevators—recommended sizes.

Calculations:

23 floors of rooms $\times$ 15 $\times$ 1.9 (convention occupancy) = 391 $\times$ 1.9 = 743

743 $\times$ 12.5 per cent = 93 persons $-$ 5 min, two-way peak.

Assume: 3000 @ 500 fpm passenger elevators, 3 ft 6 in. center-opening doors, 10 up 10 down (convention peak),

With garage.

Probable stops: 1.75(10) $-$ 1 = 16.5 $\times$ 12 = 198 sec

Lobby: up (12 + 10), down (12 + 10) = 44 sec

Garage floor (assume 1 stop) = 12 sec

Run: $\dfrac{290 \times 2 \times 60}{500}$ = 70 sec

324 sec

HC = $\dfrac{(10 + 10) \times 300}{324}$ = 19 persons

No. of elevators: $93/19$ = 4.9 = 5

Interval = $324/5$ = 65 sec. (Long.)

Without garage.

Probable stops: = 198

Lobby: (12 + 20) = 32

Run: $\dfrac{270 \times 2 \times 60}{500}$ = 65

295 sec

HC = $\dfrac{(10 + 10) \times 300}{295}$ = 20

No. of elevators: $93/20$ = 4.6 = 5

Interval = $295/5$ = 59 sec

Five elevators, 3000 @ 500 fpm minimum, 3000 @ 700 fpm recommended.
1200-person ballroom exceeds hotel capacity, must be used for outside functions—recommend at least 1 escalator, lobby to 2.

Separate garage elevator required—one 2500 @ 200 fpm elevator serving lobby, basements 1, 2, and 3.

Service elevators:

Based on 60 per cent of number of passenger elevators, three 3500 @ 500 fpm service elevators recommended.

Kitchen elevator, 4000 @ 100 fpm loading dock (street) to kitchen, to ballroom. If ballroom to be used for displays: large freight, (3 stops) street to ballroom. If 300-person restaurant on roof: demand 300 up + 300 down. Average feeding time 1.5 hr; $\dfrac{600}{1.5} = 400/\text{hr} \div 12 = 33$ per 5 min

Demand for hotel = 93 + 33 for restaurant = 126 per 5 min

Round-trip time, hotel without garage   295

Constant stop at top   18 (assume 6 passengers/trip)

                                                  313

$$\text{HC} = \frac{(10 + 10) \times 300}{313} = 19$$

$126\%_{19}$ = 6 elevators required.

Interval: $313\%_6 = 52$ sec

APARTMENTS

Recent decades have seen the growth of apartment houses from four- and five-story walk-ups to buildings of 30 or more floors. This growth is attributable to both increased land costs and improved vertical transportation. Only since 1960 has extensive application of local and express elevator groups begun in apartments. With further use of this concept apartments of 40 or more floors should become commonplace.

The demands for vertical transportation in apartments follow the normal day of the building's residents. Outgoing traffic is heavy in the morning as persons leave for work, with corresponding incoming traffic in the early evening as they return. These are the average peak traffic periods of apartments that house primarily business people.

In apartments and housing projects with a predominant family occupancy the needs of children and housewives influence the traffic pattern. Traffic reaches a forenoon peak as shopping expeditions take place and a distinct afternoon peak as the children return from school and go out to play.

In both downtown and family-type apartment buildings the critical peak traffic that determines elevator capacity occurs in the late afternoon and early evening when persons are returning for meals and others are going out for evening recreation. Studies have shown that this traffic is two-way and amounts to about 5 to 7 per cent of the building's population.

Population

We base the population of apartment buildings on the number of bedrooms provided in the building, counting so-called efficiency (one-room) apartments as one bedroom. Occupancy per bedroom varies with the type of apartment building and its rental range. The building housing business persons will be almost as densely occupied as the family type. Occupancy of the first may average 1.75 persons per bedroom because of the considerable apartment-sharing by working people. With low-rental apartments occupied by families with many children, an average of 2.0 persons per bedroom should be used. When the rents are high and rooms are spacious, an average occupancy estimate of 1.5 per bedroom is acceptable.

Elevator Capacity

The minimum recommended size of an elevator for an apartment building where the elevator is a necessity (six floors and over) is the 2000-lb car with 6 ft 0 in. $\times$ 3 ft 8 in. inside dimensions. Sliding, power-operated doors are also necessary because they are less likely to be blocked than swing-type doors. In lower-rise buildings of two to five floors, where elevators are a convenience, a smaller car such as 1200 or 1500 lb capacity can be used but moving operations will be impaired.

In large buildings, where there are two or more elevators and no service elevator, at least one of the passenger elevators should be large, 2500 lb or more, to expedite moving, which can occur quite frequently.

Elevators must be able to carry at least 5 per cent of the population for the high-rent apartment buildings and from 6 to 7 per cent for the moderate and low-rent apartments. The more economical the rent, the more children are likely and the higher the traffic peaks that will occur.

Service elevators are a necessity for a tall or high-rent apartment building. Recent statistics show that one out of every 10 families moves once a year. Assuming a move out and a move in will tie up one elevator most of a day, 500 families in a building will tie up an elevator one day per week just for moving—in addition to normal deliveries of furniture, rugs, groceries, cleaning, and various services as well as normal building maintenance. The suggested minimum is one service elevator for every 500 families. If management imposes a restriction that all deliveries must be made on service elevators this ratio should be one service elevator for every 300 families.

If frequent maid service is expected or if most occupants will be working service elevators will be a necessity no matter how large or small the apartment house is. Here it is suggested that at least one service elevator per 250 apartments be provided.

A service elevator in any apartment house may pay for itself in improved rental income. This may begin with the opening of the building. If it has only two elevators and the owner is trying to rent before the building is completed the following situation frequently occurs. To eliminate an outside hoist, the building contractor takes an elevator from the elevator contractor to use as a temporary hoist before it is completed. The remaining elevator is used by construction workmen and the rental agent to show apartments. If an apartment is rented the tenant usually wants to move in as quickly as possible and the owner is more than willing to accept the rent. Because the completion of the building and moving in cannot take place during the same hours the owner is faced with overtime moving at premium rates. This can persist for some time because when the building contractor relinquishes the elevator he has been using, it will require considerable finishing to make it ready for tenant use. In addition if both elevators are to operate as a group, their controls must be tied together by the elevator contractor, who must work on both elevators at night, at the owner's expense, to complete the installation. A third car, or a service elevator, would avoid overtime costs for both moving and elevator installation, which has often amounted to a substantial part of the cost of the extra elevator! The tenants enjoy the convenience of a service elevator and rental return per apartment is likely to be higher.

Garages

Lower-floor garages in apartment houses exact the same elevator trip time penalty as in any other type of building. If an apartment has such garage floors they should be served by all the elevators. If the tenants must wait for, say, only one of two cars to get to and from the garage they are inconvenienced whenever they use such facilities. If they pay premium rent their complaints may be quite vocal.

The same consideration of having all elevators serve any public use floors will also apply to basement laundries, storage areas, recreation areas such as rooftop swimming pools, and terrace floors. It is most important that penthouse floors be served by all the elevators of a group if not, the highest-rental floors in the building will have substandard elevator service.

SAMPLE CALCULATIONS

Because the 3 ft 0 in. single-slide door is the most common in apartments, a new value for time spent at an elevator stop must be calculated. In addition persons in apartments resent being rushed in and out of an elevator so slightly more time should be allowed per stop for transfer. The following values are suggested:

Car start and stop: Geared, 4.4 sec; gearless, 3.6 sec
Door close, 3'0" single-slide: 4.3 sec
Door open (with some premature opening):   1.2 sec
Transfer: 3.3 sec
Optimum time per stop: Geared, 12.2 sec; Gearless, 11.4 sec
Add 15 per cent as inefficiency: <u>1.8</u>   <u>1.7</u>
                       Total time: 14.0   13.1

An apartment house elevator should never be filled to capacity. Unlike office buildings, where elevator passengers seldom have parcels, someone always has something such as a baby stroller, food parcels, luggage, or laundry in an apartment elevator. As we will be dealing with two-way traffic, we will estimate car loading at no more than 10 persons up or down for a 2000-lb car and no more than 12 persons for a 2500-lb car. Probable stops will be estimated as one person per stop. For example, if we have a 2000-lb car that is expected to carry no more than 10 persons per trip, we assume it will make no more than 10 stops if it serves at least 10 floors. This might be four stops up and six stops down, six up and four down, or any combination of up and down stops not to exceed 10.

If we have a 2500-lb car it is reasonable to assume that the building is large, with many suites per floor. In that event we will say that the car will also make no more than 10 stops per round trip and carry 12 persons, two persons getting off or on at about two of the stops.

In any apartment building the maximum number of stops for an elevator should be no more than the number of passengers it is required to carry. For example, if demand is such that the elevator will have to carry only six passengers per trip, it is not expected to make more than six stops.

Example 11.2. Apartments

A. Given: 12-story apartment building, moderate rental, 18 bedrooms/floor 9-ft floor heights.

Demand: $11 \times 18 \times 1.75$ (persons per bedroom) $= 347 \times 6$ per cent $= 21$ persons/5 min.

(1) Assume: two 2000 @ 200 fpm elevators, 10 passengers/trip.

$$10 \times 14 \qquad\qquad = 140 \text{ sec}$$
$$\text{Lobby: } 14 + 10 \qquad = 24 \text{ sec}$$
$$\text{Run: } \frac{11 \times 9 \times 2 \times 60}{200} = \underline{59 \text{ sec}}$$
$$223 \text{ sec}$$

$$\text{HC: } \frac{10 \times 300}{223} \times 2 \quad = 27 \text{ vs } 21 \text{ persons. Too much.}$$

(2) Assume: 7 stops/trip, 7 passengers.

$$7 \times 14 \qquad\qquad = 98 \text{ sec}$$
$$\text{Lobby: } 14 + 7 \qquad = 21 \text{ sec}$$
$$\text{Run: } \qquad\qquad = \underline{59 \text{ sec}}$$
$$178 \text{ sec}$$

$$\text{HC: } \frac{7 \times 300}{178} \times 2 \quad = 23 \text{ vs } 21 \text{ persons. O.K.}$$

$$\text{Interval: } 178\!\!\;/\!\!\;_2 \qquad = 89. \text{ Too long.}$$

(3) Assume 2000 @ 250, 6 passengers.

$$6 \times 14 \qquad\qquad = 84 \text{ sec}$$
$$14 + 6 \qquad\qquad = 20 \text{ sec}$$
$$\text{Run: } \frac{11 \times 9 \times 2 \times 60}{250} = \underline{48 \text{ sec}}$$
$$152 \text{ sec}$$

$$\text{HC: } \frac{6 \times 300}{152} \times 2 \quad = 24 \text{ persons. O.K.}$$

$$\text{Interval: } \qquad\qquad = 76. \text{ O.K.}$$

Two 2000 @ 250 fpm elevators recommended; two 2500 @ 250 if no service car.

B. Given: 30-story apartment building downtown, 12 bedrooms per floor, 9-ft floor heights.

Demand: $29 \times 12 \times 1.75 = 609 \times 6$ per cent $= 37$ persons/5 min.

Assume: three 2000 @ 500 fpm elevators, 6 passengers/trip.

$$6 \times 13 \qquad\qquad = 78 \text{ sec}$$
$$\text{Lobby: } 13 + 6 \qquad = 18 \text{ sec}$$
$$\text{Run: } \frac{29 \times 9 \times 2 \times 60}{500} = \underline{63 \text{ sec}}$$
$$159 \text{ sec}$$

$$\text{HC: } \frac{6 \times 300}{159} \times 3 \quad = 37 \text{ persons. O.K.}$$

$$\text{Interval: } 159\!\!\;/\!\!\;_3 \qquad = 53 \text{ sec. O.K.}$$

C. Given: 30-story apartment building, low rental, 20 bedrooms per floor, 9-ft floor heights.

Demand: $29 \times 20 \times 2 = 1160 \times 7$ per cent $= 81$ persons/5 min.

Assume: Local and express elevators.

Demand: Floors 2–18, 48 persons.

Assume: three 2500 @ 350 fpm elevators, 12 passengers/trip.

$$\text{Stop: } 10 \times 14 \qquad = 140$$
$$\text{Lobby: } 14 + 10 \qquad = 24$$
$$\text{Run: } \frac{17 \times 9 \times 2 \times 60}{350} = \underline{52}$$
$$216 \text{ sec}$$

$$\text{HC: } \frac{12 \times 300}{216} \times 3 \quad = 50 \text{ persons}$$

$$\text{Interval: } 216 / 3 \qquad = 72 \text{ sec O.K.}$$

Demand: floors 19-30, 34 persons.

Assume: three 2000 @ 500 fpm elevators, 10 passengers/trip.

$$\text{Stop: } 10 \times 13 \qquad = 130$$
$$\text{Lobby: } 13 + 10 \qquad = 23$$
$$\text{Run: } \frac{29 \times 9 \times 2 \times 60}{500} = \underline{63}$$
$$216 \text{ sec}$$

$$\text{HC: } \frac{10 \times 300}{216} \times 3 \quad = 42 \text{ persons. Too much.}$$

$$\text{Interval: } 216 / 3 \qquad = 72\text{-sec. 3 cars}$$
$$\text{required for good interval.}$$

Provide: three 2500/500 high rise, arrange 1 car all stops for part-time service, and three 2500 @ 350 fpm low-rise elevators.

Typical calculations for apartment houses are shown on page 235. The evaluation factors used are taken from Table 11.1.

Note in example 11.2 C that high- and low-rise elevators are suggested to provide the handling capacity required in this large building. Three high-rise elevators are required for a reasonable interval even though their handling capacity will be more than ample, enabling frequent use of one of the high-rise cars as a service car during all but the critical traffic hours. The third car can have openings on all floors, a larger platform and special control circuits to be operated independently of the remaining cars in the group. To preserve lobby decor, a rear entrance can be provided for access to a street-floor loading dock.

Variations in apartment building sizes and heights are endless. In addition, certain minimum standards for elevators have been established by various lending and governmental agencies. The criteria for elevator service shown here generally comply with these regulations.

DORMITORIES AND RESIDENCE HALLS

Most of the aspects of apartment elevatoring already discussed also apply to residence halls and dormitories. The essential difference is that the average dormitory resident is subject to strict discipline as far as working and mealtimes are concerned. He is usually required to attend classes at certain hours and must take meals in minimum time. These restrictions create a great impact on vertical transportation.

Experience has shown that about 10 per cent of a dormitory's population seek elevator service during a critical 5-min peak, which usually occurs before suppertime and varies with the type of dining facility. If a formal dining room is provided where students must be seated at a given hour the peak will approximate 15 per cent of the population, will be a down peak (assuming lower floor dining), and will utilize the full capacity of the elevators. If there is a cafeteria, only a 10 per cent peak is expected.

Elevators of 2500 lb capacity with a 3 ft 6 in. center-opening doors are recommended for dormitories, to provide ample size for students as well as for moving operations and servicing the building. Separate service elevators are seldom required, as their functions can be performed by the passenger elevators during slow periods of the day.

Dormitory elevators should be as student- and vandal-proof as possible, as should apartment elevators when many children are present. Car operating fixtures should be of substantial construction, extraneous switches should be omitted, and operating buttons should be made of solid metal. Hall buttons, too, should be of solid metal, for it is not unusual for a student to use his foot to register a call.

The protective edge on the car doors should be of metal to foil attempts to carve it with a penknife. Light jewels can be picked out with a sharp instrument and thus should be inaccessible. For anything that is fastened with a screw, the screws should have spanner or allen heads or be avoided entirely; young minds are challenged by what may be behind the cover.

Key-operated switches are a challenge and are best omitted. If a floor must be blocked off at certain times it is best to provide a locked elevator lobby. A classic story is told about the college that was going to have elevators with skip-stop operation. The odd floors were locked off by key switches in the car operating panels. On opening day an enterprising undergraduate was selling copies of the key at two dollars per!

College students will try to overload elevators as they have done with phone booths and compact cars. Many codes allow the elevator to be shut down if filled to more than 150 per cent of capacity. We recommended a load-weighing switch that will sound a loud alarm if the car is filled to 125 per cent of capacity.

No matter what is done, vandalism and damage may be expected. The best solution has been found in some colleges; boys and girls share the same dormitory with restrictions allocating different wings at the lobby or floor entrances. The girls seem to exert a civilizing effect on the boys and vandalism virtually disappears.

Elevator requirements should be calculated on the same basis as for apartment houses. The elevators should be determined for the apartment house percentage of 6 to 7 per cent, two-way traffic and a 10 or 15 per cent capacity at mealtimes, usually a down peak. Population should be based on approximately 200 ft^2 of net area per student as shown in Table 11.1.

Floors with special facilities such as lounges, recreational areas, laundries, and cafeterias require special consideration because of their expected impact on vertical traffic.

As discussed in Chapter 2, skip-stopping is not recommended in dormitories or apartments. There is almost no saving in number of elevators and the saving in entances creates moving and building service problems. With any emphasis on serving handicapped persons, skip-stop arrangements increase management and elevator assignment problems.

One skip-stop arrangement, however, merit considerations: the creation of dormitory "houses" within the same building. The elevators serve the common floor and students walk up and down from that floor to their rooms, a plan akin to duplex apartments. Elevators must be calculated for total population on the group of floors and, with the high concentration of load at each stop, a constant stop on each floor may be expected.

SENIOR CITIZEN HOUSING

Apartment dwellings serving the needs of elderly and semi-invalid persons are receiving considerable emphasis. Each suite may have its own kitchen facilities as in a conventional apartment house, or community-type dining may be provided. The buildings are designed for persons of advancing years who can take care of themselves or require only minor aid.

Because these people are totally dependent on elevators for vertical transportation each building needs a multiplicity of units to ensure continuity of service. In addition the elevators must be designed to wait for the user, whose movements and reaction time will be slow. Many passengers will have poor eyesight and use walking aids.

Because occupants are subject to illnesses and may require the use of stretchers for medical care, at least one elevator should be planned for this contingency.

Handling capacity needs will be minimum, no more than about 5 to 6 per cent of the population in a 5-min period. Waiting will be no problem, provided the wait is comfortable; a convenient bench in the elevator lobby on each floor is suggested. Room occupancy is very light; many apartments will have only one person, which indicates an average of 1.25 to 1.5 persons per bedroom, depending on the expected use of the facility.

The elevator cars should be wide and shallow and equipped with handrails. The 2000-lb car, 6 ft 0 in. $\times$ 3 ft 8 in. deep is suggested and a 3 ft 0 in. single-slide door should be used. A light-ray device is recommended for door protection in addition to the safety edge to avoid closing before the entrance way is clear. One or more of the elevators should have a 2500-lb car, 6 ft 8 in. wide $\times$ 4 ft 3 in. deep, equipped with 3 ft 6 in. two-speed doors, to accommodate a 76 $\times$ 22 in. mobile stretcher. A separate service elevator, if provided, should be of ample size for this contingency (hospital-size recommended), and the passenger cars can be limited to 2000 lb.

Additional time should be allowed at each elevator stop for the expected slow transfer of passengers resulting in a per-stop time of about 5 sec rather than 3.3 sec. A prominent signal at each floor to indicate whether the elevator is going up or down is also suggested. Floor numbers on the door jambs are suggested in addition to the normal in-car position indicator.

Elevator calculations can proceed as for normal apartment houses with the necessary extra time values. The elevator should never be considered for more than about six passengers per trip. This can be increased to nominal capacity (80 per cent) if management supervision will be such that groups of persons are moved at one time.

A logical step from housing for the elderly is a nursing home, the essential difference being the increase in personnel service and the operating staff. For our purposes a nursing home should be considered as an institutional building and is discussed in Chapter 12.

OPERATION OF ELEVATORS IN RESIDENTIAL BUILDINGS

In apartment houses of no more than six floors the rheostatic or resistance controlled elevator, which is usually arranged without leveling,

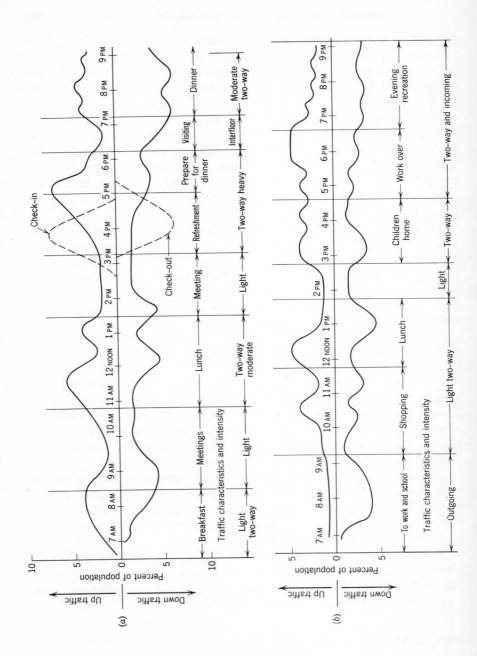

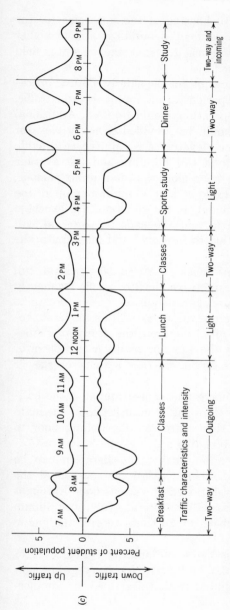

Figure 11.1 Traffic flow charts: (*a*) motel-hotel, convention traffic (in and out of elevators at main lobby); (*b*) apartment building (in and out of elevators at main lobby); (*c*) Dormitory with cafeteria (in and out of elevators at lobby).

is acceptable and most economical. In housing of the same size for the elderly leveling is essential. In other residential buildings and in higher buildings, because of the more intensive use expected, the generator field control type of elevator is recommended.

For apartments, dormitories, and housing for the elderly, normal operation during the day will include long periods of minimum elevator traffic. For this reason an on-call type of operation should be used. Additional features for heavier traffic periods should be provided if heavy elevator use is expected. For example, if three elevators are required to provide an adequate interval of operation in a tall building and the average passenger load per trip is expected to be no more than four or six persons, long periods of intensive use are unlikely and a minimum operating system should suffice. On the other hand, if the elevators are expected to carry 10 or 12 passengers per trip and the expected interval will be near the maximum, special attention to incoming and outgoing peaks is recommended.

In hotels and motels whose rooms must be 80 to 90 per cent full to provide a good investment return, intensive elevator traffic frequently occurs and more refinement in group operation is necessary. Features such as incoming and outgoing traffic operations as well as moderate-to-heavy two-way traffic operation are often required, the degree of refinement depending on the capability of the elevator plant. A two-elevator group cannot accommodate intensive traffic whereas a four- or six-car group can.

Special floors may require special operations. For example, if the ballroom floor is served by the main elevators and is on other than the main floor, it may be helpful to change the control or dispatching floor to the ballroom floor when meetings are breaking up.

For quiet periods in a hotel or motel further consideration can be given to operating elevators on call, either with all cars parked at the lobby floor for maximum security or stationed at various floors throughout the building for ready guest accessibility. Alternatively, a minimum number of elevators can be kept cruising at all times to give the guests the promptest possible response.

Traffic flow charts for the various types of buildings (Figure 11.1) are typical and will vary for particular buildings. Necessary group control can be determined in a manner similar to that described for commercial buildings.

For example, typical traffic in a hotel-motel follows an in-and-out pattern of movement as shown, depending on the activities of the guests during the day. If a convention is in progress guests generally go to and from their rooms between meetings and business sessions and fre-

quently after meals. In the late afternoon and evening there is considerable traffic between floors and to and from the lobby, consisting of guests
from other hotels or local friends and persons leaving the building for
evening entertainment and other activities.

If no convention is in progress and the motel or hotel is patronized
by business people substantial outgoing peaks occur in the morning and
incoming peaks in the evening. In addition there is a check-in, check-out
peak in the late afternoon or whenever most of this activity takes
place, as early as 11 A.M. in some areas or as late as 3 or 4 P.M. in
others.

Traffic curves shown for apartments and dormitories are also altered
by the location and use of the facility. If the dormitory is convenient
to the classrooms it is frequently used by the students during the day.
If it is remote, morning outgoing and late afternoon incoming traffic
peaks may be similar to those in an in-town apartment occupied by
business people. Each building has its unique traffic.

Traffic in housing for the elderly approximates that found in an apartment house but with greatly reduced intensity. This is partially offset
by the relatively long time spent at each stop by the elevators designed
to accommodate the elderly.

Features of Residential Elevators

Because elevators are used by many persons not familiar with them,
installations in motels and hotels should have the maximum features
that make them easy to use. Such features include prominent hall buttons
that will light when operated, readily seen directional indicators (hall
lanterns) at each floor for each elevator, and well-lighted lobbies and
elevator cars. Car operating panels should clearly present the floors
the elevator serves and both a position indicator in the car showing
where the car is stopping and a floor numeral on the edge of the hoistway door is recommended.

Recorded devices to announce the floor at which the elevator is stopping and its direction of travel are recommended to aid the guest. In
addition, these devices can be arranged to announce special events or
give safety messages if necessary.

In other residential buildings, because turnover is minimized, only
the minimum informational features are necessary. These are a hall
button that lights to acknowledge the call being registered, position indicators in the car, and a prominent directional lantern in the car to
show the entering passenger which way the elevator is headed.

Service elevators should be large enough to carry their intended loads:

carts, tables, or baggage. Additional considerations must be given to moving furniture in all residential buildings, including cars with ceilings 8 ft high as well as higher hoistway and car doors. The essential signal equipment is a car position indicator.

If the service elevator is normally a passenger elevator protective pads should be provided. A switch to remove the elevator from group operation with other passenger elevators should be provided and the elevator should operate with attendant in response to car calls only. If frequent service use is expected, a separate hall button system and an annunciator in the car is an economical means to provide the special operation.

Other chapters in this book also include suggestions for special operations or features that may be necessary for a particular building. Many of them can be used in any building to solve a present or expected problem. Elevator manufacturers are more than willing to help solve those problems and should be consulted.

ELEVATORS IN PRIVATE RESIDENCES

One area of residential elevators that is growing in popularity with the introduction of economical equipment is the elevator in a private residence. These have long been prohibitively expensive and were found only in the most palatial homes. Increased use as well as the popularity of multifloor houses has created the demand and elevator manufacturers are eager to meet that demand.

The average home elevator is a small car of about 700-lb capacity and operates at a speed of about 35 fpm. It is designed with a collapsing car gate and swing-type hoistway doors and can either be supported by the building structure or be installed in an independent tower. The car interior is designed to accommodate a standard-size wheel chair.

The installation and design varies with each manufacturer. The American Safety Code, recognizing that the elevator will be infrequently used, has allowed certain easing of rules. One important rule is imposed, however: the elevator must contain a telephone capable of reaching a central switchboard should the need ever arise.

CHAPTER TWELVE

Elevatoring
Institutional Buildings

DEFINITION

We define institutional buildings as those in which people obtain a particular care or service. They are generally public and are designed to perform specific functions. Those functions influence vertical traffic, which consists of a combination of staff and visitor traffic, such as in a hospital, or primarily visitor traffic, as in a museum or exhibition building.

The major types of institutional building are hospitals, both general and specialized, nursing homes, schools, courthouses, museums, sports arenas, exhibition halls, observation towers, and jails. Combinations are occasionally found, for example, a governmental office building and courthouse. In such a case vertical transportation must serve both the office and courthouse traffic.

Today's institutional buildings usually have extensive parking facilities that must be served. Residential areas, such as living quarters on upper floors in a hospital, may be integrated into the building and the impact of these areas on vertical transportation must be determined and served.

Existing facilities, especially in hospitals, must often be expanded to serve growing needs. A basic rule in planning the expansion of any facility is to determine the adequacy of its existing vertical transportation. Too often the vertical transportation load of the entire complex is placed on the new facility, which overwhelms otherwise adequate service. One of the best ways of evaluating the impact of the new facility is to assume that the entire facility is being built today and, perhaps by expansion of existing equipment, to develop a total solution.

POPULATION

The amount and type of service to be rendered often determines the population of a facility. This is best described by examples of each type of institutional building and is summed up in Table 12.1.

Hospitals have more critical vertical transportation demands than most other types of institutional building. Hospital staffs have been expanding even more rapidly than patient loads. Statistics show that the average staff per bed increased from 1.98 in 1954 to approximately 2.4 in 1964 and is expected to exceed 3.03 in 1974.* Concurrently, hospital visiting hours are being liberalized until most hospitals now allow visiting at any time between 9 A.M. and 9 P.M.; restrictions are placed on critical areas only. Staff per bed has proved to be a good indication of the elevator traffic in hospitals and an ideal criteria for population.

In nursing homes and mental institutions the staff per bed is somewhat lower and the elevator requirements less severe. Again the staff per bed is a good population criteria.

Population ratios in schools vary with the type of facility. In primarily classroom buildings, population densities of 10 to 15 ft² of net area per student are common. The total density in the building varies with the classroom utilization factor, which school authorities are striving to maximize and which may be as high as each seat being used about 80 per cent of the time. At present, use factors of 50 to 75 per cent are attained.

Laboratory buildings provide more space per student than do classrooms. The average is about 50 to 100 ft²; in advanced laboratories and graduate schools, averages of 150 to 200 ft² of net area per person are often allowed.

Population in library buildings varies with use. A general reading room may have densities as high as 15 to 20 ft² per person or, in some specialized areas where many book racks or files of reference material are located, density may be as low as one person per 100 ft² or more.

Courtrooms are designed for a specific primary function—a jury trial. There will be spectators, (varying in number with the importance of the trial); the judiciary staff (about 12 to 16 persons), and the jury (12 to 16 persons). By using a value of about 30 persons per courtroom

* *J. Amer. Hospital Assoc.*, Oct. 16, 1964.

Table 12.1. Institutional buildings

Type of Building	Population Criteria	Recommended 5-Min Capacity	Maximum Interval
Hospital	2.5–3.0/bed	10–12 per cent	30–50 sec
Nursing home	1.0–1.5/bed	8–10 per cent	40–70 sec
Mental hospital			
School			
Classroom	10–15 ft²/student	25–40 per cent	See text
Laboratory	50–100 ft²/student	20 per cent	40–60 sec
Library	Depends on seating	15 per cent	40–60 sec
Courthouse	30 persons/court room plus spectators	12–15 per cent	40–60 sec
Jail	Varies	See text	See text
Museum, sport arena Exhibition, observation tower	Varies	See text	See text

Recommended Elevator Sizes

Type of Building	Passenger Elevators Size; Doors, Type and Size	Service Elevator Size; Doors, Type and Size
Hospital	3000–3500 lb, 3'6"–4'0" c/o	4000–4500 lb, 4'0" 2-speed, c/o
Nursing Home Mental Hospital	2500–3000 lb, 3'6" c/o	4000 lb 4'0", 2-speed or c/o
School	3000–6000 lb, 3'6"–5'0" c/o	3500–4000 lb, 4'0" 2-speed or c/o
Court House	3500–4000 lb, 3'6"–4'0" c/o	4000–5000 lb, 4'0" 2-speed
Museum, sport arenas Exhibit, observation tower	4000–6000 lb, 4'0"–6'0" c/o	4000–8000 lb, biparting
Jail	3500 lb, 3'6" 2-speed	4000–5000 lb, 4'0" 2-speed

Recommended Speeds (fpm)

Building Height	Hospital	Nursing Home	Courthouse	Museum	Jail
2–6	200–350	200–350	500	500	200
6–12	500	350	500	500	350
12–20	700–800	500	700–800	700	500
20–25	800[a]	500–700[a]	800[a]	800[a]	700[a]
25–30	1000[a]	800[a]	1000[a]	800–1000[a]	800[a]
30–40	1000–1200[a]		1000–1200[a]		

Table 12.1. Institutional buildings (*continued*)

	Exterior Elevators	Inside Elevators
Observation Towers (2-Stop Elevators)	100'—250–350 fpm	500 fpm
	200'—350–500 fpm	700 fpm
	300'—500–700 fpm	1000 fpm
	400'—500–700 fpm	1200 fpm
	500'—700–800 fpm	1400 fpm
	600'—800–1000 fpm	1600 fpm

ᵃ For buildings of this height local-express elevators should be considered.

plus expected spectators, a reasonable population factor may be established. A probably use factor of 75 to 80 per cent may be assumed with the prospect of improved judiciary scheduling.

Museums, exhibits, sports arenas, observation towers, and so on, are designed for a stated spectator capacity. In addition an anticipated "turn-over" or entering and leaving of these spectators in a given time is considered in the over-all design. Vertical transportation must be directly related to expected population and turnover.

Jails, especially short-term jails, are often located in high-rise buildings or on the top of governmental buildings. Population is easy to determine by the number of cells, but the major vertical transportation needs are related to the staff, number of visitors, type of visiting, security, service needs of the prisoners, and the type of prison. The best determination of vertical transportation need will be based on the prison staff provided plus allowances for visitors, transfer, trials, and so on.

ELEVATOR TRAFFIC IN INSTITUTIONAL BUILDINGS

Elevator traffic characteristics vary with the type of institution. In hospitals emphasis is on interfloor traffic with considerable periods of two-way traffic. In a courthouse two-way traffic is the major form.

In classroom buildings traffic is primarily interfloor, especially during class change periods. Laboratories and libraries have substantial incoming and outgoing traffic as well as two-way traffic similar to that found in office buildings.

Traffic in arenas, theaters, and other entertainment facilities is entirely in at the start of a show and out at the end. In exhibits and observation towers flow is primarily two-way and vertical transportation systems must be designed to turn over the expected number of visitors in the time allotted to view the exhibit or panorama. If a restaurant is located in the facility the average time to be seated and served is an important consideration.

Because traffic in each type of institutional building varies with the facility, few general rules can be stated, but each building type is individually evaluated. Table 12.1 gives the expected intensity of the critical traffic and is followed in the text by examples of particular elevator problems.

As mentioned previously, parking or horizontal transportation facilities affect the vertical traffic in institutional buildings as in other types. Often it is necessary to locate such parking on various levels, which creates multiple entrance floors to the building. In this case it is best to provide shuttle transportation to a single lower terminal for the main elevators or a necessary time penalty must be included in elevatoring calculations. Further consideration must be given to how quickly autos can fill or empty a parking facility. In sports arenas especially, little is gained by excellent elevator or escalator service if bottenecks cause slow departure from the parking exits.

All elements of the circulation system must be planned as an entity. Each form of transportation: auto, escalator, elevator, bus, or subway, has a definite utilization factor that must be considered when each of these elements is integrated into the system. The vertical transportation system, representing an outlay to the owner of the facility, may be minimized to the detriment of the effective utilization of the facility itself.

LAYOUT

Special traffic-handling requirements in institutional buildings, especially in suburban areas, are posed by visitors who may never have ridden an elevator or escalator before and may never do so again. These are the people who visit a hospital once, occasionally go to a tourist attraction, have never been in a courtroom, and seldom go to a large city. They are often confused by complex buildings, may be at a peak of emotion and need the ultimate in guidance.

More so than in an office building, the elevators must be a center of attraction. The directions to them and the signs associated with elevators and escalators must be clear and well defined. Doors must be wide and car interiors should be inviting. Ample signals should be provided and the direction of elevator travel plainly indicated. Places with high visitor turnover may advantageously be equipped with audible devices to announce floor stops and the attraction at each floor.

For the staff of institutional buildings less elaborate signaling and information devices are necessary but vertical transportation must be located to minimize time consumed in horizontal movement. The transportation core should be central, located near the facilities it is expected to serve, and designed to save employee time.

When heavy public use is expected and elevators serve few floors, large cars of 5000- to 6000-lb capacity are often desirable. This procedure maximizes handling capacity because the average tourist or spectator does not expect high-frequency service or, in other words, prefers bus to taxi service.

Large elevators necessitate ample queuing space instead of alcove arrangements, and deep lobbies are required in front of the elevators where persons may congregate. A waiting group is an attraction in itself as any carnival barker will declare.

In hospitals at least some of the elevators will have to carry beds and stretchers, a common requirement for which a special hospital-shaped elevator has been designed. Because the hospital car is narrow and deep it is unfortunately not the best shape for passenger traffic. In a large hospital the vehicular or bed traffic should be separated from the pedestrian traffic. In a smaller hospital both functions are usually performed by the same elevators.

Observation towers, long popular, are being built in more and more localities to provide the sensation of viewing the area from a point hundreds of feet above the ground. Vertical transportation is essential to the success of such a tower. One of the most dramatic uses of an elevator is its operation on the outside of the tower with a glass-enclosed cab so that persons may enjoy the thrill of ascent and descent. Outside elevators require specialized design to avoid the hazards of wind and weather and to preserve architectural simplicity. These goals have been achieved by the Seattle Space Needle, the Skylon Tower at Niagara Falls, and the New York World's Fair New York State Exhibit, which has become permanent (Figure 12.1).

Suggestions for elevator layout are offered in the following pages. As with building designs, variations are infinite and competent elevator engineers should be consulted whenever a problem exists.

Hospitals

Vertical traffic in hospitals may be separated into two distinct parts: (a) pedestrian traffic, consisting of staff, doctors, technicians, volunteers,

Figure 12.1 Seattle Space Needle.

visitors, and ambulatory patients; and (b) vehicular traffic, made up of patients on stretchers or in wheelchairs, linen carts, food trucks, supply carts, portable equipment, and so on. Separating these two types of traffic is by far the best approach to hospital elevatoring.

If pedestrians and stretcher patients use the same elevators patients suffer delay and discomfort. Other persons must squeeze past a stretcher patient to get in and out of the elevator, thus slowing the entire trip.

If all the elevators in a hospital carry patients on stretchers they must be narrow and deep, a design that reduces the efficiency of passenger transfer and slows the elevator trip.

Because the number of pedestrians far exceeds the number of vehicles to be carried from floor to floor in a hospital, its elevator plant should consist predominantly of passenger-shaped elevators. The ratio is approximately seven pedestrians to each vehicle requiring vertical transportation. The other factor is that pedestrians are usually paid employees whose time is necessary to serve the patient, whereas a patient is seldom moved in a critical condition. If he is, means should be provided to give him priority elevator transportation.

For these reasons the first approach to planning proper hospital elevatoring should begin with two separate groups of elevators: passenger-shaped cars for pedestrian traffic and hospital-shaped cars for vehicles. Because the first rule is that more than one elevator in a hospital must be capable of handling patients, the minimum plant for any multistory hospital is established as two hospital-shaped cars.

The second rule is that elevators be sufficient to provide an operating interval of from 30 to 50 sec. This interval is attained by the design of the elevator plant, as is shown by example later.

A third consideration is to have a sufficient number of elevators so that at least one is accessible within a minimum time. If food service requires exclusive use of an elevator during a particular time a separate food service elevator should be provided. This elevator can be used at off times for linen delivery and other supplies that can be scheduled at convenient times.

Food service can also be handled by multiple dumbwaiters or food lifts that can be unloaded either manually or automatically. The most recent designs automatically eject a food truck at selected floors. Such automatic equipment must be engineered for its application and used by a staff that accepts deliveries at the selected floors. An elevator may be used for any kind of service, but the cart handler is required to travel with the cart.

Using heated carts or having sufficient elevators in a group so that the frequency of service (interval) matches the rate at which the trays may be loaded on the cart is, from an elevator aspect, the best type of hospital food service. Because prompt delivery of hot food to the patient is the ultimate goal, and because time spent in transit is not critical, the heated cart is preferred. Although food service in hospitals is a controversial subject, it should always be considered in light of the total transportation system, including elevators.

Dumbwaiters—sometimes in pairs for clean and soiled articles—are often used between surgical supply and operating suites and between various nursing and pharmaceutical supply floors. A dumbwaiter connecting the kitchen and cafeteria or coffee shop is also useful. If the loading dock is at a different level from the kitchen a kitchen freight elevator should be provided, of the same type as described for hotel kitchen service.

Layout

Various elevator layouts are effective in separating vehicular and passenger traffic. In small hospitals, which may require only two or three elevators, the efficiency of the passenger-shaped elevator is sacrificed to obtain the necessary flexibility of operation. In any hospital requiring four or more elevators the two separate types of elevators are recommended.

Figure 12.2 shows arrangements of two and three cars. These arrangements provide the flexibility of using the cars either from front openings only or from the rear for a true separation of traffic types. They should never be used as passages or to serve both front and rear openings simultaneously, which would double the probable number of stops. A manual or automatic switchover can be employed to change from front- to rear-entrance operation.

Hospitals are often planned for future expansion and should always include additional elevator hoistways or framing so that the elevator plant may be expanded. The ultimate expansion should be determined and the elevator plant projected to that end. If vertical expansion is contemplated elevator machinery of the basement type can be installed initially. The final overhead equipment can then be installed with minimum interference to the operating plant and the transfer made in minimum time. Alternatively, the elevator machinery can be installed in its permanent location atop a shaftway tower for the building's full ultimate height and adjusted when the upper floors are activated.

A sample layout in Figure 12.3 shows the conventional 4000-lb hospital-shaped elevator which can be arranged for both front and rear openings or front openings only. Two-speed sliding doors provide the widest opening with minimum hoistway space.

The 4000-lb car accommodates most motorized hospital beds but leaves minimum room for persons riding with the bed. If oversized beds are contemplated or if it is the hospital's practice to move patients in their beds, a larger elevator of 4500 or 5000 lb is recommended.

A hospital-shaped elevator with center-opening doors is the recommended arrangement. The doors can be closed in about half the time

Service corridor

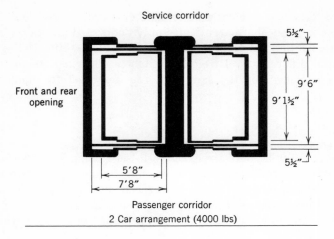

Front and rear
opening

5½"

9'6"

9'1½"

5½"

5'8"

7'8"

Passenger corridor

2 Car arrangement (4000 lbs)

Service corridor

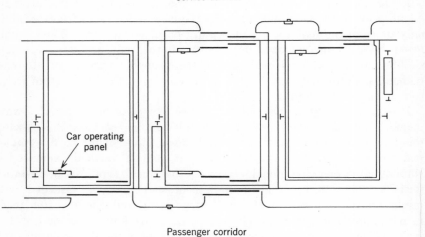

Car operating
panel

Passenger corridor

3 Car arrangement

Note:

For low rise elevator installations,
where headroom is limited an
Underslung Electric Elevator is
recommended.

Figure 12.2

254

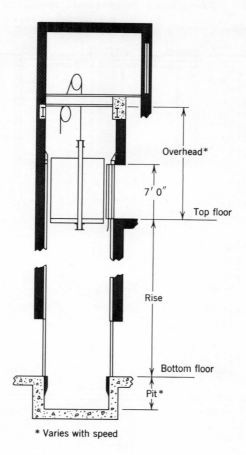

Overhead*

7' 0"

Top floor

Rise

Bottom floor

Pit *

* Varies with speed

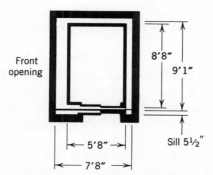

Front
opening

8'8"

9'1"

Sill 5½"

5'8"

7'8"

Figure 12.3   4000-lb hospital elevators.

255

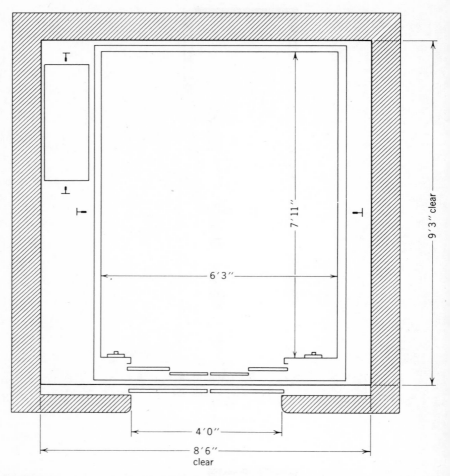

Figure 12.4   5000-lb hospital-type elevator with 4-ft 0-in. center-opening doors.

required for two-speed doors and the stretcher or bed can be moved into the elevator with minimum passenger crowding. The sample layout in Figure 12.4 shows this arrangement for a 5000-lb car. Although the hoistway is wider than with the two-speed opening, the increased efficiency is worth the investment in space.

Passenger elevators are of the conventional size and shape as for commercial buildings. For maximum efficiency in passenger handling, the 3500-lb department-store shaped elevator, shallow and wide, is recommended. As an additional feature, this size elevator accommodates a

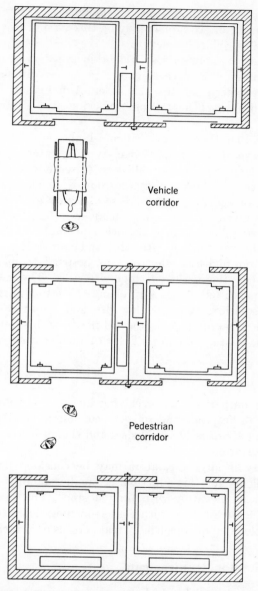

Vehicle
corridor

Pedestrian
corridor

Figure 12.5   Suggested hospital elevator layout.

257

mobile stretcher (22 × 76 in.) in an emergency. Figure 12.5 shows a unique arrangement of six cars employing this type of elevator in combination with 4500-lb vehicular elevators.

Groups of four or more cars should be installed in alcoves as recommended in Chapter 2. Service elevators require additional lobby space if elevators are placed facing each other. A minimum lobby of 14 ft is recommended for sufficient room to swing two stretchers unloaded simultaneously.

In hospitals taller than 17 or 18 floors high- and low-rise groups are recommended, especially for passenger-type elevators that would have an excessively long trip time if called on to serve as many as 18 floors. Service elevators may be in a single group if sufficient capacity is attained with six or eight cars. If more service cars are needed consideration should be given to separating them according to their functions, possibly by restricting all food service and supply to a single group and reserving another group for stretcher and staff traffic.

With low- and high-rise elevators in hospitals comes the question of travel between the low- and high-rise area. The most economical solution, as in office buildings, is to change elevators at a transfer floor. The ultimate solution would be low-rise and high-rise elevators with the high-rise cars having openings at all floors, with service to the overlapping low-rise landings on an up hall call, down car call service only.

Outpatients

Facilities for outpatients are receiving increased emphasis. To reduce the time spent in hospitals and to serve community needs, separate outpatient facilities are usually established and should be served by separate vertical transportation.

If the facility is large escalators may be considered to enhance the use of upper floors for this function. A smaller facility may be served by an elevator or elevators with limited stops. The cars should be of ample size, at least 3000 lb, with center-opening doors to facilitate the loading and unloading of wheelchairs and persons on crutches.

Calculating Elevator Requirements

As may be noted in Table 12.1, expected passenger traffic will amount to 10 to 12 per cent of the hospital population in a 5-min period. This population, for elevatoring purposes, is based on from 2.5 to 3.0 persons per bed, a ratio coincidental with the approximate staff per hospital bed. As hospital staffs increase, so will the demand on the elevators.

Example 12.1 shows how the service demand is translated into elevator

Example 12.1. Institutional Buildings—Hospitals

A. Given: 400 beds, 10 floors, 12-ft floor heights. Passenger traffic: 400×3.0/bed $= 1200 \times 12$ per cent $= 144/5$ min; vehicular traffic: $400 \times 4/100$ beds $= 16$ vehicles/5 min.

Assume: four passenger elevators, 3500 @ 500 fpm, two-way and interfloor traffic, 10 passengers up, 10 passengers down.

Stops: $1.75(6) - 1 = 9.5 \times 12 = 114$ sec

Lobby: $12 + 20 \times 1 \qquad\qquad = 32$ sec

Run: $\dfrac{(11 \times 12) \times 2 \times 60}{500} \quad = \dfrac{32 \text{ sec}}{178 \text{ sec}}$

HC: $\dfrac{(10 + 10) \times 300}{178} \times 4 \quad = 132$ persons versus 144. O.K.

Interval: $178/4 \qquad\qquad\qquad = 44.5$ sec. O.K.

Vehicular traffic: time per vehicle, average trip:

Load vehicle for down trip:	15 sec
Door close, car start:	5 sec
Run ½ height of building:	8 sec
Unload:	15 sec
Door close, car start:	5 sec
Run ½ height:	8 sec
Load second vehicle up trip:	15 sec
Door close, car start:	5 sec
Run:	8 sec
Unload:	15 sec
Door close, car start:	5 sec
	104, say 100 sec.

Each elevator can serve 2 vehicles $\times 300$ sec $\div 100 = 6$ vehicles in 5 min. Three elevators 4000 @ 500 fpm are required to serve 16 vehicles.

Interval: $100/3 = 33$ sec. Good.

B. Given: 200 beds, 6 floors, 12-ft floor heights. Passenger traffic: 200×3.0/bed $= 600 \times 12\% = 72/5$ min; vehicle traffic: $200 \times 4/100$ beds $= 8$ vehicles/5 min; combine passengers and vehicles: Use 4000 @ 350 elevators, 6 passengers up, 6 passengers down plus 1 vehicle either way.

Assume: 3 elevators.

Stops: $1.75(3) - 1 = 4.25 \times 12 \qquad = 51$ sec (passenger stops)

$\qquad\qquad\qquad\qquad 2 \times 15 \quad = 30$ sec (vehicle stops)

Lobby: $12 + 12 \qquad\qquad\qquad = 24$ sec

Run: $\dfrac{5 \times 12 \times 2 \times 60}{350} \qquad = \dfrac{21 \text{ sec}}{126 \text{ sec}}$

Passenger HC: $\dfrac{(6 + 6) \times 300}{126} \times 3 = 84$ versus 72. O.K.

Vehicle HC: $\dfrac{1 \times 300}{126} \times 3 \qquad = 9.6$ vehicles versus 8. O.K.

Interval: $126/3 \qquad\qquad\qquad = 42$ sec. O.K.

facilities. The characteristic traffic is a combination of both two-way and interfloor traffic. Our calculation is based on a two-way traffic approach and assumes that interfloor stops will coincide.

Critical traffic periods occur at a number of times during the day. One of the most important is in the forenoon when doctors are visiting patients, tests are being given, and some of the staff are lunching; another occurs about 3:00 P.M. when hospital nursing staffs are changing shifts. Visitor peaks are apparent in the early afternoon and in the evening.

Vehicular traffic reaches a peak about 8:30 to 9:00 A.M. when patients are transferred for operations and therapy, the cleanup from the morning meal is in progress, supplies are transferred, and maintenance activity is in full swing.

The vehicular peak may amount to from three to four vehicles per 100 beds in a 5-min period depending on the scheduling of treatment and delivery of supplies. For utmost efficiency, vehicle traffic should be scheduled for the fullest possible elevator utilization. There will be a certain amount of personnel riding the elevators, which detracts from the predicted performance; however, we have assumed that the vehicle has exclusive use of the elevator, which can be arranged by special operation or good scheduling.

Dumbwaiters or other specialized facilities for food handling and supply delivery can reduce the 5-min vehicular demands on elevators closer to three vehicles per 100 beds, about the minimum with normal scheduling. A figure as low as 2.5 per 100 beds is possible with an intensive industrial engineering study and complete scheduling as well as personnel practices forbidding a person to hold an elevator.

In view of the foregoing calculations it is recommended that the three-vehicle-per-100-beds basis be retained as a minimum even with extensive facilities for specialized functions, and that sufficient vehicular type elevators be installed to provide a good operating interval with those traffic conditions. In that way ample elevator service can be assured.

NURSING HOMES AND MENTAL INSTITUTIONS

Institutions for long-term care may be referred to as nursing homes. They include hospitals for the chronically ill, mental institutions, postoperative care centers, nursing homes, homes for the aged, and other facilities in which patients or residents remain for an extended period and receive less intensive care than in a hospital.

Elevatoring such buildings is approached much the same as for general hospitals. If the facility is large, with 300 or more beds, complete separation of vehicular and pedestrian traffic should be considered. If many patients are expected to be ambulatory the elevator traffic will be heavy if recreation and dining facilities are concentrated on the lower floors; the need for vehicular-type elevators is minimum.

As a population factor, if definite staffing plans are not established, from 1.0 to 1.5 persons per bed may be used, the higher figure related to the higher degree of patient care. For critical 5-min elevator capacity a handling capacity of from 8 to 10 per cent of the population, two-way traffic should be provided. A longer interval range is permissible because of little urgency in day-to-day activities.

With a high incidence of ambulatory patients, the primary elevator system should consist of passenger-shaped elevators. A minimum of one hospital-type car should be provided for the necessary transfer of supply carts and occasional stretcher movement. As an economy measure this could be one of the elevators in the passenger group arranged for independent special service.

In mental institutions security can be provided by locked elevator lobbies. The practice of keying all elevator call buttons has led to various abuses including forced locks, sticks in key ways, and forged keys, and is not recommended.

SCHOOLS

As land for horizontal expansion becomes unobtainable and the inefficiency of a sprawling campus become apparent, more and more schools are expanding vertically. With proper attention to vertical transportation, there is no limit to possible height. The University of Moscow is a vertical school in a single building of about 30 floors with the living space, classes, and libraries all in one building.

Six- or seven-story buildings with classroom space for 2500 to 3000 students are perfectly feasible when served by escalators plus an elevator or two for necessary freight and handicapped student needs. Science departments, with their long laboratory periods, are ideally located in high-rise buildings and require approximately the same elevator service as an office building. School libraries, by proper allocation of floor use, can be multistory buildings. General reading rooms can be located on the lower floors served by escalators, and specialized book collections can be located on upper floors with only necessary elevator service.

Classroom Buildings

In classroom buildings vertical transportation demand is the most severe during the time alloted to changing classes. From 3 to 15 min may be allowed for this purpose, depending on the type of school. Secondary schools, usually in buildings of limited height, allow the least time between classes to discourage student mischief in the halls. Longer class change times are required for larger schools and extensive campuses.

During the peak 5-min of the class change period as much as 50 per cent of the student population may seek vertical transportation. As an average we will consider 40 per cent. Severe vertical transportation demands also occur when evening classes start in downtown colleges. These classes usually start about half an hour after businesses close, by which time the student must travel to the school and have something to eat. He will arrive about 5 to 10 min before classes start and create an incoming 5-min peak on the elevator system of from 25 to 40 per cent of the student population. We shall consider 30 per cent as nominal.

Student population is determined by multiplying the total number of classroom seats by a utilization factor. For day sessions in most colleges this factor ranges from about 50 to 75 per cent depending on the refinement of classroom scheduling, which institutions are trying to improve. For high schools and evening colleges, a use factor of from 80 to 90 per cent of the available seats is not uncommon. As may be surmised, the use factor is an important determinant in elevatoring a classroom building.

Escalators are by far the best means of vertical transportation for a school with 1500 to 2000 students. They provide service to every floor, can be reversed to serve heavy incoming and outgoing peaks, and can be used for building heights up to about 11 floors. Typical applications appear in the chapter on escalators. In addition to the escalators an elevator or two is required for the handicapped and for the movement of furniture and supplies. The elevators should be of substantial size (about 3500 lb minimum) and should be readily accessible. It may be necessary to provide an attendant during class change periods to limit use of the elevators to authorized personnel.

In smaller schools, where elevators are provided as the prime means of vertical transportation, the overwhelming demand during class change periods may require restrictive stopping. Elevators would be allowed to stop at either the even or odd floors to reduce the number of possible stops. As a result about half the students would walk from floor to floor, possibly halving the elevator demand. Since three- and four-story walk-up schools are not uncommon, stops at every third or fourth floor would not be unreasonable.

All elevators should stop at the served floors. Skip-stop arrangements with one car serving, say the odd floors while another car serves the even floors would be self-defeating because no one would be encouraged to walk. Professors and handicapped students may ride in separate elevators, usually the service or freight elevators.

A sample of a calculation for a school elevatoring problem appears in the chapter on two-way and interfloor traffic.

Laboratory Buildings

Science or other types of laboratory session are generally longer than normal classroom periods. A student with a project is required to complete it and usually may leave when he is finished. The net result is that the vertical transportation problem is one of an incoming peak with very little other concentrated traffic during the day.

If the science building is elevatored as an office building, based on sufficient elevator capacity to fill the building in a 20- or 30-min period, service should be adequate for all other traffic periods. Elevators should be designed for a 5-min incoming peak of from 15 to 20 per cent of population, based on expected occupancy ranging from 50 to 200 ft^2 of net area per student, depending on the type of facility.

With good scheduling—for example, starting various laboratory sessions at 15-min intervals—the elevator plant may be minimized. If scheduling becomes the basis of elevatoring it should be well recorded, as building use can change and school administration often does.

Laboratory sessions are well attended so that the utilization factor is high. In many laboratories large and unwieldy apparatus is often moved in and out, requiring oversize service or freight elevators. If occasional excessive loads are expected, a safe-lift type of operation on one of the elevators can be used. Rooftop observatories and greenhouses may also require elevator service, which can be provided by one of the main elevators with the necessary penthouse structure or by a two-stop underslung type of elevator of limited speed and capacity, operating between the top main elevator stop and the roof.

LIBRARY BUILDINGS

A high-rise building is ideal for a library. The lower floors, connected by escalators, can provide ready access to the common reference works and general reading. The upper floors can house specialized references and rare book collections and could require minimum elevator service. The very nature of a library, the long-term storage of information, permits this segregation of function and traffic.

The elevatoring of any library depends on the expected use of the various floors and will require extensive preliminary planning.

In an undergraduate library, considerable student turnover is expected in the general areas. Observations have shown that a full turnover of the available seats or spaces for reading occurs about every hour. The calculation of vertical traffic demand will then be two times the number of student spaces divided by 12 to give the average two-way demand on the elevators in 5 min. In other words from 15 to 20 per cent of the population of the library will seek vertical transportation in a 5-min period, two-way traffic.

Population is based on the number of reading spaces provided and the nature of the carrels, either locked or open. Population density also depends on the provisions for and use of seminar rooms, special collections, special libraries, either visual or audio, and other factors peculiar to modern libraries.

Elevator calculations should proceed as for other forms of two-way traffic. Handling of book carts and automatic delivery of books to the check-out desk may warrant consideration of automatic-ejection types of dumbwaiter.

COURTHOUSES

Elevatoring a courthouse concerns activities in the courtrooms themselves as well as the various functions connected with a courtroom trial. The court clerk's office, where necessary pretrial papers are filed, is a critical area responsible for a constant flow of lawyers and messengers between it and the entrance to the building. Circulation is expedited by locating these facilities on the main floor.

Another critical area is the reporting room for jurors. All the prospective jurors gather in this area and are moved in groups of 20 or so to the various courts for examination.

A usual requirement in courthouses is the separation of the judges from the general public, which calls for separate vertical transportation.

Transportation of prisoners in a criminal court requires security arrangements and may have to be restricted to a special elevator or elevators. Alternatively, this function may be combined with the service needs of the courts, which include normal maintenance and, possibly, the transportation of displays and records.

Finally, the general public and participants in civil suits as well as the courthouse staff require vertical transportation. If the courthouse facilities also houses extensive office facilities such as those for the district attorney and investigative staffs, vertical transportation requirements in part resemble those of other office buildings.

These requirements suggest that elevatoring a courthouse begins with study of the general plan of the building and extent of its various facilities. A major determinant is the number of courtrooms and the percentage likely to be in full use at a given time. 100 per cent usage is improbable but a factor of 75 per cent is reasonable.

For each court in session about 30 persons will take part in a criminal trial, plus spectators or in a civil trial with a jury. In civil trials without juries only a few persons are involved, hence, if jury trials are always considered as population criteria, conservative elevatoring will result.

Observation has shown that the starting and ending or recessing of trials overlap by about 30 min, so that about half the population enters the courtrooms while another half leaves. For example, if there are 20 courtrooms in a building about 15 will be in use at one time. At 30 persons per court a population of 30 times 15 or 450 persons plus spectators is possible. If these people turn over in half an hour, the demand for vertical transportation is 450 divided by 6 or 75 persons every 5 min, two-way traffic. If elevators are filled to only half their capacity and operated at the acceptable intervals of 40 to 60 sec, capacity should be ample for spectators, who can be controlled.

Although judges may require separate transportation, their elevators can also be used to carry juries, either prospective or charged. At least two separate elevators in a private alcove may accomplish these tasks. Judges, because of their status and limited number, should and do receive priority service. Because jurors are usually escorted and each group may receive exclusive service, elevators large enough to transport the expected number of jurors in each group should be provided.

If the building includes office functions as well as courthouses and their related functions, additional elevator service may be needed. Elevators established for the courtroom traffic should be checked to determine if they can also serve the incoming requirements of the office staff in a manner similar to that for a single-purpose building. A further check for possible conflict during lunchtime should be made and the number of elevators and intervals adjusted accordingly.

JAILS

Short-term jails for holding persons awaiting trial, indicted offenders, or short-term prisoners are ideally located above the courthouse. Transfer problems are minimized and, in a high-rise structure, all necessary facilities can be provided with maximum security.

Short-term prisons located on the upper floors of courthouses or municipal buildings require a separate group of jail shuttle elevators for access to and from the street. Security is strengthened by separate local elevators from the jail sky-lobby to the cell levels (Figure 12.6).

Determining the elevators necessary for a prison depends on staff, operation, and number of transfers in and out during the course of a day. Transfers consist of persons being moved to long-term prisons, prisoners reporting for trial, and new arrivals. Lawyers are allowed to visit prisoners in either the cell area or a visiting room. This entails additional transfer.

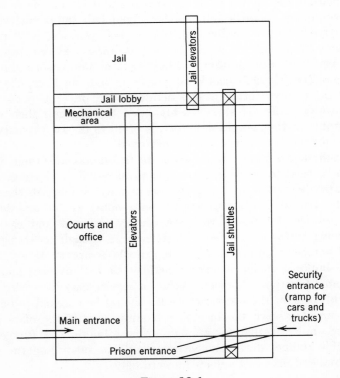

Figure 12.6

Recreation and sick call, if these facilities are located away from the cell floors, require vertical transportation. Meals, however, usually take place in the cell area.

Security is accomplished by locked elevator lobbies and by attendants on the elevators. Prisoners are usually escorted, with the escort calling the elevator, which should be equipped with a vision panel so the attendant can see what is taking place before opening the doors. A form of riot control, such as a foot-operated or elbow operated switch to call for aid or send the elevator to a secure lobby, is advisable.

Closed-circuit television can be provided for in-car surveillance. In the event of difficulty special controls to call the elevator to a protected floor should be provided.

The extent of vertical transportation requirements must be established and sufficient elevators furnished. Because of security requirements operation efficiency is poor, so ample extra transfer time should be allowed. Larger elevators, 3500-lb minimum, should be used to facilitate truck handling and the transportation of groups. The elevators should be used for all purposes, that is, by both passenger and vehicle, to minimize attendant staffing.

MUSEUMS, EXHIBITS, SPORTS ARENAS, AND OBSERVATION TOWERS

The value of such buildings depends, in part, on how quickly persons can be moved into, through, or out of the facility. The vertical transportation problem in a sports arena is obvious: to put persons in their seats in the shortest possible time for prompt presentation of the event. "The shortest possible time" varies with each facility, depending on such factors as parking, ticket selling, and other attractions, such as betting at a horse race. As a guide, transportation should be sufficient to serve an average crowd in 30 min.

In a museum or exhibition hall a more leisurely pace is expected. Aside from performances at particular times, an hour or two may be allowed for visitors to fill the building to capacity. Vertical transportation needs are for turnover rather than rapid filling or emptying as in a sports arena.

The key to the success of an observation tower is the vertical transportation and the area provided for viewing or dining. A visible indication of appeal is a line of persons waiting at the ground level for elevator service up into the tower.

Observation areas are often placed atop taller buildings and served by additional capacity in the high-rise group so that an elevator may be used for the visitors during peak hours without affecting tenants in the building. A separate lower lobby is recommended for the observation-deck elevators.

Escalators

For low-rise, heavy-traffic applications, escalators are the recommended means of transportation. They can serve the most people, can be reversed for incoming or outgoing traffic, and require the least space in relation to their traffic-handling capacity. Local and express escalators have been furnished for some sports arenas to provide the necessary service to a succession of upper levels with the additional benefit of separating ticket holders for special areas before they board the escalator.

Elevators

Two-stop elevators are the other preferred means of high-capacity vertical transportation. Because all persons board at one level and exit at others, they can serve structures of any height and minimize passenger confusion. Introducing a third stop exacts a substantial time penalty besides creating confusion for passengers.

If an observation tower facility has more than two main upper levels, serious consideration should be given to shuttle elevators between the various levels. All persons would then go to one of the upper main levels by the major elevators and transfer to the shuttle elevator for the other upper levels.

Refreshment Service

Service needs, especially refreshments, are of prime importance in any facility. Refreshment facilities should be stocked between events, using service or freight elevators provided for that purpose. These elevators should be located near loading docks or storage areas on the lower level and close to the refreshment stands on the upper levels to minimize truck transfer time. Elevators should be large and heavy enough to accommodate either industrial truck or hand cart loading. Freight type, vertical biparting doors should be used to gain maximum space in the elevator interior.

Elevator Capacity

Passenger capacity rather than frequency of service is the prime objective in elevatoring facilities of this nature. Elevator speed should be proportional to the height of the structure as in Table 12.1. Because elevators are the most critical equipment for observation towers, consideration must be given to both service and passenger use. Deliveries should be scheduled at off-peak visitor periods and ample cab interior protection should be provided.

GENERAL

All the general rules for equipment location and passenger information and guidance apply with a special force to the elevatoring of institutional buildings. The large number of visitors, many unfamiliar with elevators or escalators, requires that particular care be taken to avoid confusion and operating inefficiency.

Elevator operation must be simple and the signals explicit. An occasional visitor to a tall building is more inclined than the regular occupant to take any elevator that stops at a floor, no matter which way it is going. For this reason signs and directional arrows must be prominent and unequivocal in indication. Visual signs may be supplemented by automatic recorded devices that audibly announce direction of travel and elevator destination.

OPERATION

As described in Chapter 10 on commercial buildings, an operational study must be combined with equipment analysis to gain full utilization of the vertical transportation plant. Fixed methods of operation that oppose the elevators to traffic will rob the most adequate elevator plant of its effectiveness. That is why it is essential to provide traffic-responsive operating features.

In Figures 12.7, 12.8, and 12.9 a series of traffic flow charts is presented for principal types of institutional buildings. The charts also indicate some of the expected traffic conditions and the operation necessary to meet those conditions. Persons responsible for design as well as the operation of the building must see that these requirements are fulfilled.

Each chart shows the percentage of building population traveling in each direction at a particular time. This percentage will vary for the

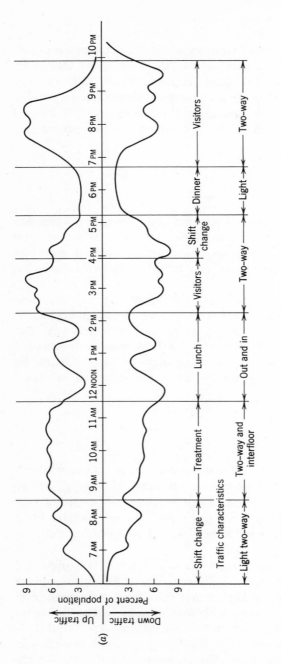

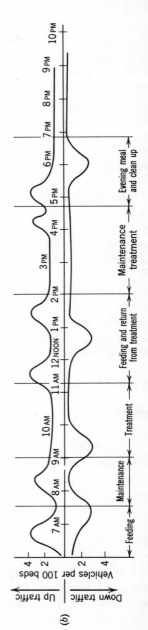

Figure 12.7 Hospital elevator traffic (in and out of elevators at main floor): (*a*) pedestrian traffic; (*b*) vehicular traffic.

270

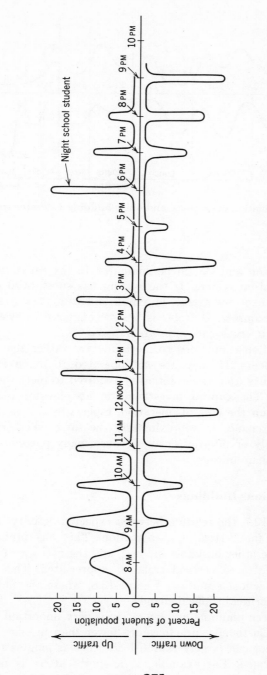

Figure 12.8 Schools—classroom building (elevator traffic in and out at main floor) urban location, day and night classes. Based on hourly class changes, 10-min class-change period.

271

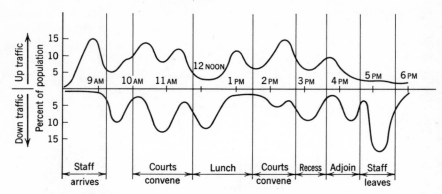

Figure 12.9   Combination courthouse and office building (elevator traffic in and out at main lobby).

individual institution and should be compared to the capabilities of its vertical transportation system. If the system has substantial capability in relation to the expected traffic, minimum operating features for each traffic period are required. If traffic is heavy compared to system capabilities, additional operating features are necessary.

Elevators are often engineered to meet interval rather than handling capacity requirements. If they are not operated to make full use of their handling ability and at the intensity required to meet the interval, they are wasted. The capital investment in an elevator plant is far more expensive than the cost of operation, especially if it is automatic. The cost of maintenance is approximately the same whether elevators are used intensively or intermittently, because many parts are replaced due to age rather than mileage.

Operation in Various Buildings

Note in Figure 12.7, the relation between expected activity in a hospital and its need for vertical transportation. This has probably been observed in all the other buildings studied, and the necessity for relating a building's activities to vertical traffic is appreciated. This is clearly borne out in the school situation, Figure 12.8, where the class change periods create the critical traffic demands.

A relation between planning and operation is very important in institutional buildings. Customary practices are fewer than in office buildings, in that management can largely establish its rules as long as the desired function is performed. For example, if a sports arena is not opened until 15 min before a performance, vertical transportation needs are entirely different than in the facility that is opened 1 hr before. Similar observations apply to hospitals that insist on too-short feeding or visiting schedules or courthouses that insist on exclusive elevators for judges and will not consider using the same cars for other purposes at other times.

The successful elevatoring of institutional buildings is predicated upon understanding relationships between all factors involved.

CHAPTER THIRTEEN

Material Handling
and Service Elevators

DESIGN CRITERIA

Two approaches may be taken to design the elevator plant for an industrial or material handling function. The first is to put in large, heavy-duty elevators related to the expected function of the plant and let the industrial engineer decide later how to use them. The second more desirable approach is to plan the elevators from the start to fit into plant operations.

No matter what the approach, a certain amount of time and motion study is required in the application of an elevator for material handling. As with passenger elevators, certain time allowances are required for loading, closing doors, running, and so on. This chapter reviews those requirements and establishes general guidelines for such elevatoring.

SIZE AND CAPACITY

We presume that the necessary elevators have a size and capacity of more than 6000 lb, which is beyond the normal passenger range. As a general proposition, if passenger-sized cars with 4000 lb capacities and passenger-type elevator doors can be used in an industrial plant, it is far more economical to do so, with suitable interior protection of course. Passenger-shaped and sized cars usually require less special equipment, can be delivered in less time, and are more standard with most manufacturers. In addition, platform loading requirements, that is, the capacity of an elevator related to the area of the platform, are generally more stringent for passenger than freight elevators.

A requirement for a large cab with relatively light loading (large volume) leaves little choice except to use a freight elevator with lesser freight-type platform loading. Similarly, use of industrial trucks to load and unload require a special elevator. The entire elevator structure and lifting mechanism must withstand, hold, and level the full load of the elevator plus the load of the industrial truck.

The various classes of freight handling elevator are defined in the American Standard Safety Code for Elevators, as *A, B,* and *C.* The general requirements for each class are the following:

Class *A*: *General Freight*—loading by hand truck

No single piece of freight to exceed one quarter capacity load of the elevator, based on not less than 50 lb/ft^2 of platform area.

Class *B*: *Motor Vehicle*—garage type elevators

Automobiles and trucks only. Capacity based on not less than 30 lb/ft^2 of platform area.

Class *C*: *Industrial Truck Loading*

Elevator loaded by industrial trucks. In general both the elevator and the hoistway structure must be able to support the impact load and the combined weight of the elevator and the truck. Capacity not less than 50 lb/ft^2 of platform area. Elevator capable of supporting 150 per cent of rated capacity load. These requirements are modified if the truck loads but is not carried on the elevator.

Additions and alterations to the foregoing rules may be found in the latest edition of the code.

In contrast, passenger elevator platforms are rated from about 70 to 130 lb per ft^2 depending on total platform area. If a freight elevator is intended to be used for passenger service it must be rated as a passenger elevator and special door operation provided, as will be described later.

Freight elevators are available in sizes from 2500 to 25,000 lb or more. Some can carry loads of 100,000 lb and others fully loaded box cars. The highest rise, largest freight elevators each have 40,000 lb capacity, a speed of 200 fpm, and can serve 15 floors. They handle loaded trailer trucks and have platforms 17 ft wide × 34 ft deep, the standard trailer-truck size at the time of their installation in 1932. More recent installations, of lesser rise and speed have platforms of 40 to 45 ft long and capacities of 60,000 lb for more modern trailer trucks.

Because of the time required to load or unload a freight elevator, speed is generally of secondary importance. Elevator travel at high speed is uneconomic if 4 or 5 min are necessary to transfer its load. Practical speeds are proportional to building height and required loading time, with quicker transfers warranting higher travel speed. Speed should be sufficient so that traveling will consume only about 25 per cent of total round-trip time.

LOADING AND UNLOADING

Loading and unloading will take most of a freight elevator's use time depending on the loading method used. Loading pallets by hand truck may require from 15 to 20 sec to transfer each pallet load on or off the elevator. If the car is to be loaded with four pallets, over a minute will be spent in loading or unloading. Time for door operation must be added to the loading time.

Freight elevators usually have vertical biparting doors, consisting of upper and lower panels that counterweight each other (Figure 13.1). With manual operation a door of this kind can be opened or closed in 6 to 8 sec plus about 6 sec to open or close the vertical lifting gate

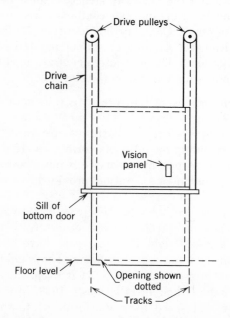

Figure 13.1   Vertical biparting door.

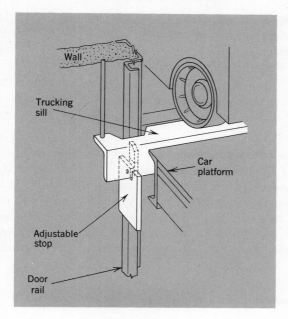

Figure 13.2

on the elevator. With automatic operation the door and gate can be simultaneously opened or closed at a speed of about 1 fps. The average 8-ft high opening can thus be closed or opened in about 4 sec, as each panel only has to travel half the height.

Vertical biparting doors allow an opening almost the full width of the elevator and the structural steel frames of the opening are less susceptible to damage than the formed metal frames of passenger-type entrances. The door panels are completely hidden before loading can begin and thus are less likely to be struck by a moving truck as can happen with horizontally sliding doors. Sills can be reinforced to withstand truck wheel impact (Figure 13.2). Automatic operation permits a measure of premature opening, about 1 sec less for opening if the elevator has automatic leveling.

The time required to transfer a single pallet load with an industrial truck obviously varies with the transfer distance. If we assume transfer directly off or on the elevator, each pallet can be moved in 10 to 15 secs and total loading or unloading of four pallets will require no more than about 40 to 60 sec. The typical cycle would be as follows:

Door opening time (with premature opening):	3 sec
Unloading (or loading) time:	40 sec
Door closing:	4 sec
Time to start and stop elevator:	4 sec
Time per stop:	51 sec
Inefficiency, about 20 per cent	9 sec
Total time per stop:	60 sec

If we load at one stop and unload at another, running time at full speed is simply added to twice the time per stop indicated above to determine the time required to handle four pallet loads. If we assume a running time of 1 min (which of course varies with speed and rise), the total round-trip time is 3 min, or, depending on study requirements, 20 trips per hour or 80 pallets per hour. Similarly, if the elevator is to be loaded and unloaded at the same stop, the additional loading time should be allowed and the longer round-trip time calculated.

Automatic Loading and Unloading

Automatic loading of a freight elevator by a pallet conveyor or rolling trucks and automatic pullers or pushers is often desirable. The loading device is mounted on the elevator and, to calculate round-trip time, the time for automatic transfer is added to the door and running time of the car. With devices of this nature automatic leveling is a necessity and the limit of leveling (plus and minus floor-level tolerance) depends on the transfer device used. The load itself can act as the signal for elevator to operate either by a predetermined program or a reading means on the particular load.

Safety is of utmost importance, and local industrial safety codes as well as good practice will determine the need for hoistway doors and car gates. Much also depends on whether there is room for persons to ride the elevator in addition to the load and loading mechanism as well as other protective means. It is strongly recommended that all operations be made automatic to eliminate personnel in proximity to the elevator and transfer mechanism.

If people are to ride on any freight elevator, certain provisions should be made. If only personnel necessary for freight handling are allowed on the car and prominent signs to this effect are displayed, the elevator is considered strictly freight. If other employees use the elevator for transportation to upper floors, the American Standard Safety Code requires the following features.

Biparting doors must have sequence operation so that the car gate closes before the hoistway door can close. The hoistway doors must open before the car gate. A protective safety edge must be added to the car gate so that the closing gate will stop and reopen if it encounters an obstruction in its descent.

If sequence operation is provided, the elevator with biparting doors may have an automatic closing operation. This means that, as with a passenger elevator, the doors begin to close a time interval after they are opened so that the elevator can be called from floor to floor without an attendant. Without these provisions the doors must be closed by a constant pressure button after each stop. Because people tend to be careless about closing doors, a door-open bell is often added which automatically rings when someone calls for an elevator at another floor and the elevator doors are not closed.

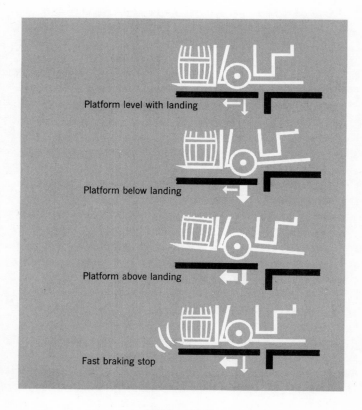

Platform level with landing

Platform below landing

Platform above landing

Fast braking stop

Figure 13.3

The door-close button is often mounted on a pendant so that the driver of an industrial truck does not have to dismount to close the door.

STRUCTURAL REQUIREMENTS

Freight elevators loaded and unloaded manually require little extra structure in the hoistway beyond normal rail supports. If the elevator is to be rated for a high capacity with possible industrial truck loading and unloading, extra rail support must be provided.

The entire impact of the truck stopping, running, and reversing is transmitted to the building structure through the elevator rails. The

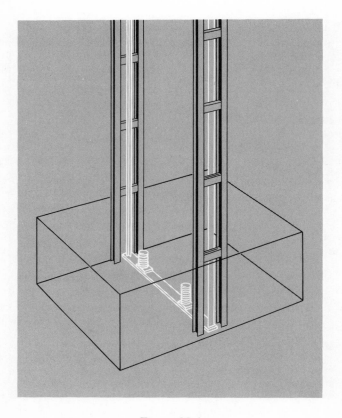

Figure 13.4

diagram in Figure 13.3 shows how these forces react. An example of an extra rail structure to absorb these forces is shown in Figure 13.4. The necessary structure for each installation must be calculated and engineered for the particular elevator size and capacity.

The elevator manufacturer normally calculates the forces while the architect or structural engineer is responsible for providing the supports in the building. The letter shown below and Figures 13.5 and 13.6 are one company's form for transmitting the necessary information.

All other parts of the elevator must be designed to withstand the extra loads of industrial truck loading. The platform, for example, requires extra-heavy flooring either of steel plate or industrial-type wooden blocks on end; the platform structure requires a multiplicity of stringers to distribute the load and prevent distortion; and the carframe and hoisting machine or hydraulic pistons must be of heavy-duty design.

Manufacturing Company
Anywhere

Subject: Industrial Truck Loaded Elevator
Building Number
Anywhere
Contract Number

Gentlemen:

Freight elevators carrying industrial trucks, automobile trucks or passenger automobiles exert forces of large magnitude on the building structure. In order to assure a safe and satisfactory installation, it is essential that the supports you provide for the guide rails will be of adequate strength and stiffness. We are therefore furnishing you, on the reverse side of this sheet, the rail forces and stiffness requirements for your elevator. A brief explanation of the effects of these forces is outlined below.

Very truly yours,
John C. Smith
Sales Department

FORCES AT LOADING

When the loaded truck enters the elevator, it exerts heavy loads at the front edge of the platform. These loads produce a couple—the top guide shoe exerts a force on the guide rail towards the loaded edge of the platform and the lower guide shoe exerts a force away from it. With entrances at the back of the elevator, these forces will be reversed. These rail forces (designated R_2) produce bending moments in the rail and its support—the double H columns act as a beam placed vertically.

The R_2 forces also produce turning moments in a horizontal plane, bending one column towards the hoistway wall and the other away from the hoistway wall.

In addition to force R_2, there is a force R_1 tending to spread the rails apart due to eccentric loading of the platform. This force produces direct bending moments in the columns.

Duty	20,000 lbs.	Safety type	Roll
Car size	12' 0'' x 18' 0''	Safety load	42,000 lbs.
Service	Industrial truck	Vertical height between guide shoes	152''

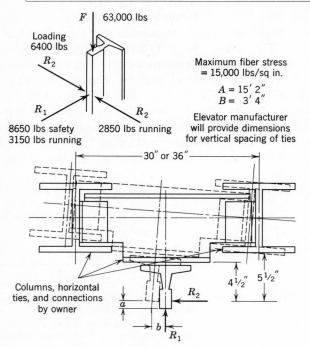

F | 63,000 lbs

Loading
6400 lbs
R_2

Maximum fiber stress
= 15,000 lbs/sq in.

$A = 15' 2''$
$B = 3' 4''$

R_1 R_2

8650 lbs safety   2850 lbs running
3150 lbs running

Elevator manufacturer
will provide dimensions
for vertical spacing of ties

30'' or 36''

Columns, horizontal
ties, and connections
by owner

$4\frac{1}{2}''$ $5\frac{1}{2}''$

a R_2

b

R_1

Section X–X

See table below for values

Condition	Net forces	Maximum allowable deflection
Loading [a] (as indicated)	$R_1 = 3150$ lbs.	$a = \frac{1}{8}''$
	$R_2 = 6400$ lbs.	$b = \frac{3}{16}''$
Running [a] (at S)	$R_1 = 3150$ lbs.	$a = \frac{1}{8}''$
	$R_2 = 2850$ lbs.	$b = \frac{3}{16}''$
Safety [a] (at S)	$R_1 = 8650$ lbs.	$a = \frac{5}{16}''$
	$F = 63000$ lbs. [b]	–

[a] These conditions need not be considered as acting simultaneously.
[b] For design of pit supports, this force must be doubled for impact.

Figure 13.5

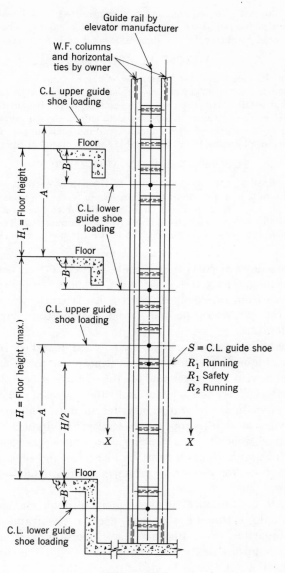

Figure 13.6

Since these forces are at loading and are transmitted to the columns through the guide shoes and the rails, they occur at determinable points above and below the loading levels. Refer to Sketch "A" for dimensions and table for values of forces.

FORCES AT RUNNING

Forces R_1 and R_2 also occur during running of the car and have the same effects. Force R_1 can be the same magnitude as for loading or somewhat larger. Force R_2 will be somewhat smaller. However, since the running forces R_1 and R_2 occur during the entire travel of the elevator, it must be assumed for design purposes, that they will be applied to the center of each column span and each support for the column (floor beam, spreader beam, etc.). Refer to table for magnitude of forces.

FORCES AT SAFETY APPLICATION

At safety application, the stopping action of the safety exerts a large force "F" vertically on the rails in a downward direction. These forces are transmitted through the rail to the pit floor. There is also a large force R_1 due to eccentric loading, which tends to spread the rails (similar to loading R_1 and running R_1). The loads due to safety application can occur anywhere in the entire car travel. See table for size of these forces.

Car interiors deserve particular attention. Steel or oak rubbing strips should be mounted along the sides and adequately supported to withstand the blows from carelessly driven trucks. If trucks are to be carried locations of the car operating panel and hall button fixtures demand special consideration.

Material handling elevators also have to be installed in "problem" environments ranging from an explosive atmosphere to an area in which normal cleaning with hot water and steam requires a completely waterproof installation. Corrosion control and other elements of maintenance of structural steel in the elevator installation must also be considered. All safety devices as well as ropes and electrical equipment must operate properly in these difficult environments, and special provisions must be made for each hazard. Hazards must be identified and precautions taken in the specifications for elevator equipment to guard against premature wear or danger.

The architect or structural engineer must provide at each level the necessary structural framing that will become the frame and sill for the vertical biparting door. Because these doors as well as the lifting car gate may require extra space above the top landing or in the pit, elevator overhead and pit must be structured to suit.

Structural requirements for freight elevators, as may be surmised, are somewhat more critical than those for passenger elevators. Aspects are too numerous and variable to cover in this book. Early consultation with selected elevator manufacturers is advised when freight elevators are planned.

SERVICE ELEVATORS

Service elevators in commercial, residential, or institutional buildings are generally passenger elevators with special provisions to handle over-size loads or hand trucks. They usually have abuse-resistant interiors, and must comply with code requirements for carrying passengers, and are usually equipped with horizontal sliding doors. These doors allow full automatic operation with maximum efficiency.

If the full width of the car platform must be utilized, vertical biparting door should be used and automatic operation attained with sequence operation.

Service elevators can be of any practicable platform size or ceiling height provided the platform area conforms to safety code requirements. Cars with heights as great as 13 ft and doors with corresponding dimensions have been installed. Capacities of 8000 lb are not uncommon, with 6000 lb a usual size for a large commercial building.

The size of a building's service elevator should be determined by the largest or bulkiest load likely to be carried. If the load is expected only on rare occasions special provisions such as a removable car front with swinging door panels can be provided at the necessary floors. In this way the general efficiency of the elevator is not impaired and special provisions for the occasional large load can be instituted when required. An example of such provisions is shown in Figure 13.7.

A freight elevator need not be a heavy-duty installation if a light-duty, slow-speed elevator will economically solve a material handling problem. Safety codes allow the drum-type noncounterweight elevator to be used for freight elevators and many variations are available. The drum-type machine must lift the entire weight of the elevator car plus the duty load, hence horsepower requirements are much greater than for traction-type elevators and correspond to equivalent hydraulic elevators. Elevators of this type are designed as sidewalk elevators or as interior convenience elevators used, for example, between a kitchen and loading dock.

As described in Chapter 8, a light-duty freight elevator can be obtained as a self-supporting unit by utilizing the elevator rail structure to minimize the loads on the building structure as shown in Figure 13.8. A drum elevator is limited in rise to the rope capacity of the drum. Similarly, a hydraulic elevator is limited in rise to the practical depth the piston hole may be drilled as well as the column action of the piston. With both drum and hydraulic elevators electrical power

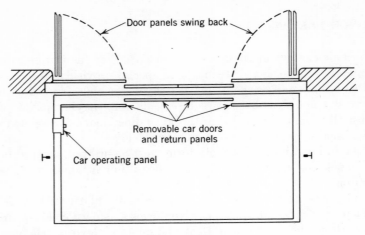

Figure 13.7

requirements must be based on the entire load of the elevator, including the weight of the car plus the duty load.

OPERATION OF FREIGHT ELEVATORS

The grouping and operation of freight elevators depends on their role in the over-all industrial or storage system. Freight elevators are seldom used in large groups, the usual installations being individual units. Two major forms of automatic operation are available as well as a number of manual operations.

Automatic operations are either collective or single automatic. In the collective operation each call is remembered and the elevator answers all the up hall calls on the up trip, reverses at the highest call, and answers all the down calls on the down trip. The operation is useful if one loading is not expected to fill the elevator and additional loads can be taken on at other stops. If occasional full loads are expected a freight-service bypass feature may be added, allowing persons to use a special switch within the car to bypass hall calls.

The single automatic operation allows the person who has control of the elevator exclusive use of the car for that trip. The hall call buttons should incorporate lights to indicate if the elevator is in use. When the light goes out the elevator may be called to a particular floor and be used by the next person. This operation is preferred whenever the load is such that it would fill the elevator and additional stops would

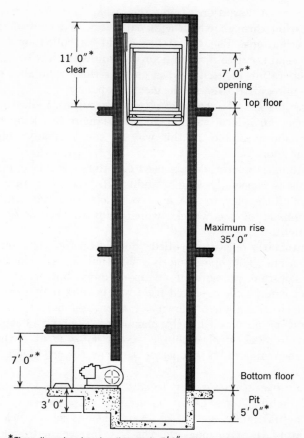

11' 0"* clear

7' 0"* opening

Top floor

Maximum rise 35' 0"

7' 0"*

3' 0"

Bottom floor

Pit 5' 0"*

*These dimensions based on the use of a 7' 0" opening height as shown, and on the use of bi-parting hoistway doors and a folding gate on the car.

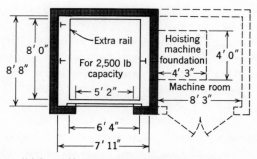

8' 0"

8' 8"

Extra rail

For 2,500 lb capacity

5' 2"

6' 4"

7' 11"

Hoisting machine foundation

4' 3"

4' 0"

Machine room

8' 3"

Hoisting machine can be located at either side of hoistway.

Figure 13.8

287

be unnecessary. A variation of this operation is to have a central dispatching station through which a dispatcher would control the elevator use and destinations. The dispatcher would be called by telephone or intercom to send a car to a given floor and to dispatch it to the unloading floor. This operation is often used in garages when a number of elevators in a group are required to serve the garage capacity.

For a multiple single automatic elevator group an indicator light over each entrance can inform the garage attendant or truck operator which elevator will be available. In this way he can be ready before the car arrives at his floor.

When automatic operations are used elevators should be automatically leveled. This is especially true if industrial trucks or autos are to be driven on or off the elevators. A nonleveled elevator platform must withstand the impact of the wheels, which adds to the forces on the car and rail structure.

A semiautomatic operation called "double button" is often used with freight elevators. The operation is such that a car can be called to a floor by constant pressure of an up or down button at the landing. The elevator can also be operated from within the car by similar constant pressure on either an up or down car operating button. Leveling may be automatic or accomplished by means of "inching" buttons used to jog the car to floor level within a restricted zone at each floor with the doors open and only to operate the car toward floor level, never away from it.

A valuable operation for any freight elevator is a system known as "tail-board inching," which can be used to stop the elevator platform above the actual floor level, at the same height as a truck backed up to the elevator. An extra long guard is installed below the elevator platform to avoid the danger of a person or object falling into the hoistway.

Car switch operation has often been used on freight elevators. The operation requires an attendant whenever the elevator is operated. It is not popular in present-day use, and if an attendant is required during a period of the day dual operations such as collective with or without attendant are furnished. When the system uses an attendant, he has full control of starting, stopping, and door closing by appropriate switches. When the system is "without attendant," these operations are performed automatically in response to car or hall calls.

If the industrial plant or warehouse requires a group of elevators, many of the operations outlined for passenger service may be adapted for freight service. The final choice would depend on the door-operating system employed. Because it is difficult to ensure that persons will close biparting doors after they use an elevator, the accepted system is to employ a door-open bell that will sound if someone is calling the car while the door is open. Use of sequence operation with biparting doors and a safety edge on the car gate is one means of providing automatic operation if the time penalty is acceptable.

Large openings for passenger-type doors, if hoistway space is available, will ensure prompt automatic operations of the elevators. The freight elevator will not open to full width, however, and there may be difficulty in loading. If loads are light and bulky, such as racks of garments in a department store or clothing factory, the passenger-type entrance may be desirable.

Provided it is safe, any type of operation for a particular production cycle can be engineered. Elevator manufacturers are equipped to determine and advise what can be done and should be consulted.

ELEVATORS IN INDUSTRIAL PLANTS

Years ago, when pianos rather than television sets were in vogue, a typical piano factory was a multistory building. Light parts of the piano were manufactured on the upper floors, all raw material being taken to the top. The foundry and finishing shops were on the lowest floors. The myriad small wooden pieces were assembled as they traveled down, becoming larger and larger sections until they became the completed piano on the shipping floor.

Many modern industrial processes now follow a similar sequence. Because land costs were moderate when many manufacturers started, their plants were usually horizontally oriented. Transportation of raw materials and finished products was also economical. Transportation and land costs have been rising, so that the vertical factory is becoming more and more economical and, with dependable vertical transportation, quite feasible.

By engineering vertical transportation on the basis of the production process, a completely integrated factory can have compact vertical design. Large elevators can carry raw materials to upper floors and conveyors, dumbwaiters, or small elevators can bring the finished parts to the lower floors for assembly. Personnel can be moved swiftly to and from their jobs by elevators or escalators.

The role of gravity cannot be ignored in a vertical factory. In a cannery, for example, raw tinplate sheets are moved to upper floors for shaping into cans and rolled down to the food-processing floors for filling, sealing, labeling, and shipping.

The number, size (area), capacity, and well as required speed of manu-

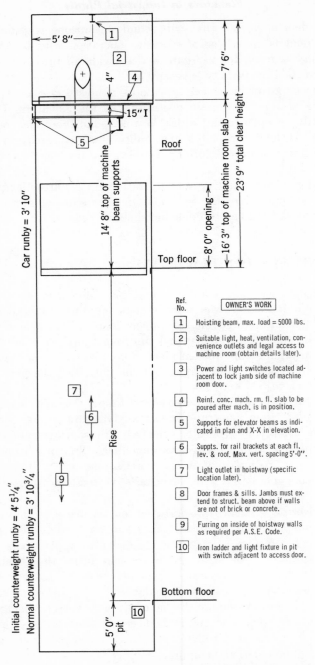

Figure 13.9   Geared freight elevator, resistance

290

facturing plant elevators can be determined by simple calculation based on indicated need. Each area requiring transportation must be studied and the expected volume estimated for an applicable time period. Elevators to handle this volume can be based on the following factors:

Time to Load. This time, varies with the type of loading: fork-lift truck, hand truck, cart, or hand. Fork-lift truck loading is fastest but also creates the greatest strain on the elevator equipment.

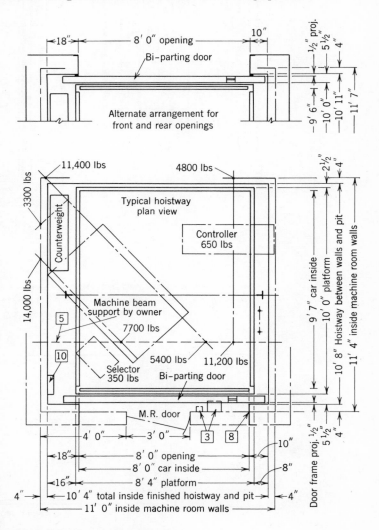

with leveling, 8000 lb @ 50 or 75 fpm.

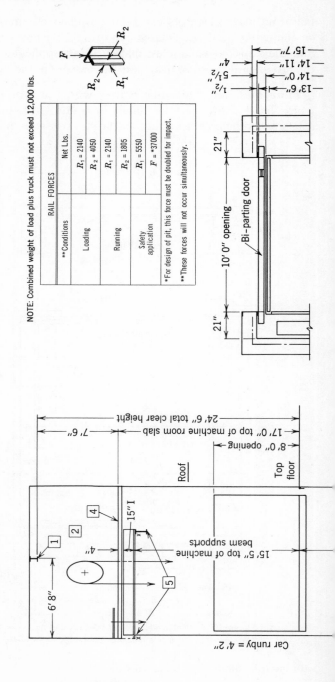

NOTE: Combined weight of load plus truck must not exceed 12,000 lbs.

RAIL FORCES		Net Lbs.
**Conditions		
Loading	$R_1 = 2140$	
	$R_2 = 4050$	
Running	$R_1 = 2140$	
	$R_2 = 1805$	
Safety application	$R_1 = 5550$	
	$F = *37000$	

*For design of pit, this force must be doubled for impact.

**These forces will not occur simultaneously.

Bi-parting door

10' 0" opening

21"   21"

13' 6"   ½"
14' 0"   5½"
14' 11"   4"
15' 7"

24' 6" total clear height

7' 6"   17' 0" top of machine room slab

8' 0" opening

Roof

15" I

4"

15' 5" top of machine beam supports

6' 8"

Top floor

Car runby = 4' 2"

292

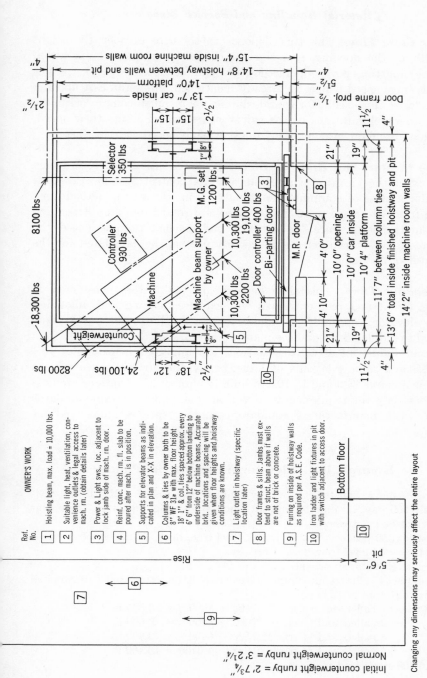

Figure 13.10 Geared freight elevator, variable-voltage, 12,000 lb @ 100 fpm.

OWNER'S WORK

Ref. No.

1 Hoisting beam, max. load = 10,000 lbs.

2 Suitable light, heat, ventilation, convenience outlets & legal access to mach. rm. (obtain details later)

3 Power & Light sws., loc. adjacent to lock jamb side of mach. rm. door.

4 Reinf. conc. mach. rm. fl. slab to be poured after mach. is in position.

5 Supports for elevator beams as indicated in plan and X-X in elevation.

6 Columns & ties by owner both to be 8" WF 31# with max. floor height 18' 1" & col. ties spaced approx. every 6' 6" from 12" below bottom landing to underside of machine beams. Accurate brkt. locations and spacing will be given when floor heights and hoistway conditions are known.

7 Light outlet in hoistway (specific location later)

8 Door frames & sills. Jambs must extend to struct. beam above if walls are not of brick or concrete.

9 Furring on inside of hoistway walls as required per A.S.E. Code.

10 Iron ladder and light fixtures in pit with switch adjacent to access door.

Changing any dimensions may seriously affect the entire layout

Initial counterweight runby = 2' 7³⁄₄"

Normal counterweight runby = 3' 2¹⁄₄"

Door Close Time. This time depends on the type of door, the height or width of the opening, and the use of power or manual operation. Vertical biparting power-operated doors can be operated at 1 fps per panel average speed which, as already mentioned, allows an 8-ft opening to be closed in 4 sec. Horizontal sliding doors must comply with the kinetic energy limitations of the safety codes, which limits their speed. With an attendant present, horizontal closing speed can be faster.

Time to Start and Run the Elevator. Acceleration and retardation varies with the elevator equipment and its control system. Practical limits for a class of equipment, obtainable from elevator manufacturers, will be from 4 to 8 sec to get up to speed and retard to a stop depending on ultimate speed. Once the elevator has reached running speed the speed required to transverse a given distance can be calculated for the floor-to-floor distance.

Unloading Time. This time depends on the factors considered in loading. Front and rear entrances will expedite loading and unloading of the elevator, especially if industrial-type small tractor and trailers are used to pull loads around the plant.

Typical industrial elevator situations are analyzed in examples 13.1 and 13.2 and sample layouts of large, heavy-duty freight elevators are shown in Figures 13.9 and 13.10. An infinite number of variations are possible to satisfy the requirements of various plants, but certain standards in line with manufacturers standard equipment are recommended for economy.

Example 13.1. Elevators in Industrial Plants

Required to move: Pallets 4 ft $\times$ 4 ft by 6 ft high, each weighing 2500 lb, approximately 200/day. Loading by fork-lift truck, truck weight 8000 lb. 80 per cent of weight on front wheels.

Distribution: 50 per cent load to fourth level from dock, 36-ft rise; 50 per cent load to second level from dock, 12 ft rise.

Determine: Elevator size & speed.

Size: Assume: 4 pallets/trip; minimum size 8 ft $\times$ 8 ft interior, 10,000 lb; nominal size 8 ft 4 in. $\times$ 12 ft 0 in.

Rating: 1 pallet and truck $2500 + 8000$ $= 10,500$ lb
        2 pallets and truck $5000 + 8000$ $= 13,000$ lb
        3 pallets and ½ truck $7500 + 6400$ $= 13,900$ lb
        4 pallets and ½ truck $10,000 + 6400$ $= 16,400$ lb
   16,400 static load required.

12,000-lb car with static loading (50 per cent over capacity).
Number of elevators required (assume 100 fpm).

To fourth level:

Load at dock 15 sec/pallet (from observation):	60 sec
Door close:	4 sec

Run to fourth level, 4 sec accelerate and retard +

$$\frac{36 \times 60}{100} = \text{26 sec}$$

Unload:	60 sec
Door close:	4 sec
Return:	22 sec
Total time, 4 pallets:	176 sec, say 3 min
Total time, 100 pallets: 25 trips $\times$ 3 min	= 75 min

To second level:

Same as above except running time:

$$4 \text{ sec} + \frac{12 \times 60}{100} = 11.2, \text{ say 11 sec } (22 - 11) \times 2 \qquad = \text{less 22 sec}$$

Total time, 4 pallets:	172–22 = 150 sec =	2.5 min
Total time, 100 pallets:	25 $\times$ 2.5 =	62.5 min
Total time, 200 pallets:	75 + 62.5 =	2 hr 17.5 min

1 elevator, 12,000 @ 100 static loading sufficient.

Example 13.2. Elevators in Industrial Plants

Required: Determine number of industrial carts that can be moved average 6 floors (72-ft rise) by one elevator per hour. Maximum load each cart, 6000 lb, tractor load 8000 lb. Front and rear openings on elevator.

Assume: Tractor can pull and deposit 2 carts on elevator. Alternate tractor and one cart each trip (sufficient tractors).

A. 2 carts/trip:

Tractor and 1 cart:	6000 + 8000 = 14000 lb
½ cart, cart and ½ tractor: 3000 + 6000 + 4000 = 13000 lb
2 carts:	2 $\times$ 6000 lb = 12000 lb
Time to load two carts (by observation):	15 sec
Uncouple (by observation):	15 sec
Drive off, close doors:	10 sec

Run 72 ft (assume 100 fpm) $\dfrac{72 \times 60}{100} = 43 + 4$ sec: 47 sec

Couple tractor and drive off:	25 sec
Walk back, close door:	15 sec
Run back to lower level:	47 sec
Total/2 carts:	174 sec

Number of carts/hour $\dfrac{3600 \times 2}{174} = 41$ carts.

B. 1 cart per trip and tractor:

Drive on:	15 sec
Close doors:	4 sec
Run:	47 sec
Unload tractor and cart:	15 sec
Second tractor drives on while first is unloading:	
Close doors:	4 sec
Run:	47 sec
	132 sec/cart

Number of carts/hour 3600 ÷ 132 = 27 (approximately).

Result: 2 carts/elevator best way. Elevator should be rated at 14,000 lb for occasional cart and tractor trip. No static loading required. Size depends on size of cart and tractor.

Readily available sizes of freight elevators are shown in Tables 13.1 and 13.2.

Table 13.1. Loading by hand or by hand truck

Capacity (pounds)	Platform (width)	Size (depth)	Maximum Speed (standard equipment)
2,500	5'4''	7'0''	No limit
3,000	6'4''	8'0''	No limit
3,500	6'4''	8'0''	No limit
4,000	6'4''	8'0''	No limit
5,000	8'4''	10'0''	Usually 700–800 fpm
6,000	8'4''	10'0''	Usually 700–800 fpm
8,000	8'4''	12'0''	500 fpm
10,000[a]	8'4''	12'0''	350 fpm
12,000[a]	10'4''	14'0''	350 fpm

[a] Elevators of this size should always be considered for industrial truck loading.

Table 13.2. Loading by industrial trucks

Capacity (pounds)	Platform (width)	Size (depth)	Maximum Speed (standard equipment)
10,000	8'4''	12'0''	350 fpm
12,000	10'4''	14'0''	300 fpm
16,000	10'4''	14'0''	300 fpm
18,000	10'4''	16'0''	300 fpm
20,000	12'4''	20'0''	200 fpm

ELEVATORS IN WAREHOUSES

The nature of the warehouse operation determines the type of freight elevator required. If it is for a long-term, low-turnover storage with bulky but light loads a large, slow-speed elevator with manual operation and manual doors may be sufficient.

If the warehouse is a fast turnover facility making extensive use of industrial fork-lift trucks its elevators must be so designed. Their number and size will be a direct function of the expected turnover.

As indicated earlier in this chapter, a time cycle of elevator loading and operation must be established to determine the average time per load. This is projected for the number of loads that must be transported and the elevator requirements determined accordingly.

A number of automated elevator systems are applicable to material handling and may be considered for a particular warehouse problem. The systems may be divided into two categories: those in which the load is moved by means of a vertical conveyor to the elevator and those in which the elevator moves, in essence, to the load.

Conveyor systems to feed a stationary elevator are generally supplied by conveyor specialists. Initiating and limit switches on the conveyor control elevator response. The elevator arrives and conveyor equipment on the elevator platform transfers the load. A limit switch signifies the completion of transfer. Disposition of the load is controlled either manually or by program, with the elevator moving the load to another floor and automatically unloading.

One type of automatic transfer includes the use of an elevator with a tilting platform. Cylindrical loads, like rolls of newsprint, are rolled onto the elevator at the loading floor by either a pusher or a floor tilter. When the elevator arrives at its destination the elevator platform is tilted and the load rolls off.

An elevator in a tower moving on tracks is the heart of the "Speed-Park"* system of automated material handling. This moving elevator system was originally developed to park automobiles by picking them up with a fork-lift mechanism, moving them onto the elevator laterally, and, by a combination of vertical elevator motion and horizontal tower trolley motion, indexing to a vacant stall and laterally depositing the automobile in that stall.

This successful operation is readily adapted to warehouse elevatoring when pallet loads can be lifted on or off the elevator by a similar lifting

* Developed by "Speed Park" Corp. New York, N.Y.

mechanism and deposited for storage. A complete computer system can be used in the control of the operation to recall the place of storage with punch cards to retrieve loads as required. No manual operation is necessary.

Another form of moving elevator system is the "Systematic"* parking system, which utilizes an extra-long elevator platform with a laterally moving dolly on the platform. The automobile or other load is pulled onto the platform by the dolly, indexed to an available stall both vertically and laterally, and deposited. Retrieval reverses the procedure. At present the operation of the dolly is manual but complete automation is possible.

ELEVATORS IN GARAGES

Garage elevators trace their history to the early 1900's when both horses and carriages were carried on elevators to upper floors for stabling or storage. Early horse elevators had a gate between the horses and the elevator operator and channel troughs in the platform so it could be washed down. Modern garage elevators do not need the trough, but protection against the vehicle being driven into the extreme end of the elevator is advisable.

A garage elevator is designed for operation by an attendant who parks or retrieves automobiles at the upper floors. Landing buttons can be pendant-mounted and door-close buttons and operating panels in the car are located so that the attendant can operate them by leaning out of an automobile window.

Time can be saved by a garage elevator with both front and rear openings. The attendant can drive in the front and out the back, thus saving 10 to 20 sec per elevator trip.

A typical sequence of operation with a single elevator entrance, drive in, back out is as follows:

Door open:	4 sec
Drive in:	10 sec
Door close:	4 sec
Run to upper stop:	depends on rise and speed of elevator
Door open:	4 sec
Back out:	20 sec
Door close:	4 sec

* Developed by "Systematic Parking" Spokane, Wash.

The cycle is then repeated by adding the running time to return for the next car.

With the drive-through type of elevator, back-out time is replaced by drive-off time, which can be as little as 10 sec.

The number of elevators required for a particular garage will be a function of the number of floors, the number of cars to be turned-over (parked and unparked in a given time), the number of attendants available, storage space at the entrance floor, and the speed with which customers can pay their bills and drive out to the street.

All the factors are important and are reflected in the economics of the elevator installations. Little is gained by an elevator plant that can deliver a car a minute if the local streets are so congested that it takes 70 sec to leave the garage.

If the garage depends on elevators for its operation, a minimum of two is recommended to maintain continuity of service. A garage elevator usually has a 7000-lb capacity to handle large limousines. The dimensions of the 7000-lb car are a platform 8 to 10 ft wide by 24 ft long. The 8-ft width is used when it is intended to operate from within the auto. If larger cars or trucks are to be handled, capacity and dimensions should be increased.

Garage elevators have lost favor in recent years to the popularity of the self-parking garage because of the high cost of attendants. The problem of getting the most parking space out of a limited downtown plot of land remains, and when motorists are willing to pay higher rates for parking convenience, garage elevators and necessary attendants are feasible.

Automated garages represent another approach to the problem of convenience with economy in parking. The Speed-Park and Systematic systems referred to earlier are both designed to provide parking within minimum land and attendant requirements.

With the Speed-Park system the attendant, usually a girl, acts as both parking operator and cashier. The patron drives his car to a loading position from which, once the car is clear of obstructions, the automatic parker lifts it onto an elevator in a traveling tower and deposits it in a stall. The action is initiated by the attendant who takes a key for a vacant stall and inserts it in a special control computer. The operation is entirely automatic; the key acts as the coding device as well as the patron's check for his car. Retrieval is done in the opposite manner; the patron returns the key and the computer directs the car to be unparked to an unloading position and computes the charges the attendant collects. If a key is lost a car may be searched for based on the time of parking by unparking several cars and identifying the

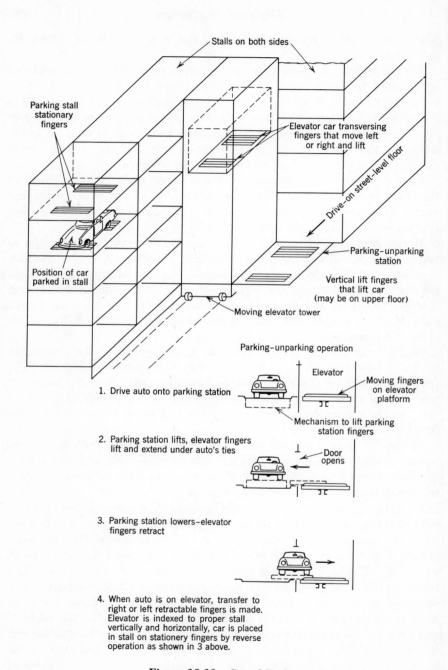

Stalls on both sides

Parking stall stationary fingers

Elevator car transversing fingers that move left or right and lift

Drive-on street-level floor

Position of car parked in stall

Parking-unparking station

Vertical lift fingers that lift car (may be on upper floor)

Moving elevator tower

Parking-unparking operation

Elevator

1. Drive auto onto parking station

Moving fingers on elevator platform

Mechanism to lift parking station fingers

2. Parking station lifts, elevator fingers lift and extend under auto's ties

Door opens

3. Parking station lowers–elevator fingers retract

4. When auto is on elevator, transfer to right or left retractable fingers is made. Elevator is indexed to proper stall vertically and horizontally, car is placed in stall on stationery fingers by reverse operation as shown in 3 above.

Figure 13.11   Speed Park.

300

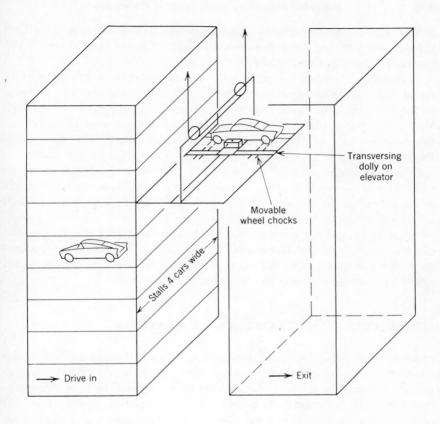

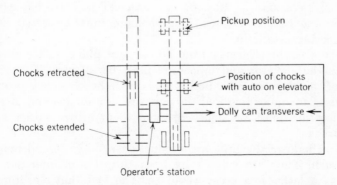

Figure 13.12 Plan view of elevator platform showing parking dolly. Systematic parking.

proper one. Complete searches can be made by an attendant walking through the parking area. A schematic description of the "Speed-Park" system is shown in Figure 13.11.

Systematic Parking, as previously noted, employs a movable dolly on an extra-wide elevator platform. The patron leaves his car in front of the platform. The car is deposited in a stall and the cycle is repeated. Unparking takes place in a reverse manner and the car is placed on the opposite side of the platform to be driven away. The Systematic Parking system is shown in a descriptive sketch in Figure 13.12.

Other automatic parking systems have employed "ferris wheel" turntable arrangements or moving elevator towers with automatic unloaders or an attendant unloading. Whatever the method, its economics as well as reliability must be carefully considered. The cost of land for a self-parking or ramp-type garage must be balanced against the cost of the elevator equipment and mechanism for an automatic garage or an attendant elevator garage. In addition the cost of attendants must be weighed against the complexity and cost of automatic equipment.

OTHER FREIGHT ELEVATOR CONSIDERATIONS

Aside from total load and methods of loading freight elevators, the environment in which loading takes place must be considered. Unless special hazards in a plant dictate otherwise, durability is a prime requirement. If hazards such as chemical atmospheres, abrasive or explosive dusts, or moisture exist the elevator equipment is governed by the same considerations as any other electrical and mechanical installations in the hazardous area. This is more fully discussed in the chapter on special installations.

To gain the greatest efficiency from an elevator plant, sufficient space for access to the elevator and unloading must be allowed. This is one advantage of an elevator with both front and rear openings, provided one side is used for unloading and the opposite side for loading. A minimum consideration must be sufficient room to maneuver either hand- or fork-lift trucks.

Elevators in industrial plants are production equipment and must be treated as such. They are subject to down time for maintenance and repair just as a lathe or a press would be. The fact that elevators are unusually vital, not only to the productive function but to the movement of people, must be recognized and acted on. If the entire operation of a plant depended on one machine a standby would probably be considered, and the same logic should be applied to plant elevators. The alternative would be to have available spares for any parts that might fail to permit replacement in minimum time.

A greater understanding in the use of freight and industrial elevators might have been gained from the foregoing pages. Effective elevatoring—the design and application of an elevator installation—depends on systematic consideration of all relevant factors.

CHAPTER FOURTEEN

Multipurpose Buildings and Special Elevator Applications

MULTIPURPOSE BUILDINGS

With the increasing emphasis on land usage, the concept of the multipurpose building is gaining favor. A building may well combine working space on its lower floors and residential space above. In a university, including classrooms in a dormitory building may permit 24-hr use of the structure.

In hospitals, especially, the nursing staff may have quarters on the upper floors. This practice is common in many Catholic hospitals, where the sisters' living area is on the top floors.

Staff residential or nursing home space on the upper floors of a hospital is one way to improve utilization of the building.

Such facilities, which usually require less vertical transportation than the hospital itself, may be provided at less cost as an upward extension of the hospital building than in a separate building on a separate site.

The secret to successful multiuse of a building is separation of its multiple functions by separate vertical transportation and lobbies. Persons entering the residential area, for example, need not interfere with persons using other areas of the building. The various functions should be separated by vertical height or, possibly, by a mechanical floor.

Children who may live on apartment floors over an office building should not be allowed to ride the elevators with the tenants of the offices or, for that matter, to play in the office building lobby.

Elevatoring of such multipurpose buildings can be based on separation of the several functions and minimization of interfering traffic. If the expected elevator traffic patterns for the functions do not coincide, elevatoring can be established for the major function and sufficient service made available for the minor function. If the two functions are expected to coincide, as in combination office and apartment buildings, separate groups of elevators should be considered (Figure 14.1).

The combination office and apartment building typifies a possible conflict between traffic entering the offices and leaving the apartments. Although the building is expected to be in a downtown area, it is not necessarily true that all persons who live in the apartments will work

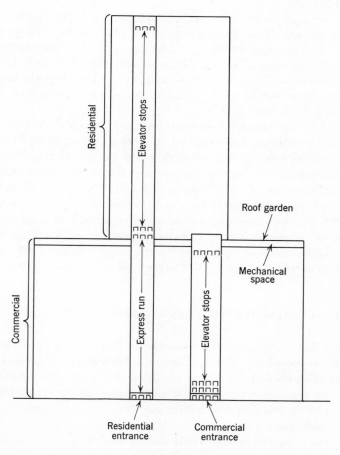

Figure 14.1

in the same building. Similarly, when office staffs are leaving and apartment tenants are returning home, there may be conflicting traffic. In addition the problem of office and apartment space security and the safety of children, as mentioned earlier, is always present.

One of the most successful approaches to the office-apartment combination is the sky-plaza concept. A separate lobby is located on the lowest apartment floor and connected to the street by shuttle elevators. Apartment tenants ride these elevators to the sky-plaza and change to the local elevator, which takes them to their floor. The sky-plaza is enhanced by swimming pools, shops, or a restaurant. This is the elevatoring arrangement of the John Hancock Center in Chicago, where 44 floors of apartments are located above a 40-story office, store, and garage building (Figure 14.2).

A hotel with extensive convention facilities, such as ballroom and meeting rooms often used by others than the hotel guests, can be considered as a multipurpose building. Separate vertical transportation for outside guests increases the value of the meeting facilities and minimizes their interference with hotel guests. Guests, even when they are attending the meeting room functions, appreciate the reduced congestion on the main passenger elevators.

In estimating the vertical transportation requirements of the separate functions in a building the expected maximum usage of each facility and the possible time of use of each must be considered. If periods of maximum use do not overlap, the vertical transportation is calculated for the maximum use. In addition to the quantity of service required, the nature of the traffic must be carefully calculated. Its direction is either in unison or opposed and proper elevator provisions must be made. An important example is the inclusion of restaurant facilities on the top of an office building. The normal lunchtime traffic of the tenants is usually in direct opposition to that of the restaurant patrons.

UNUSUAL APPROACHES TO ELEVATORING

The sky-plaza system, mentioned earlier in this chapter for elevatoring apartments on top of an office building, has been used for a hotel above a department store and for many facilities above garages. Besides the separation of functions, this concept gains more usable space from the lower floors of a building by minimizing the space required by local and express elevators.

Each of the proposed World Trade Center towers in New York is conceived as three 40-story "buildings" on top of each other. The lobby

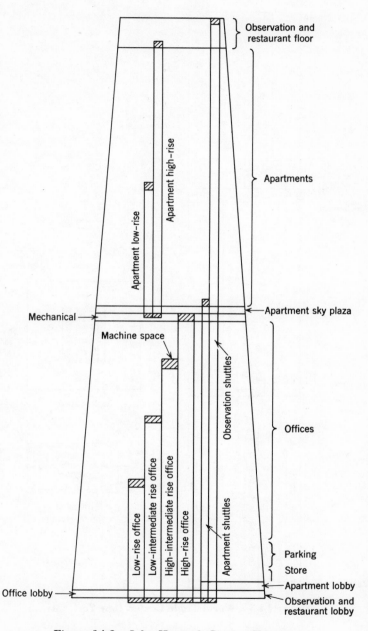

Figure 14.2   John Hancock Center, Chicago.

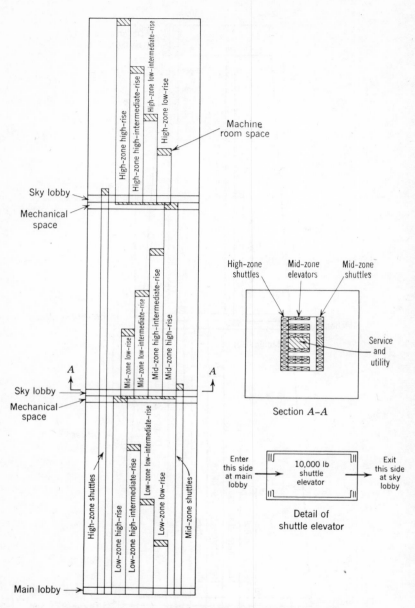

Figure 14.3   World Trade Center, New York City.

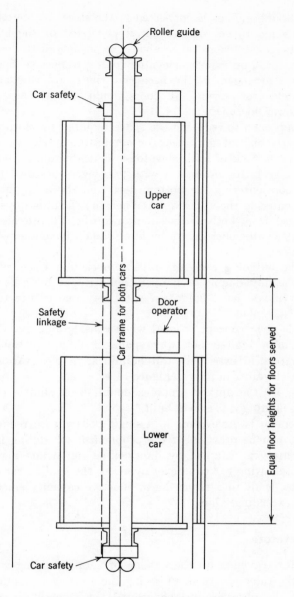

Figure 14.4   Double-deck elevator.

of each of these buildings is connected to the street by shuttle elevators. A person wishing to go, say, to the upper third of the building, will ride a shuttle elevator nonstop to about the seventy-fifth floor and there change to a local or express elevator to his respective floor. Without this sky-plaza arrangement the necessary shafts for conventional local and express elevators serving all floors would consume almost the total area of the lower floors (Figure 14.3).

Another approach to reducing the space required by elevators in taller buildings is the use of multideck or compartment elevators. Here the upper and lower deck of each elevator is loaded simultaneously (during the incoming rush, for example), with passengers destined for the odd-numbered floors entering the bottom deck and those for the even-numbered floors entering the upper deck. When the elevator stops, passengers are discharged from both decks simultaneously. To provide an efficient double-deck elevator operation a building should have a substantial population per floor.

During the outgoing rush the reverse operation takes place. In the middle of the day double-deck operation with both decks stopping at all floors or a restricted operation with only one of the two decks in service can take place.

The double-deck concept is ideal when considerable elevator capacity is required in a limited hoistway space. Such applications would be shuttle elevators in extremely tall buildings, in observation towers or as passenger elevators in mines (Figure 14.4).

An article by the author proposes double-deck shuttle elevators for a mile-high building if it is ever built.*

The concept of two elevators in a single hoistway to reduce the space consumption can be practical if the problem of scheduling is effectively overcome. Safety is attained by interlocking signal and machine drives so that the following car can never overtake the leading car. This operation however, leads to a reduction in effective capacity since round-trip time can be exceedingly long.

Outside Elevators

An elevator traveling up the outside of a tall building is a dramatic sight. For the rider the thrill of seeing the scenery in motion is unsurpassed; for the observer on the ground the smoothness and majesty of the moving mass is incomparable. From the engineer's point of view outside elevators pose many challenging problems. Notable applications

---

* *The Florida Architect,* March 1964.

of outside elevators have been made at the Fairmont Hotel in San Francisco, the observation towers mentioned in Chapter 12, the Regency Hotel in Atlanta (Figure 14.5) and a host of other lower-rise installations.

From the design aspect the outside elevator must be weather and windproof as well as exceptionally safe. Windproofing is helped by eliminating all possible ropes and troughing traveling cables and governor ropes. The compensating ropes are eliminated and extra motor horsepower provided for the uncompensated load. The top and bottom of the elevator cab are enclosed and streamlined, and the elevator car doors are positively locked while the car is away from the landings.

All hoistway switches and electrical installations are completely waterproofed to withstand driving rain. When wintertime operation is expected, rails are electrically heated and ice scrapers are mounted on the guide shoes. A glass cab may be air conditioned for passenger comfort

Figure 14.5   Fairmont Hotel, San Francisco.

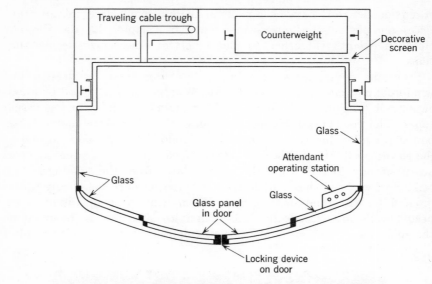

Figure 14.6   "Wall climber" design—observation elevator.

on hot days or heated on cold days. For windy days special rope guards may be provided to bridge and hold the hoisting ropes to keep them from blowing.

Outside elevators are usually of the wall-climber design, in which the car frame and guide rails are set as close to the back of the car as possible. The final effect provides maximum viewing area for the passengers (Figure 14.6). Admission is generally charged for an observation tower and an elevator ride, so passenger satisfaction is essential.

An alternate approach may be a conventional elevator with glass sides that operates within a glass-enclosed shaft. Because safety codes generally restrict the use of glass inside an elevator, special approval from authorities is often necessary and the glass must be shatterproof, tempered, or have extra strong characteristics (Figure 14.7).

Among notable installations using this concept, the Security Life Building in Denver, Colorado has an elevator in a glass-enclosed shaft operating from the ground to a thirty-eighth-floor rooftop restaurant. The Prospect Point observation tower at Niagara Falls has two glass-enclosed elevators operating from the top of a cliff to the base of the falls. The NASA Vehicle Assembly Building at the Cape Kennedy Space Center in Florida is an example of a special-purpose glass-walled eleva-

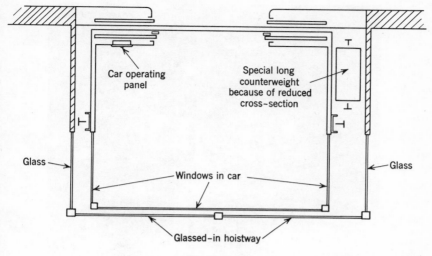

Figure 14.7

tor; it enables officials and guests to view rocket assembly from the elevator.

Glass-walled elevators in interior spaces are less exacting than those on the outside of buildings and usually require only conventional operating equipment.

Elevators in Corrosive, Explosive, Dusty, or Wet Locations

Safe vertical transportation must often be provided in areas where hazards exist detrimental to either the equipment or its operation. Such locations may be found in storage facilities for flour or other dusty, often abrasive materials, or in petroleum refineries or chemical processing plants handling corrosive or explosive substances. Wet locations include elevators in mines, those exposed to the weather, as in the observation towers previously mentioned, or located at waterside or, perhaps, used to handle wet ashes in a power plant. More recently, elevators operating in the vicinity of rockets fueled with liquid hydrogen and liquid oxygen must endure special hazards (Figure 14.8).

Whatever the hazard or location, conventional elevator equipment would be subject to rapid deterioration from the elements or may present potential dangers to personnel and material.

Classes of hazard are recognized by the National Electrical Code, which sets forth rules for the treatment of electrical equipment in such

Figure 14.8

locations. Common sense and engineering considerations must be applied to the other parts of the elevator exposed to hazards. For example, if all the electrical equipment is required to be watertight, all the structural parts of the elevator including the ropes, machine, and rails should also be protected against deterioration from water. Similarly, if the elevator equipment must operate in a corrosive atmosphere, as in a fertilizer or chemical plant, all metal parts as well as the electrical equipment should be treated to withstand corrosion. These considerations may often lead to installing wooden rather than steel guide rails and providing a safety mechanism that operates on wood. A damaged section of rail can be replaced, as in the early days of "safety" elevators.

For hazardous locations inflammable or explosive atmospheres the National Electrical Code has certain classifications, summarized as follows (the Code must be referred to for complete definitions).

Hazards are divided into two types:

Division 1, in which the hazard may exist at any time because of activities such as transferring liquids, mixing, or spraying, in the area.

Division 2, in which the hazard may exist because of mishap from leakage or some other accidental means.

Within each division are degrees of hazard listed as classes:

Class I hazards are caused by liquids or gases that are volatile and flammable, the most critical explosive hazard for electrical equipment. These areas require equipment classed as explosion-proof, in special boxes immersed in oil, or in boxes in which an inert gas is introduced to purge the equipment of volatile vapors.

Class I is further divided into groups to refer to the specific type of explosive atmosphere present:

Group A: acetylene gas.
Group B: hydrogen, manufactured gas.
Group C: ethyl ether, ethylene, cyclo-propane.
Group D: gasoline, naphtha and other solvents, natural gas.

As may be realized, the foregoing is only a partial list. Today's plants may process both hazardous compounds and those that may be hazardous in combination with other compounds. As an example, liquid oxygen, when exposed to ordinary petroleum products, forms an explosive mixture, which requires that not only the electrical system but even lubricants normally used in bearings and on elevator ropes be hazard-proofed.

A second classification of hazardous conditions is *Class II,* which includes combustible dusts, in the following groups:

Group E: metallic dust (which may also be explosive).
Group F: carbon dusts (which may also be explosive).
Group G: grain dusts.

Not only may an explosive atmosphere exist but many dusts are abrasive and cause premature wear of unprotected machinery. Even if a nonexplosive dust is apparent, switches, rotating elements, and bearings must be sealed and protected. Elevator controllers, for example, with many moving contacts subject to wear and fouling by dust, require means to keep them in a clean atmosphere. These means may include pressurizing the machine room or placing the controls in sealed cabinets with adequate ventilation.

Class III hazards are those caused by flying fibers that are easily ignited. These might be cotton fibers in a cotton refining plant, or wood dust. A hazard of this class arises from an accumulation of dust that can interfere with operation of the equipment.

Specifying elevator equipment for installations of this nature requires a considerable number of pages. The architect or engineer specifying such equipment should establish the type and extent of the hazard. As an example, *Class I, Division 2,* Group B, would indicate a possible explosive hazard of hydrogen gas. He should then consult with equipment manufacturers to determine the necessary precautions and draw up elevator specifications accordingly. Much additional detail should be included in the preliminary drawings to insure provision of all necessary safeguards.

Similar treatment may be applied to elevator installations in wet or dusty areas. The severity of the environment as well as the amount of normal protection for the equipment must be determined. For example, will the atmosphere be foggy? Will the elevator be exposed to water as when cleaned with a hose? As has occurred in an atomic energy plant, will it be stored under protective water between the times the reactor is recharged?

Similarly, elevators in highly corrosive atmospheres must be thoroughly studied before the actual equipment is installed. All working parts must be free to operate when usual metal pins or bearings would freeze from rust. Bronze bushings, stainless steel pins and safety parts, special hoist ropes, and so on, must all be provided to reduce the hazard.

Shipboard Elevators

When elevators are installed aboard ships many special factors must be considered. The equipment must be waterproof and designed to resist corrosion, as these conditions are to be expected on a ship. Traveling cables must operate in troughs to avoid tangling when the ship rolls. The elevator control equipment as well as the elevator car must be able to operate during rolling and pitching in moderate seas. All the equipment must be able to withstand the extra forces imposed by motion of the ship.

Counterweighted elevators are used aboard ships for passenger-sized cars. The counterweight should be equipped with a safety for the obvious reason that if it ever broke loose it may go right through the bottom of the ship. Layout conditions on shipboard are more exacting than on land. Space is at a tremendous premium, and fitting a reasonable-size elevator in a hoistway trunk is quite a challenge. As with any special

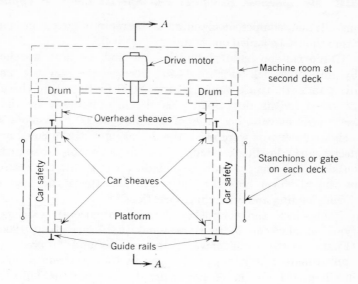

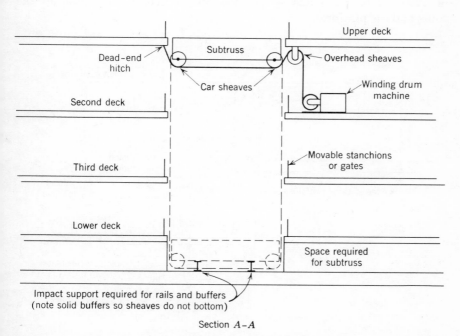

Section *A–A*

Figure 14.9   Shipboard cargo elevator—top landing flush with top deck. (Note pit required for sub-truss. With shallow pit, overhead structure required.)

317

installation, competent manufacturers' representatives or consulting engineers should be called on for aid.

Cargo can be handled by elevator and, as in a warehouse on land, by fork-lift truck (Figure 14.9). Because the elevator may be loaded by a fork-lift truck weighing from 8000 to 10,000 lb, the elevator must be rated for its duty load plus the load imposed by the truck. This may mean elevators capable of handling 15,000 lb or more. If a counterweighted elevator were used, the deadweight of the counterweight would decrease the loading capacity of the ship. For this reason cargo elevators on ships are usually drum machines, rated to lift the entire deadweight of the platform plus the duty load and the static load of the truck during loading and unloading operations.

Flight-deck and deck-edge elevators of aircraft carriers are notable types of elevator. With tremendous platforms about 1800 to 2000 ft² (Figure 14.10) these elevators are raised and lowered at a speed of approximately 200 fpm by a roped hydraulic arrangement as described in Chapter 1 for the earlier hydraulic installations. Oil under pressures of 1200 psi or more drives the cylinders, which in turn pull up the ropes and the platform.

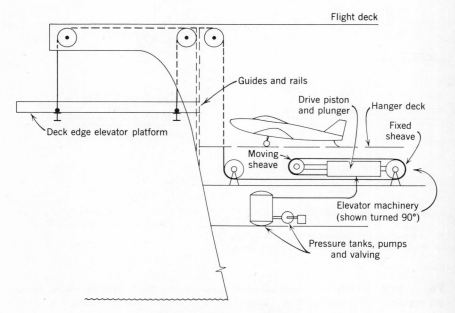

Figure 14.10   Deck-edge elevator.

UNIQUE ELEVATOR INSTALLATIONS

With certain designs of buildings or structures it is often necessary to provide other than vertical transportation, that is, at an incline or in a curvelinear path. Many unique elevator installations have been accomplished to meet such challenges.

One such notable installation is in the Washington Masonic Monument in Alexandria, Virginia, where the elevators are located in the corners

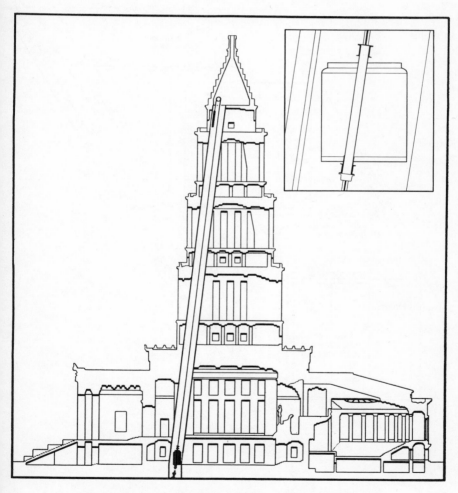

Figure 14.11   Washington Masonic National Monument.

of the structure and rise at an angle of 7° from the vertical. What makes this installation doubly unique is that the elevators are operating at a speed of 700 fpm and have a capacity of 3000 lbs. (Figure 14.11). Before this installation any elevator with an angular rise was limited to 200 fpm or less.

Elevators rising at an incline require appreciably more shaft space

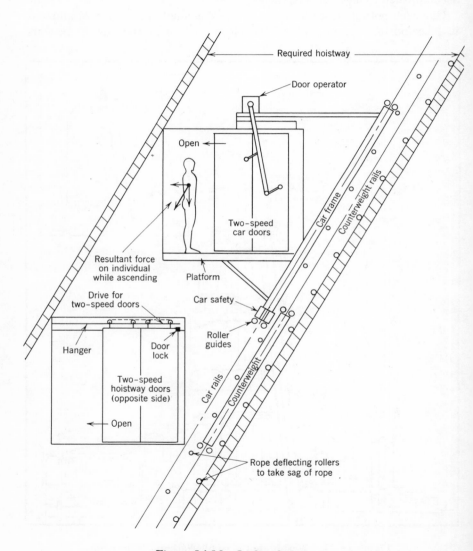

Figure 14.12 Inclined elevator.

and many more special considerations than purely vertical elevators (Figure 14.12). Up to a limit of about 3° the doors may be placed at the front of the elevator; beyond that a side location must be considered. Once the angle of incline exceeds about 7°, speed becomes severely limited for standing passengers who may be thrown by the inertial effect of starting and stopping.

Unique elevators may have other features. An elevator with a round platform is in operation in the Johnson Wax Company in Racine, Wisconsin. Serving the 15-story Heliolab, this elevator travels 600 fpm and has round car and hoistway doors as well as a round platform. The building was designed by Frank Lloyd Wright, who also designed the Price Tower in Oklahoma, where the elevators are hexagonal rather than rectangular.

Triangular, octagonal, semicircular, and other shapes have been used for the elevator platform. From the point of view of passenger handling (and cost) the rectangular shape as outlined in Chapter 2 remains the best. But the use of an unusual shape is not to be discouraged for a unique building. If adequate compensation is made for the inefficiency of passenger service, and if the elevator is a new and exciting design, it may well be a success with everyone connected with the project. Such is the case with the elevators of the Regency Hotel in Atlanta, Georgia. These elevators have keyhole-shaped platforms, operate on the outside of the shafts in the hotel's enclosed courtyard, have glass cabs, and are ornately decorated both inside and outside and lighted with special effects—truly a sight to behold (Figure 14.13).

Elevators can be unique in size also. The largest commercial elevator on record was a special lift used to move a swimming pool full of water onto the stage of the Hippodrome Theater in New York City. This lift had a capacity of 250,000 lb and traveled at a breathtaking speed of 12 fpm. As previously mentioned, many elevators are designed to handle loaded trailer trucks and freight cars. For this type of equipment capacities vary from 60,000 to 100,000 lb and are usually hydraulically driven at speeds of 50 to 100 fpm.

No matter what the vertical transportation problem or how unusual the circumstances, there is usually a solution. The solution may be ingenious and probably costly in comparison to conventional elevators because each part must be custom-designed to fit with all others and must usually be hand-fabricated. The solution must be custom-made if there is none readily available. For a true economic analysis, consider the cost of the alternative: not having transportation at all.

Consideration of the number of foot-pounds of energy plus the time saved by proper vertical transportation reveals many factors in favor of the unique solution (example 14.1A).

Figure 14.13   Hyatt Regency Hotel, Atlanta.

Example 14.1. Elevator Value Analysis

Problem: Unload pallets from trailer truck and transfer to storage area on upper floor. Truck holds 10 pallets. Assume that fork-lift truck requires 60 sec to handle one pallet.

A. With conventional freight elevator, 2 pallets/trip (60 sec to run):

1. Unload pallets at dock from truck:	10 min	1 man
2. Transfer pallets to elevator:	10 min	1 man
3. Carry pallets to upper floor (5 trips):	5 min	1 man
4. Unload elevator:	10 min	1 man
5. Transfer pallets to storage area:	10 min	1 man
Total	45 min	5 men

B. With elevator to carry trailer truck to upper floor unloading dock:

1. Unload pallets:	10 min	1 man
2. Transfer to storage area:	10 min	1 man
Total	20 min	2 men

C. Provide automatic conveying system and elevator to storage area:

1. Unload truck onto conveyor:	10 min	1 man

If we assume the process is continuous and manpower and fork-lift equipment cost $10/hour, the cost per 60 pallets is:

A. $45; if the "use"[a] cost of elevator A is x, then total cost is $45x$.

B. $20; if the "use"[a] cost of elevator B is $2x$, then total cost is $40x$.

C. $10; if the "use"[a] cost of system C is $3x$, then total cost is $30x$.

It appears that a unique solution may be the cheapest in the long run— depending on particular circumstances, of course.

---

[a] Use cost is cost of amortized installation plus cost of maintenance, insurance, space required, power, etc.

CHAPTER FIFTEEN

Elevator Specifying and Contracting. Elevator Modernization

PREPARING TO BID

Once preliminary designs of a building have been approved, tentative financing arranged, and the firm intention to proceed established, the task of preparing specifications for the various building systems is necessary.

Up to this point it has been assumed that the architect has worked with consulting engineers or manufacturers' representatives to determine and allocate space for elevators and/or escalators of the necessary size and number. It has also been assumed that he has asked all elevator companies from which he expects to obtain bids to review his space allocations for equipment fit. Failure to do so may invite a protest at the time of bidding or require drastic changes in drawings once the bid has been accepted.

Providing proper space is crucially important in designing for public contracts when those who can bid cannot be restricted as on private installations. On private installations the owner may limit the bidding to only two concerns or may even choose to negotiate a contract with one supplier. The alternative, of course, is to detail the entire project completely and make the space requirements, hence the working drawings, a condition of bidding. This is often done but precludes the acceptance of any innovation in space utilization developed by a particular manufacturer. It may also require redesigning the space if equipment budget considerations necessitate lesser quality.

Specifications

Once the method of bidding is determined on either a preliminary or complete basis, preparation of specifications may proceed. These must be complete if completely unrestrictive bidding is expected or may be a simple outline if the bidding is restricted to two or three concerns.

Areas that must be covered in the specifications are as follows:

1. Special conditions of the particular project, such as restrictions on the contractor, methods of payment, insurance requirements, necessary reports, and safety precautions. These are expected in construction projects and many standard forms of terms and conditions have been issued.

2. Scope of the work that includes any special services the elevator contractor is expected to offer, such as special painting of the structure, type and extent of postinstallation service, availability of elevators for temporary use by the building before actual completion, particular hazards, plus anything that may be out of the ordinary in the particular installation.

3. The owner's responsibility should be outlined. This includes construction of the hoistway, any patching and cutting, setting of inserts for rail brackets provided by the elevator contractor, providing power for tools and for the preliminary operation of the elevator, as well as any other item that is normally the owner's responsibility or may be on the particular job. Statements as to the procedure of approval of shop drawings and samples of finishes should be included in this section.

4. An outline of the elevator equipment required should be given. This includes capacity, speed, rise, number of entrances, type of machinery expected, signals, type of door and door operation, cab description or dollar allowance for a cab design to be determined later, plus any items considered necessary for the particular job. This outline will be followed by specific paragraph descriptions in later sections of the specifications.

A dollar allowance for a particular cab is a means of deferring the decision on the architectural treatment of the cab just as a decision on the colors to paint the doors or other features would be deferred. Because elevator equipment takes considerable time to manufacture before actual installation begins in a building, details of visual treatment may not be firm when specifications are first being prepared. By using an allowance, the actual price of the installation is established and the architect is allowed latitude in final design. If what he wants costs more or less than the allowance the difference is negotiated at a later date.

5. Specific descriptions of the elevator installation will include such items as features of the elevator operating system, because these features will vary with different manufacturers. Minimum requirements should be spelled out or a statement that either company X, Y, or Z's standard control and operating system will be acceptable. Further description of the door operation and expected door protection should be included. Signal fixtures and operation should be described in detail. Extra features such as double risers of hall buttons, special services, special operations, and any other features the elevator contractor is expected to provide should be described in this section.

6. Alternatives may be added to the specifications if, for example, the base bid price is low enough to warrant extra expenditure on higher-speed equipment. An alternative may be used to call for additional equipment that may be desirable but not necessary. Alternatives may be requested should the owner decide to build part of a facility now and the rest at a future date. In any event the alternative should clearly state the intent and, if for future installation, the expected delay.

Basic to any elevator specification is the provision that the successful contractor will comply, as a minimum, with provisions of any local codes, the American Standard Code for Elevators (ASA 17.1), the National Electrical Code, and any fire codes. Although compliance with codes is generally understood, some areas are outside their jurisdiction and, in many instances, local building codes are more liberal than recognized national codes.

If the building has been elevatored on the basis of performance criteria as described in Chapters 3, 4, 5, and 6, these criteria should be included as part of the elevator specification. Lesser performance will usually require less advanced equipment and may cause the building's elevator service to suffer. In addition the lowest bid may not be the most desirable from this aspect.

Bidders should be qualified before they are invited to bid; they should be able to demonstrate their competence to install equipment of the nature required. The architect or owner's representative should investigate all the installations cited as qualifying examples. If elevator service in a particular building is expected to be critical, as in a hospital, the bidder should also have adequate maintenance facilities in the immediate area. Failure to qualify on this point may result in each shutdown requiring excessive travel time for which the owner will have to pay and be without elevator service.

Proposal Bidding

The alternative to specification bidding is to outline briefly the elevator requirements and request various elevator concerns to submit a detailed proposal describing what they intend to furnish. This requires evaluation by the owner of all the criteria of a suitable installation for him.

Unless the invitation to bid specifically states that the lowest bid will be accepted, the owner is under no obligation to accept a low bid. This has been established by litigation and the term "lowest acceptable bidder" is often used. It would be totally unfair, for example, to compel the owner to award to a bidder who is a few dollars low when a competitor has taken considerable interest in a project and has provided help in establishing the layout and preparing budget prices and feasibility studies.

Negotiation

Often elevators are not bid separately but as part of the general contract for construction of a building. The general contractor then becomes the shopper for an elevator subcontractor, possibly seeking one who promises to meet the plans and specifications at the lowest price. If the owner does not approve of the elevator contractor who submits the lowest bid, he must add to the general contract the difference between the lowest bid and that of the elevator contractor he prefers.

Many abuses of this bid shopping system have become apparent. These include discounting of the subcontractors' bids before the general contractor submits his bid to the owner plus shopping of the subcontracts after the general contractor wins the job. This practice is akin to an auction. The general contractor has an elevator contract to award and will seek the lowest possible price to leave himself the largest net return. Corrections of this abuse have included the naming of principal subcontractors when the general contract is bid or the use of bid depositories where the established price is deposited and insured once the general contract is let.

No matter what plans and specifications are used to describe the elevator work, their scope and completeness provides only a partial guide to a good elevator installation which depends, essentially, on the reputation and the ability of the installer. For this reason it behooves the buyer to exercise care in his choice of possible bidders and to employ restrictions so that only acceptable firms will have the opportunity to install elevators.

INNOVATIONS

If the elevator installation is contracted for early in the planning of a building, the owner may be able to take advantage of innovations various elevator manufacturers can offer. Certain features are called innovations because if they were included in the firm plans and specifications, they would eliminate many companies from the bidding.

If the bid is taken before working drawings are established, full advantage may be taken of reduced space for installation permitted by equipment of improved, more compact design. For example, one elevator manufacturer has designed hoistway and door equipment to require less space than other manufacturers. If the manufacturer of the more compact equipment is given a contract early enough, the space saved can be added to rentable area or used to improve the width of corridors.

Large manufacturers of elevators have complete organizations that not only design, manufacture, and install their equipment but also maintain it on a contractual basis. With all this experience and with continued research and development, they find ways to do things better and cheaper. Smaller elevator concerns often buy equipment from various suppliers from one job to the next. These elevator contractors are dependent for innovations on what their suppliers have to offer, and because each supplier is not interested in the total elevator installation the end result may be a poorly integrated installed project.

ESTABLISHING A CONTRACT

When the bidding negotiation is complete a contract is established. This may be a letter of intent until final details of terms and conditions are agreed on, a signed proposal submitted by the elevator company, or the owner's signed contract. The work of manufacturing and installing the elevator equipment can then begin.

One of the first steps is taken by the elevator contractor in preparing and submitting a layout to the owner for approval and inclusion in his working drawings. This layout (Figure 15.1) shows details of the elevator installation in the building in the space allocated coordinated with the building's plans. The architect must check the layout with his plans and approve it. Once the layout is approved the elevator contractor will get the necessary building permit from municipal authorities to proceed with the installation. Simultaneously, the owner is expected to confirm the power to be supplied by the local utility in the completed building.

Once a layout and power confirmation is obtained, the elevator equipment is manufactured. The elevator company's construction superintendent will arrange for the rail brackets or inserts to be placed while the building is rising. At the proper time rails will be delivered and installed and the actual elevator installation will proceed.

Meanwhile, other drawings are submitted to the architect or owner, including approvals for operating fixtures and finishes, for doors and entrances, and any other items having optional treatment. By a certain time the elevator contractor will need power to start up the elevator and complete the installation. This will be well before the elevator is complete because the moving platform is often used as a scaffold to install the doors and to finish up interior hoistway equipment. The owner must supply the mainline switch in the motor room plus wiring to studs on the elevator controller. He must also provide lighting power to a point in the hoistway, usually midway, at which traveling cables to the elevator car lighting may be connected.

TEMPORARY OPERATION

The general contractor or the owner may wish to use an elevator for temporary service long before the building is complete. This understanding must be established in the plans and specifications and the time of temporary service determined, usually a stated number of days or weeks after the hoistway and power become available. The extent of temporary operation may be such that the elevator contractor has to provide a temporary hoisting machine or the general contractor provide a temporary location for the hoisting machine at some point below the permanent machine room level.

Labor contracts have recognized that construction craftsmen are not required to walk up more than a certain number of floors. This requirement is met by a temporary elevator, usually the regular elevator platform with a temporary plywood cab and wooden doors on the hoistway. In many localities an operating safety test is performed and the temporary operation is licensed. To allow work to proceed on adjoining elevators the hoistway is enclosed in wire screening or otherwise protected. The elevator is operated by an attendant and often stops only at every third or so floor.

The number of floors served by such temporary elevators must be established early because concentrated effort is usually required to get

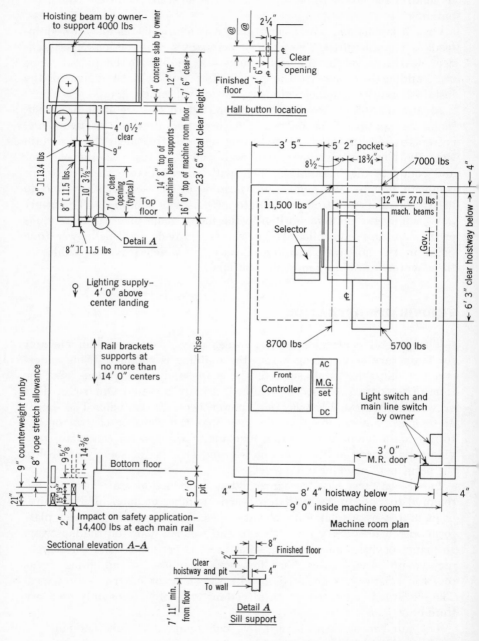

Figure 15.1 **Geared, variable voltage**

330

the equipment on the job and running. To meet the building's construction schedule, overtime work by the elevator installer at heavy cost is usually necessary. The number of temporary elevators is based on the number of men expected to be on a job at a particular time. A traffic study is made to determine how quickly the men can be moved and elevator operation is established to best serve the general contractor's interest. Even when the workmen must wait for an elevator their pay accumulates from the time they left the construction shanty on a lower floor.

ACCEPTANCE

Once a permanent elevator is complete it may be turned over and accepted by the owner, at which time an elevator being used for temporary operation can be completed by the elevator contractor. Elevator

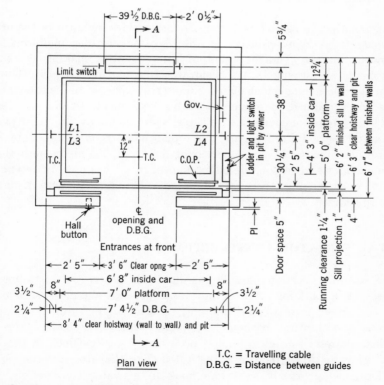

Plan view

T.C. = Travelling cable
D.B.G. = Distance between guides

passenger elevator, 2500 lb @ 200 fpm.

men are often the first on the job and the last ones to leave, starting with the foundation and finishing only when the tenants are moving in. To complete their job, elevator installers must have all the elevators in a group running so that group controls may be tested. With the general contractor wanting to use a car to complete his work, tenants wanting to use one to move in, and passengers requiring the others, it is no wonder that the final stage of completion is drawn out.

The contract is essentially complete when the architect or owner accepts each individual elevator installation. By this time a government inspection and safety test has taken place and the elevator has been licensed. The contractor has made his inspection and items of deviation he noted have been cleared up. The elevator is turned over when the owner signs an acceptance, at which point the new installation service begins.

NEW INSTALLATION SERVICE

New installation service is a maintenance service included in the original contract. A representative of the elevator installer maintains the equipment for an average period of three months, making necessary adjustments and seeing that the elevator is operating properly. During this period the management of the building is expected to make arrangements for continued maintenance of his equipment, by his own staff or by a maintenance contract with the elevator company. In either event, if a major part failure occurs, its replacement is guaranteed by the elevator installer for a usual period of one year, based on normal use of the elevator and reasonable maintenance. If, for example, maintenance were poor or lacking, there would be considerable argument if normal use were claimed.

ACTUAL ELEVATOR CONSTRUCTION

The foregoing sections simply highlight the process of installing an elevator in a building. The actual work depends on close scheduling with the other parts of the building so that an elevator installation proceeds smoothly and without interference with other trades. Step-by-step installation of an elevator has been thoroughly outlined in the National Elevator Manufacturer's Institute's *The Elevator Erection Manual.* Designed primarily as a handbook for elevator constructors, this book covers many of the considerations necessary for installing elevators.

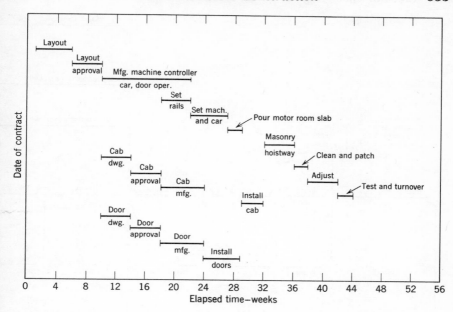

Figure 15.2   Gantt time schedule. Simple elevator installation.

These consist of reading elevator layouts, rigging and hoisting of equipment, fastening to steel and concrete, setting brackets and rails, erecting the carframe and platform, setting the machine and overhead sheaves, roping and electrical wiring, plus all the other facets of an elevator installation. The interested reader should refer to that book; it does a thorough job of description well beyond the scope of these pages.

Coordination and timing is the key to the success of any construction project. To this end various means of scheduling are used, the most common being Gantt charts and the Critical Path Method, or CPM. A sample of each is presented in Figures 15.2 and 15.3. The CPM shows the involvement of other trades in the actual task of installing an elevator, whereas the Gantt chart shows the required schedule of material arrival on a particular job.

Schedules are charted for a single elevator installation and do not indicate actual time periods. Each project is totally different with its complexity, size, and height determining the time required. As can be imagined, installation scheduling for a multigroup elevator project will be exceedingly complex compared to a smaller system. Similarly, an apartment house elevator is a relatively simple situation and formal schedules will probably not be prepared as they can be discussed verbally

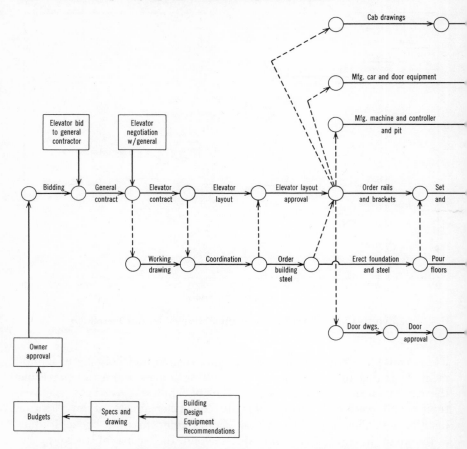

Figure 15.3 Critical path schedule, showing single simple elevator construction schedule (no time scale).

and depend on a hoistway ready date. In a commercial or industrial building, however, where considerable tie-in with other trades may be necessary, formal scheduling may be essential and should be considered before bidding, possibly with dates and delivery time included in the contract terms. We discuss this aspect in detail later in this chapter.

The charts reveal the importance of approvals. Although it may be difficult for an owner to decide a year or so in advance what type of metal fixture he wants in his building, these fixtures are essential parts of the elevator and so must be ordered early. For example, the hall button must be mounted in an electrical box imbedded in a masonry wall. Because the ultimate style of the hall button fixture and its mount-

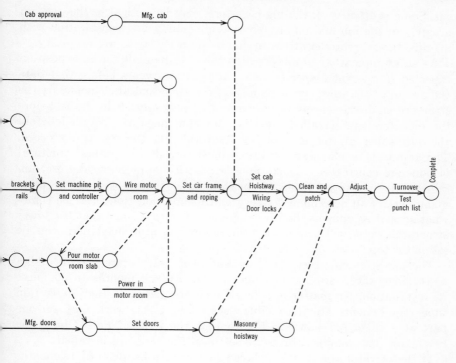

ing box must be coordinated, the design must be firm long before the walls are built.

Similarly, hoistway doors are generally made with a factory-applied baked enamel finish. Because the doors must be installed before the locking mechanism, door color is one of the earliest approvals. This is often deferred in apartment house construction, where elevator doors are installed with a prime finish only and the final finish and color are applied when the building is complete.

The elevator industry is attempting to permit the delay of choosing finishes by creating arrangements whereby the finished surface is applied later. A good example is the removable panel cab installed as a plain sheet steel cab in which the wall panels are hung in sections. Panels can be removed or changed depending on the later desires of the owner or to utilize the cab for freight service.

Delivery Scheduling

As plans for a building become firm and actual construction begins, the need to have certain items installed at certain times becomes apparent. Some equipment, including elevators, may be critical to the over-all progress of the job and require considerable study and consultation with manufacturers' representatives to determine when items are necessary.

As an example, take an observation tower to be built for an exposition expected to open at a specific date. At least two years before that date the design of the tower must be made firm. Its essential elements are the structure and the elevators, because the tower must be built before the elevators are installed and the elevators must be installed before the furnishing of, for example, a restaurant on the top can proceed. The architect, in planning the tower, must consult with either structural or concrete contractors to determine a practicable delivery and erection schedule for the tower itself. He must likewise consult with the elevator manufacturer to determine delivery and installation times for the somewhat special equipment the tower requires. Let us assume that the tower structural work will require a year before elevator machinery can be set on the top.

The elevator manufacturer may require a year before he can design and deliver the necessary machinery and, say, six months to complete its installation. No matter how many men are placed on the job, certain time requirements are irreducible because men can work only on one part at a time. As shown in Figure 15.2, the Critical Path Chart, the machines, for example, cannot be set until the rails are installed.

If the elevator contract is delayed for six months, or until 18 months before completion of the project no time is left for contingency and the schedule is critical. If the delay is longer the elevator project must be considered for overtime and costs will skyrocket. If further delay is encountered it may be impossible to complete in the given time; no inducement will make it possible.

The first essential for any construction or elevator installation is to establish a realistic original schedule. To avoid delay during the progress of a job two courses are open. One is to provide the schedule and the necessary manpower to coordinate all trades to maintain such a schedule, which is accomplished by progress reports, follow-up, expediting, and prompt approvals by all concerned. This procedure is usually the most satisfactory and is used by the knowledgeable contractors in the field.

The second means is to establish an expected delivery date a given number of days after receipt of the contract and impose a penalty on the contractor if the date is not met. If the time is reasonable and the penalty is not excessive, the elevator contractor can accept, provided his liability is limited to only those delays subject to his control and responsibility. If the time is too short he has three choices: to refuse to participate in the job; to include, if possible, the necessary overtime to complete within the time allowed; or to estimate how many more days the job will take than the allotted time and include the cost of the penalty in his bid.

The architect can rest assured that, if a penalty job is accepted, every delay, every inaccuracy, each interference between trades, delays due to weather and labor difficulties, and so on, will be recorded, and any delay, including time to receive approvals, will be imposed to extend the introduction of a penalty. The cost in paper work and argument may far exceed the gain expected by the penalty. As may be surmised, it is far better to schedule a job properly and make necessary allowances for contingencies than to try to substitute penalties for poor scheduling. In fact, it is far better to offer a bonus for completion before a specific date, which can introduce a competitive spirit and accomplish, in a positive way, what a penalty is intended to do. Stated otherwise, if a job is to be completed in a hurry, the owner should be willing to pay for fast completion.

RELATION OF ELEVATOR WORK TO OTHER TRADES

Because an elevator, escalator, or moving ramp becomes an integral part of a building when it is completed, considerable coordination is required between equipment installation and construction of the other parts of the building. Recognizing this, the general contractor keeps track of all the trades so that interference is minimized and the work flows smoothly. It also behooves the elevator installer to get his equipment in place at the proper time so that the other trades will not interfere.

For example, in a steel building, the rail brackets should be set and fastened before the beams are fireproofed. If not, the elevator contractor may have to have the concrete cut away before he can fasten his brackets. The machine room supports must be in place before the elevator machine beams are set. If the other trades fail to complete this task, the installation is delayed. Unless the elevator contractor gets his door sills in place before the finished floors are poured, considerable cutting and patching will be necessary. Similarly, boxes for hall button and hall lantern fixtures must be set before walls are built. Proper power is necessary early enough so that the running elevator can be used.

When the job is ending a considerable amount of cleaning up must be done. Plaster dust and loose masonry abounds and must be cleaned up. The hoistways act like flues everytime an elevator hoistway door opens. As the air conditioning in the building is balanced, door locks must be adjusted, for the conditioned floors will be at a different air pressure from the hoistway and wind will tend to hold doors open.

As tenants move in, turmoil unavoidably prevails. The new elevators may be erratic in operation as the equipment is tuned up. Tenants under pressure to settle down and resume normal work may not at first find the new quarters meeting their highest expectations.

In a large building the elevator contractor may have left the system in a state of adjustment designed to meet the initial traffic conditions. As the building becomes occupied and tenants' habits become established, additional tuning to adjust performance to traffic is necessary. This may include adjusting the value of weight that causes elevator dispatch and bypass operation, the time when peak traffic operations are established, and the traffic responsiveness of the group of elevators.

If the building is slow in being occupied these adjustments must necessarily be delayed—a condition that emphasizes one of the advantages of having the elevator manufacturer maintain the equipment on a contract basis. Adjustments that must be made will then be done at the necessary time. The alternative, with owner maintenance, is either to have the owner's mechanic do it or issue a separate order to the elevator manufacturer.

Representatives of the elevator manufacturer should call on the building management as the building is being occupied. They will give the owner instruction for maintenance, parts leaflets, aid in overcoming operational problems, and all the services necessary to make the installation a credit to the manufacturer as well as the owner. A reputable elevator company strives to satisfy a customer so that he will recommend the installation to others in the market for elevators.

CHANGES AND ALTERATIONS

Occasionally an unpredictable development may require interrupting progress of an installation to make a change. The variety of such changes is immeasurable. A prospective tenant of the building may want an additional entrance on the elevator, floor designations may be changed to suit somebody's fancy, additional control features may be warranted, as well as a host of other factors.

If the need for a change becomes apparent early enough it can often be made without delaying the job. If the change is late scrapping of ready worked material or extensive changes to installed equipment may be necessary. Needless to say, changes should be carefully investigated to limit them to only those features that involve minimum scrapping or rework.

Once equipment is installed it may be desirable to add further operating features, possibly to handle a traffic situation unanticipated at the time of planning or to meet the changed requirements of a particular tenant. The extent of such work can readily be explained by the elevator installer and its cost estimated. This may be a matter of adding relays to the controller, interrupting existing wiring, or so simple an alteration as reconnecting existing switches. The knowledgeable elevator company will be able to show what changes are necessary and what they should cost.

After equipment has been in operation for a number of years it may need repairs or modernization. On a geared machine the worm and gear may have to be replaced. On any machine drive sheaves may require regrooving or brakes may need relining. If the contract specifies full maintenance by the elevator manufacturer the cost of such repairs is included in the contract and the owner is free of the responsibility. If the owner maintains the equipment he must contract to have the necessary repairs done, usually by having elevator companies submit proposals and accepting the most favorable.

If renovation is desired for either appearance or operations the owner can ask elevator companies to submit proposals for such work or hire a consulting engineer or architect to negotiate the work for him. It is usually best to negotiate with the original installer who should know the equipment best.

Renovation may be necessary because elevator service falls short of standards in a modern building or to bring architectural appearance up to date. Two-speed doors in the original installation may be replaced by center-opening doors to improve round-trip time. A comparison of floor-to-floor operating time with that of a modern building may indicate wasted elevator capability.

As firms often expand at the same address rather than move, a building 15, 20, or more years old may have changed in size and nature of population since it was originally built. The nature of the building may have changed from a diversified office occupancy to single-purpose as firms take more floors in a particular building.

In the same period of time elevator operating systems, signals, fixtures, entrance designs, control systems, and so on, as offered by manufacturers, will have improved to gain more efficiency from a given elevator. The elevator machine and safety, which can be called staples in the industry, can often be used with the new features. By using as much of the original machinery, which represents a major portion of the cost of an installation, a new and modern elevator can be created in an existing building.

The cost of the change, however, may be equal to installing a new elevator in a building under construction. Changeover is costly because existing equipment must be removed before new can be substituted, a process not necessary in a building under construction. Additional costs arise because remaining equipment in a building that is being modernized must be kept running. Construction work in an occupied building is not performed under most efficient conditions and special safety precautions must be observed in respect to the building's tenants.

The results of such modernization may be dramatic. New operating equipment may be able to reduce the passenger waiting and riding time by 10 or more seconds per trip. When we consider, for example, a building with 1000 persons, each person making about eight elevator trips per day, the time saved will amount to over 5500 man hours per year. At an average pay of three or more dollars an hour, the cost of a modernization could be returned in the space of a few years or in even less time if this increased man-hour efficiency can encourage the tenants to pay additional rent.

CONVERSION AND MODERNIZATION

One of the most fruitful means of realizing operating savings in elevator modernization is conversion from attendant to nonattendant operation. This is feasible in any building unless the attendant is required to load freight on the elevator. Even this limitation can be minimized with dual control to allow automatic operation during the less busy times of the day.

Many of today's buildings were constructed before the discovery in the 1950's that people could operate elevators on their own in any type of building, even with heavy traffic. Before that time over 50 per cent of the elevators sold were attendant operated; since then over 95 per cent have been installed as nonattendant.

Kinetic energy limitations imposed by safety codes permit faster car door closing speed in attendant than nonattendant elevators. This is more than offset on a nonattendant elevator by the promptness with which the doors are closed. An attendant, since he assumes the responsibility, has to be sure no one is in the way or, to be courteous, that no one is coming. An automatic elevator does not have that concern. The safety edge on the door and the reduced speed of closing protect the passenger and, if he continues to interfere with door closing, forces him out of the way with a gentle nudge. Improved group operation and the elimination of delays caused by attendants provide a greater frequency of elevator operation so that a person who just misses an elevator will receive service within a short time.

Modernizing an elevator not only reduces cost by eliminating the operator, but may also improve service by reducing round-trip time and minimizing operating delays. The efficiency of an elevator is measured in part by how quickly the car can travel from stop to stop, determined by a simple comparative stopwatch test on a number of similar installations. The elevator is operated up one floor and down one floor. As the doors start to close, the timing is started and continues until the platform is level or the doors are fully open, whichever is later, at the next floor. The time is recorded and the procedure repeated for a one-floor run in the opposite direction. It does not matter where the recording is started or ended as long as it is consistent on all of the installations observed.

For reliable readings, the load in the elevator should also be reasonably consistent or differences in car loading, which may add a second or two with heavier loads, accounted for. The results of this time study should be as follows:

The time required to make a one-floor run with approximately the same loading conditions should be about equal in the up and down direction and for any floor of equal height in the building. If the up trip with an empty car is faster than the down trip with an empty car, readjustment in the elevator system is needed since its electrical circuits are not compensating for the changing load. This is especially true with generator field control elevators, whereas with ac resistance control or hydraulic elevators an appreciable difference may be normal.

For a generator field control elevator with 3 ft 6 in. center-opening, power-operated doors, nonattendant operation, the time required from the start of door closing to the door fully opened and car level at the next higher or lower floor (12-ft floor height) should be about 8.5 to 9.5 sec. This is the standard performance of which modern elevator systems are capable and will consist of the following elements:

Time to close the doors and start car (3 ft 6 in. center-opening doors): 3.0 to 3.5 sec

Time to run about 12 ft from the time the car starts to move to the time that the car is stopped at the next floor for elevators of 500 fpm or more: 4.5 to 5.5 sec

Time to open the doors at the next floor with the doors starting to open about 6 to 8 in. before the car is level: 1.2 to 1.8 sec

With different doors (two-speed, single-slide, or wider openings) and with greater floor heights the time will be longer. If the elevator is a geared type, with a speed from 200 to 350 fpm, the average time will be 1 to 3 or more sec longer, depending on speed under the same conditions of doors and floor height.

If a traffic problem exists in a building, performance less than the foregoing is penalizing elevator service. An improvement of a second or two per floor-to-floor trip can be multiplied by the number of stops an elevator makes each trip. This will add a percentage improvement in elevator roundtrip time, hence increased handling capacity, and will reduce operating interval. Consultation with elevator manufacturers' representatives can often determine how this can be accomplished.

Achieving improvement in an old building may mean an extensive overhaul of the equipment and addition of a new control system. For a newer building readjustment and minor repairs may make the difference.

New dispatching or operating controls may be warranted if users frequently complain of long waits for service. As outlined in Chapter 7, the dispatching control must keep the elevators spaced in relation to prevailing traffic. If this is not done the elevators tend to operate together and hall call waiting time becomes excessive. If there is a suspicion that this is happening a recording meter may be connected to each call button to measure the number and duration of such calls. This can be compared to the operating interval of the elevators by simultaneously measuring the number of departures from the main floor, assuming that cars are operating between it and the upper floors. The average wait of the hall calls should be somewhat less than the average time between departures (operating interval versus waiting time). If waits are greater than or equal to the interval, a dispatching deficiency exists and corrective measures should be made.

The comparison of hall call waits and interval can be confusing if there is considerable car call traffic on the elevators or if the elevators serve more than one main entrance, an upper floor cafeteria, or other unusual traffic generators. The comparison can also be confusing if the cars spend a disproportionate amount of time parked at a terminal or an upper floor. Anything that delays cars, either electrical signals or traffic emanating from other than main floors, must be evaluated.

Elevator manufacturers' representatives should be called on to aid in analyzing the traffic situation in any building. Adjustment of the present dispatching system, additional features, or replacement may provide the necessary improvement.

In some situations elevators are not sufficient to handle the traffic, even with the maximum potential improvement in operation. This may be because of an initially inadequate elevator plant, false economy, a major change in building occupancy, or other reasons. In such a case consideration must be given to changing the nature of the traffic by staggering working hours or reassigning space. Other approaches to solving the problem may include radical changes in elevator operation such as adding new equipment or complete renovation to improve speed or capacity.

An opposite situation may also exist. By modernizing equipment and improving performance, fewer elevators may be able to do the same job. For example, there is a building in which nine modernized elevators replaced ten manually operated ones and many buildings in which four cars are presently doing the work that previously required five. In the latter case the gain was attributable to a combination of improved performance from the modernized elevators plus minor readjustment of tenant working schedules. The released hoistway space was welcome for new power feeders and air conditioning ducts. In earlier chapters of this book the relationships between elevators and people were shown. As we discussed various types of building the relationship between traffic and elevator handling capacity was developed. In an existing building all these relationships are apparent and can be re-evaluated to create the proper elevatoring for existing conditions. The construction project, once completed, is translated by the people occupying and using the building into the conditions that all the estimates of handling capacity and elevator performance tried to predict. Once the facts are at hand a better-elevatored building can emerge.

CHAPTER SIXTEEN

Economics of Elevatoring

COST

When we think of providing services for a building we must be concerned with two cost considerations. One is the cost of the initial construction and the second is the cost of (or return from) that investment over the economic life of the building. It is often said of vertical transportation, as well as other building services, that good service does not cost but rather pays. An application of this principle was considered in Chapter 15, the conservation of productive man-hours by time-saving vertical transportation.

In elevatoring any building the cost-return considerations start with the initial plans. Many factors external to the building itself establish the ground rules. It is very seldom that land is unlimited and that any type of building, low-rise or high-rise, can be chosen for a given site. Zoning regulations must be complied with and the restrictions of land use on a particular plot must be related to the building height. In areas where land use may be free, needs for parking and access to parking must be considered. The cost of walking long horizontal distances, in terms of time consumed, should be compared with vertical travel by elevator or escalator.

A functional analysis of the building must be undertaken. Related facilities and the communication between them must be considered. To what extent must people performing their services, such as doctors in a hospital or executives in a business, come together to confer face to face, or can they use appropriate means of electronic communication, possibly including two-way television? Do materials have to be moved from person to person or department to department or is the process one of in and out? Storage functions must be considered. For example,

344

can materials be stored in a vertical plane to be moved into production lines when the demand arises or must each item be processed continuously?

In formulating the initial plans the foregoing alternatives are usually considered. As with any plan, the approaches taken may represent compromises because there is often more than one way to solve any problem. In elevatoring a building the final result will generally be one of compromise between requirements of initial cost, space consumption, service quantity, and passenger-time conservation.

MULTIPLE APPROACHES TO ELEVATORING

In earlier chapters of this book various elevatoring problems and possible solutions are discussed. They include the use of high-rise and low-rise elevators rather than a group of elevators making all stops, escalators rather than elevators in low-rise buildings, separating vehicular and pedestrian traffic on elevators, providing shuttle elevators for garage levels, and other plans. Their objective is either maximum handling capacity with acceptable riding and waiting time or, if a long trip is in prospect and handling capacity secondary, minimum waiting and riding time.

All Stops Versus Low-Rise and High-Rise

In the foregoing chapters there are some very clear-cut examples. The selection of high- and low-rise elevators or a single group of elevator exemplifies the multiple effects of a choice on building design and operation. The two arrangements are shown in Figure 16.1. Either plan with a total of eight elevators, is usually quite feasible for a building 18 to 22 floors high. Arrangement (a) is accomplished with a single group of eight elevators which, if they serve 22 stops, have a total of 176 hoistway entrances. All eight elevators will have the same speed; for a building of this height, about 700 fpm. Arrangement (b) has two groups of four elevators, operated local and express with the low-rise group serving say, floors 1 through 12 and the high-rise group serving the first floor, skipping floors 2 through 12, and serving floors 13 through 22. The eight elevators will require only 92 entrances. The speed of the high-rise elevators will be the same as arrangement (a), 700 fpm, but the low-rise can be lower speed, 500 fpm, because travel distance is shorter. If we assume that the size of the cars is the same in both cases, say 3500 lb, the local and express arrangement will require less building space.

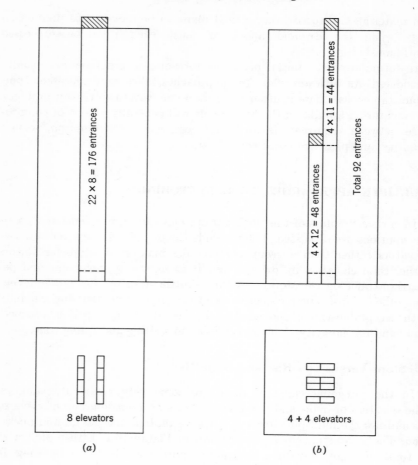

Figure 16.1

From the passenger's aspect the single eight-car group will have one advantage and one disadvantage. The chances of getting an elevator will be high because any passenger can take any of the eight elevators and waiting interval will be short. Once he boards an elevator his ride may take longer with more interruptions, as the tendency to make stops is increased with 22 floors served.

The building management has a number of advantages. Once the peaks are over it is a relatively easy matter to detach a car for maintenance or service work. Lobbies are in the same place throughout the building.

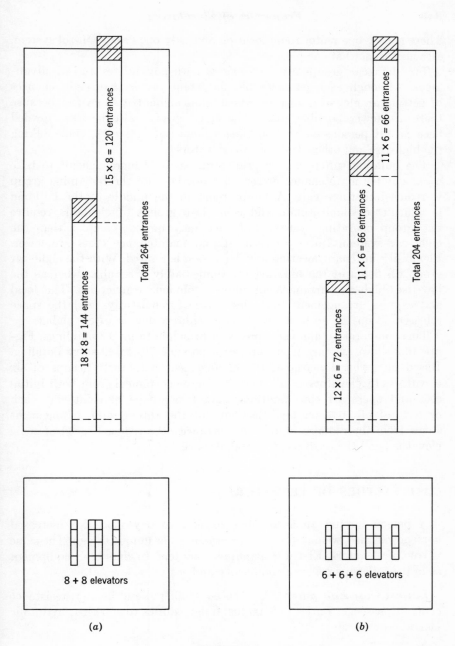

Figure 16.2

There is only one motor room location and only one group control system, although somewhat complex.

Two four-car groups give passengers both advantages and disadvantages. Although each pasenger has only four rather than eight chances of getting an elevator, once he boards the car his trip is swifter because there are fewer possible stops. The elevator may also be less crowded because all persons in the building cannot ride all cars, some taking the high-rise and others the low-rise elevators.

The building suffers a few disadvantages. It is more difficult to take a car out for maintenance or service work because the remaining group is reduced to three cars. A motor room in the middle of the building is difficult to sound-isolate and cool. Two groups of elevators require two group operating systems but each may be less complex than the eight-car system. Initial investment and maintenance costs are lower. Flexibility in tenant location and expansion is limited. With the eight-car group all floors of the building are immediately accessible, whereas the low-rise, high-rise arrangement imposes obvious restrictions. The local and express arrangement takes less space for hoistways and the space released is on upper floors where its rental value is often higher.

This comparative analysis applies in principle to larger buildings. Figure 16.2 shows two arrangements for a possible 30- to 40-story building. Based on given dimensions, the arrangement with three groups of six elevators, 18 elevators in all, may be more economical from both initial cost and operating considerations than two groups of eight cars each or a total of 16 elevators. Economy of the three-group arrangement stems from the reduced number of entrances, the reduced speed of some elevators, and the recovery of rentable space.

COST FACTORS OF ELEVATORS

A person buying an automobile expects to pay more for increased horsepower, size, weight, operating accessories, or unique design. The same is true of elevators. Elevator manufacturers tend to class their equipment as in the following order of complexity and cost:

Lowest Cost Equipment. Low speed (100 fpm and below), resistance control; passenger duties to 2500 lbs, freight duties to 4000 lbs; hydraulic elevators; rises up to 60 ft.

Moderate Cost, Low Speed. Resistance control with leveling; speeds of 100 to 150 fpm; passenger duties up to 4000 lbs, freight duties to 8000 lbs; two-car group installations; rises from 60 to 100 ft.

Moderate Cost. Generator field control to 200 fpm; passenger duties to 4000 lbs, freight duties to 10,000 lbs without industrial truck loading; spring buffers in pit; rises up to 100 ft.

Moderate Cost, Higher Speed. Passenger and freight elevators from 200 to 350 fpm; two and three car groupings; static loading freight elevators of any speed; oil buffers in pit, chain compensation; rises over 100 ft.

Moderately High Cost, High Speed. Elevators of 500 to 700 fpm; oil buffers; rope compensation; three or four or more car groups.

High Cost. Any speed of 800 fpm or higher.

Of course, any special design in the above categories tends to destroy the stated relationships.

Figure 16.3 attempts to depict the foregoing cost relationship in a graphic manner. Categories overlap and dimensions of the chart change with increased duty load as well as with speed, the only criterion shown. A proportional increase in floors served is assumed with any increase in speed.

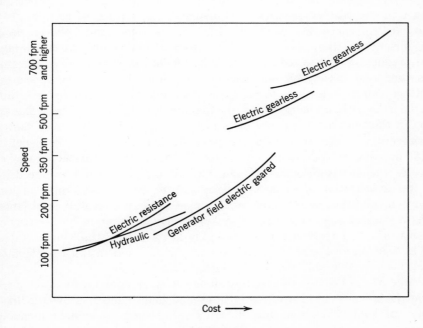

Figure 16.3

The main breaking points in elevator cost come with the differences in equipment classes. Dealing strictly with passenger elevators, there is a sharp cost differential between a resistance control elevator and a generator field controlled elevator both of the geared type. Because of elevator code requirement for oil buffers at speeds higher than 200 fpm, another breaking point between geared generator field controlled elevators at 200 fpm and those at higher speed occurs. The difference between geared and gearless elevators appears between 350 and 500 fpm, whereas with speeds higher than 500 fpm a steady increase in cost occurs when elevator machines of greater horsepower are required to attain a higher speed or a higher rise.

The picture is further complicated by differences in machines required between various capacities at various speed. For example, because the market for elevators of 2000 to 2500 lb at 500 fpm in apartment houses is comparatively large many manufacturers have developed special machines to satisfy that market at a reasonable cost. If a heavier duty, say 3000 lb, is required a heavier machine may be necessary with a considerable difference in cost. Similarly, this same machine may be capable of handling 3500 or 4000 lb and the cost differential may be minor between 3500 lb at 500 fpm and 4000 lb at 500 fpm.

Market conditions and the demand for elevators play an important part in the cost of elevators and demand alters price. Architects tend to vary the space they establish for elevators from plan to plan, making it difficult for the manufacturers to stock elevators or take advantage of production runs to reduce costs. If a standard type and size of elevator is used and decoration and change are confined to surface treatment of the cab and doors, a much lower price can be and usually is established. As with any commodity, the manufacturer's cost savings is passed on to the consumer. If many manufacturers are selling similar elevators, competition tends to reduce the price further and the buyer benefits. In consequence the architect benefits if standard elevators are used because the elevator's share of the over-all building cost is reduced.

Standardization of elevator design has progressed considerably in European countries, necessitated by shortages of housing as well as of labor. As a consequence, the complexity of an elevator unit in an apartment house of equal dimension is considerably below that of the United States. The time (man-hours) required to manufacture and install the elevator has been considerably reduced by such standardization.

One of the benefits of standard design with its consequent lower price can be elevator service where none existed before and improved utilization of land. This trend has started and is becoming evident in many ways. In areas where the ground floor space of a building is not of high commercial value the area can be used for parking and the space above is used for commercial purposes. In stores and other buildings the basement and second-floor space becomes as valuable as ground floor space if escalators or elevators are used. The economy of high-rise construction is enhanced by a less expensive, standardized elevator.

A low-rise elevator serving two or three floors can be extra economical. A hydraulic elevator operating at slow speed can be installed at low cost because it requires minimum hoistway space and minimum structural supports. Its operating cost may be higher than a comparable electric because the entire elevator load must be lifted each trip. In comparison, a counterweighted electric elevator requires more hoistway space but operates at considerably less power demand.

The convenience of having any elevator must be compared with the demand that will be placed on the elevator. If many persons are expected to use the elevator, the improved performance of the electric elevator may be a significant advantage over the slower hydraulic.

Resistance versus Generator Field Control

In a taller building where the cost of drilling for a hydraulic elevator may be prohibitive and a moderate-speed elevator is required, the geared electric type is used. The comparative differences to be resolved are between the costs of the ac resistance controlled geared elevator and the generator field control elevators. The factors responsible for the difference are the ac motor of the former versus the ac/dc generator and dc drive motor of the latter. If high speed is a requirement the generator field control must be used. If speed is not a prime consideration resistance control may suffice. If intensive service, good leveling, and minimum floor-to-floor time are prerequisites the generator field control elevator is a necessity.

Because floor-to-floor performance is less important for freight elevators, both the hydraulic and resistance electric operation can be applied in the sizes and speeds of freight elevators. The hydraulic is generally limited by the required height of travel. Depending on soil conditions and the number and size of cylinder holes required, the cost of drilling may be a serious economic factor. The hydraulic, however, can be used to lift exceedingly large loads, whereas an electric, although height limitations are minor, may require machines of very high horsepower to lift loads of over 20,000 to 30,000 lb any distance at a reasonable speed. Another consideration is that, with the electric operation, the load must be supported by the building structure, whereas hydraulic load is directed to the ground through the plunger.

If loading is by industrial truck an elevator designed to handle the static load and loading impacts must be provided. If the final speed of operation is low a resistance electric or hydraulic can be used. If a speed of 100 to 200 fpm or more is required the generator field controlled electric is employed. With either electric or hydraulic handling the impact loads on the elevator require substantial hoistway rail structure support.

Geared versus Gearless

In a building that requires elevator service of the highest quality the choice between geared and gearless equipment may be difficult in borderline cases. The areas of ambiguity are usually from six to ten stops in commercial and institutional buildings and from 20 to 25 floors in resident al buildings. Over these heights gearless elevators are invariabily superior.

The geared elevator machine is less costly because it employs a high-speed motor that is much easier to manufacture than the slow speed dc motor of the gearless machine. The difference in cost, assuming equal rise, number of stops, and the lifting capacity, may be 10 to 15 per cent higher for the gearless elevator. The difference in performance can be, depending on the degree of manufacturing quality of the supplier, as much as 2 or 3 sec slower for a geared elevator in a given floor-to-floor operation. Acceleration rates of geared elevators are also slower.

In addition to the difference in performance the service life of the gearless machine is almost endless. Because there are relatively few wearing parts, replacement or repair cost is practically nil. With the geared elevator a worm-and-gear life of about 20 years may be expected, depending on initial quality and over-all maintenance.

The efficiency of the gearless elevator is higher, about 80 per cent. The geared elevator, because of losses in the power train, has an efficiency of about 65 per cent. The pluses and minuses may be summarized as shown in Table 16.1.

The improved performance of the gearless elevator plus its additional speed gives at least 10 per cent better elevator service than the geared elevator. We have arbitrarily assumed that the difference in price, in the example, is 15 per cent greater. To the foregoing considerations must be added the financing of the additional investment, actual maintenance cost (assumed in the example to be 5 to 6 per cent of the initial investment per year) which vary with locality and intensity of service plus all the other cost considerations beyond the scope of elevatoring itself.

Table 16.1

	Geared	Gearless
Cost of elevators	x	$1.15x$
Cost of power	y	y
Efficiency	.65	.8
Cost of passenger travel	$1.10z$	z
Maintenance cost	$.06x$/year	$.05(1.15x)$/year
Expected life	40 years	40 years

Relative cost:

Power: y = \$100/year

Initial elevator cost: x = \$100,000

Passenger travel: z = \$18,750/year based on each elevator serving 250 persons, six trips/day, each trip averaging 1 min, 250 days/year, and each person receiving an average wage of \$3/hour.

Total cost, geared: $x + 40\left(\dfrac{y}{0.65}\right) + 40(1.10z) + 40(0.06x) =$ total cost

$100{,}000 + 40\left(\dfrac{100}{.65}\right) + 40(1.10 \times 18750) + 40(6000) = 1{,}171{,}153$, total cost

per elevator

Total cost, gearless: $1.15x + 40\left(\dfrac{y}{0.8}\right) + 40(z) + 40[0.05(1.15x)] =$ total cost

$1.15(100{,}000) + 40\left(\dfrac{100}{0.80}\right) + 40(18750) + 40[0.05(1.15 \times 100{,}000)] =$

$1{,}100{,}000$ total cost per elevator

Although the cost differential between a geared and gearless elevator may not appear to be great on a single-car basis as shown in Table 16.1, it is seldom that a single car is installed. If a gearless elevator provides 10 per cent better service than a geared elevator, a six-car geared installation may well be served by five gearless elevators. If we consider that the five gearless units will provide service equivalent to 5.5 geared units for a given situation, the cost savings over a period of years then becomes appreciable.

We have tried to point out that the most important consideration is not in the cost of the elevator but in the service it renders. This is one of the intangible attractions of a good building. Tenants are seldom aware of the actual difference in service from one building to another yet they share a general feeling that something is lacking in the poorly serviced building.

Actual Costs

The purchaser of an electric elevator is buying three major units plus a quantity of necessary accessories. The three main units can be defined as the motor room equipment, the car and its safety parts, and the pit assembly. The necessary accessories are the individual entrances at each floor together with the rails and wiring from floor to floor. If we lump the three major assemblies together we can consider the group to be a basic elevator and add a cost increment per floor served.

The cost per floor served will vary with the type of entrances. A single-speed elevator entrance is much less complex than either a two-speed or center-opening type of entrance and this difference must be taken into account. The differences in hoistway structure, rails, wiring, operating fixtures, and so on, will vary to a certain degree with the ultimate complexity of the elevator. For example, a simple push-button landing fixture will cost less than one with more elaborate buttons that light when operated. Similarly, directional hall lanterns will increase the cost per floor served.

An additional cost differential between low- and high-speed elevators will be apparent when the difference in the number of ropes or the size of the rails is considered. The slow-speed light-duty elevator may be supported by four or five ½ in. wire ropes and have guide rails that weigh 8 ppf. The high-speed elevator may have eight ¾ in. ropes and rails that weigh 18 ppf or more. This consideration is important not only in the stops served by the elevator but in the floors that may be passed by a high-rise elevator with an express run.

The basic cost of the elevator will, of course, vary with the speed, duty, control, and grouping. The resistance control elevator will require the minimum of motor room and pit as well as car safety equipment, whereas the high speed, gearless elevator will require the maximum. With either type of elevator the design of the cab is a factor. This design is often established as an allowance in a contract for an elevator. The allowance, which may be from $1000 to $10,000 or more, is assumed to be sufficient to purchase and install a desired design of cab. As the design is changed, additions to or subtractions from that allowance are made and the final price is established. For example, if the basic design includes formica panels and incandescent lighting and the architect wants rosewood veneer and fluorescent lighting, the difference in cost is calculated and added to the final bill.

The allowance procedure is often used for other items such as the main-floor entrances, which may be of natural metal or special finish rather than the same finish as the upper floor entrances. Allowances may also be used for signal fixtures, special signs, items that can be added after the elevator installation is complete, or extended services such as special instructional booklets and spare parts. Basically an allowance is used if for any reason an item cannot be specified in detail in advance but an estimated cost must be included in the total price of the job.

Because the major cost of the elevator is in the basic machinery and structure, unless they can be radically changed the final price of the installation may not be much different. For example, the cost of the electrical control for performance of dispatching may only be 5 or 10 per cent of the total price of the entire installation. Furthermore, the cost difference between the best quality of operation and the minimum as reflected by electrical control may only be 10 or 15 per cent of the total electrical control, making a difference of only 1.0 to 1.5 per cent in the total cost of an installation. Major cost factors can often be found in the quality of door operation, differences of architectural features, and minimizing of structural features.

Much of the basic cost of an elevator is in the material and labor to install the machinery, the car, the pit equipment, and the rail structure essential to complete the running elevator. Significant economies may be achieved in the initial elevatoring of a building when the number of elevators required is established. Once this is done the usual procedure is to establish a budget cost so that the total financing of the project may be considered. The budgets are established by elevator concerns and should include the projected cost of the elevator installation a few years hence to allow for higher labor costs, inflation, and so on. The budget should also include an allowance for additional features that are of little interest at the time of budgeting but will be desirable at the time of building.

A budget can seldom predict the condition of the elevator market at the time of the bidding or negatiating for elevators. If the market is good and all the facilities of the companies are fully utilized higher equipment prices can be expected. If productive capacity is idle prices may be lower. The wise architect keeps close tabs on market changes and adjusts his budgets accordingly. He should also keep close tabs on the differences between what he ultimately specifies and what has been initially budgeted.

Interested elevator concerns give budgets that are as realistic as possible. They know that excessively high budgets discourage projects and reduce the future work available. They can only budget what is indicated to them so that complete information at an early stage is almost as important as at the time of bidding.

The experienced manufacturer will, at the time of bidding, consider a number of factors before quoting a price for the elevator installation. He must recognize his costs, the price and availability of labor at the time the installation will go ahead, the ability of his factory to produce efficiently and on time, the equipment involved, and previous prices or budgets for comparable equipment.

With information from all sources, the bidder will alter his price to protect his company's position and to secure the job if it is desirable. He is judged by the profit he returns and the need to keep sufficient work in the organization to absorb overhead costs. The difference between elevator work and a commodity sold over the counter is that the former must be produced in the future, at a cost that cannot be predicted with absolute certainty. The commodity, on the other hand, has been produced and cost is a historic fact.

For that reason prices for elevators have not been nor are they likely to be catalogued. Elevators are seldom sold F.O.B. in pieces but are installed in a building and completed for use as part of the total elevator contract. The parts of an elevator are impossible to break out into unit prices, since, if the installer is delayed installing the rails, for example, he will try to make up lost time on another part of the job. By the same token, a rail installed on the top floor of a 50-story building costs considerably more than the same rail installed on the lower floors.

COST IN RELATION TO BUILDING COST

Total cost of an elevator installation will vary with the type of building. If the total cost of an office building is considered as all the incidental costs of construction, the total cost of the elevators may run from 8 to 15 per cent of the entire project. Statistics of this nature are published in periodicals and by the various appraising services, which should be consulted. The operating costs of buildings are developed by various agencies such as the National Association of Building Owners and Managers and various real estate as well as specialized operating groups such as the American Hospital Association and the Association of School Plant and Ground Administrators.

Operating costs vary with different types of building. The average yearly full maintenance cost of an elevator will be from 4 to 6 per cent of the initial investment. Full maintenance includes all preventative care of the equipment plus periodic weekly to monthly inspections and emergency repairs in the possible event of failure. The total cost to the customer is based on a long-term contract and includes a reserve for major replacements of the motor armatures, worm and gear, ropes, and so on, so that the buyer can be assured his maintenance contract is a complete protection. Many manufacturers offer such service on a contract basis for equipment they have made and installed and are well qualified to determine the frequency with which periodic attention is required for a particular installation. Some installations, because of their size or critical service, will even warrant a manufacturer's maintenance technician on the job throughout the working day.

In comparison to other building equipment power consumption of counterweighted elevators is usually so low as to be of little consequence. The highest-rise and heaviest-duty passenger elevators may not require more than 100 to 200 kwh of power per working day. An average elevator may require no more than 50 kwh per day, and the average 10 to 12-story apartment building may need no more than 10 kwh per day.

In total power requirements demand charges may be significant. This was outlined in Chapter 8 and should be carefully considered in total cost studies.

Years ago the elevator attendant was a major element of elevator operating cost. With his uniform, supervision, locker room, reliefs, and fringe benefits, it was estimated that in 1953 each elevator in a building had an attendant cost of $7000 per year. In buildings where 24-hr service was required this cost went up to $20,000 per year. The only vestige of an attendant that remains is a floor director in prestige buildings. He is a public-relations man and a guide to building visitors. With a completely automatic system his relation to the elevators, except to note trouble, is practically nil.

In some buildings having an attendant on the elevator is a mark of special service. This cost must be recognized and then charged to building services rather than elevators. It may be thought that the attendant is necessary to tenant safety, but properly designed protective systems have obviated that need. Properly designed protective systems can consist of an adequate alarm mechanism on the elevators, television surveillance if desired, means to prevent elevator operation in the event of tampering, and adequate security at all entrances to the building itself. Too often a front door is locked and the service entrance in a basement is left open.

SUMMARY

Those who wish to be able to establish the price of an elevator from a book such as this may be disappointed. Any price quoted herein would be as stale as yesterday's newspaper. Elevator prices fluctuate with applicable material costs and labor rates. The range early in 1966 was from about $12,000 for a three-stop hydraulic passenger elevator of 2000-lb capacity operating at 75 fpm to $150,000 for a 3500-lb capacity elevator operating at 1200 fpm in a 40-story building and serving about 12 stops. The curve between these two extremes is discontinuous. For example, a 20-stop apartment elevator of 2000 lb at 350 fpm may cost about $35,000 dollars; a gearless elevator, 3500 lb at 500 fpm serving 10 stops may run about $70,000 to $80,000; and a large freight elevator of 10,000-lb capacity may be only $15,000 in a five-story building.

The price and efficiency of labor will also vary by locality. The pay of elevator construction mechanics in New York City in 1966 was $5.96 per hour whereas the pay in Atlanta was $4.67 per hour (excluding benefits). In Los Angeles about 220 working days with good weather can be assured. In New York the average is less than 180 days. On the other days men do not work or must work under conditions of wet or cold, which lowers efficiency and increases elevator cost.

Elevator manufacturers are pleased to approximate elevator cost for a given project once the initial specifications are determined. They must quote daily and have a substantial knowledge of price and construction trends. They are reluctant to tabulate prices for a number of arrangements because the cost of preparing accurate estimates simply for study conditions requires manpower in scarce supply and is quite high. As computers assume the tasks of keeping records and analyzing statistics this may become more readily accessible, but even this is a remote possibility because with only 8000 or so elevator installations a year the cost of computer time versus that of a clerk may not be economical.

The elevator industry is only a small segment of the industrial capacity of the United States. It is highly specialized and one of the most highly regulated in product design. The American Safety Code for Elevators is recognized throughout the country as a stringent and model code. If automobiles and aircraft had to be built to its design and safety standards, they would possibly weigh two times as much and carry one-half their present capacity. The value of this code is attested by the records: elevators carry far more passengers far more safely than any other form of transportation.

As far as safety is concerned, people can take it for granted when they use a modern, well-maintained elevator or escalator. We hope this book will contribute to continuing the safety and further enhance the effectiveness and economy of this most-used means of transportation.

Index